You're one step closer getting your perfect computer

BUILDING YOUR OWN PC is best and only way to make sure that you get the perfect computer for you. Buying a pre-built model may cost you roughly the same amount of money, but you have to put up with the manufacturer's choice of components, which may not suit your particular needs.

When you build your own PC, you can make sure you have the right processor, memory, storage space, monitor and graphics card to suit you. In fact, building your own computer is like having a bespoke suit: it fits your needs perfectly.

Fortunately, doing the work yourself doesn't have to be difficult. Our step-by-step workshops and advice will help you choose the right components at the right price, build your computer and install your choice of operating system. With essential troubleshooting tips and advice at the back, you can start building your own PC with absolute confidence.

The book is bang up to date with the latest technology, including Windows 7, Microsoft's best operating system yet. With a full guide to its new features, we'll help you use your new computer, too.

The main thing you'll get from building your own computer is the satisfaction that you've got exactly what you want, rather than just another box. So, whether you want a powerful gaming PC, a Linux computer for browsing the web, a way of sharing storage space or a Media Center PC for recording your favourite TV programmes, your perfect computer is within your reach.

Happy building!

David Ludlow, Editor
david_ludlow@dennis.co.uk

Contents

From choosing the right kit to putting it all together and installing your software, our step-by-step guides will help you build the perfect PC

Chapter 1
ESSENTIALS

Find out what kit you'll need before you start building your PC, and learn some essential skills

Chapter 2
CHOOSING AN OPERATING SYSTEM

Find out how Microsoft's latest operating system compares to previous versions of Windows, as well as the free open-source alternative, Linux

Chapter 3
CHOOSING YOUR HARDWARE

We explain what to look for when choosing the kit for your new build

Chapter 4
BUILDING YOUR PC

Step-by-step guides to creating the perfect PC

Chapter 5
POWER ON

Take control of how your computer works

Chapter 6
INSTALLING AN OPERATING SYSTEM

Everything from configuration to installing drivers

 ## Chapter 7
WINDOWS 7

Your complete guide to Microsoft's latest release

 ## Chapter 8
NEW PC ESSENTIALS

Our pick of the best free software around

Chapter 9
TROUBLESHOOTING

Having problems? Don't panic – here are our tips and tricks to get your PC running smoothly

JARGON-BUSTER

All the buzzwords and technology explained

CHAPTER 1
ESSENTIALS

BEFORE YOU RUSH out and buy the bits for your new computer, there are some essential things that you need to know. Here, we'll show you what tools you'll require, the kind of workspace you should work on, the skills that you'll need and how to download the latest drivers for your new kit.

IN THIS CHAPTER

PC builder's

CAREFUL PREPARATION IS the key to every successful build, and the very first step is to get together the basic tools for the job. Over the next two pages, we'll show you how to put together a PC builder's toolkit that costs just a few pounds, but contains a range of hardware and software, which you can use again and again to tackle any build or future upgrade project with confidence.

WHAT YOU'LL GET WITH YOUR KIT

When you buy the components for your new PC, they will include a number of essential items. Your motherboard manual will have details of your motherboard's specifications and features, and an explanation of its ports and connectors. It'll also give you help with BIOS options and updates, and talk you through any bundled utility programs.

Your motherboard's box will contain all the data cables that you'll need to connect your hard disks and optical drives. There will be more cables than you need, so keep the other ones spare for future upgrades. Check the box carefully for any additional ports, such as rear-mounted USB, FireWire and eSATA. These will be easy to fit and your motherboard's manual will explain how.

Your case should have a manual that tells you how to take it apart and how to fit your components inside. Your case will generally ship with the screws that you'll need to fit your motherboard and other peripherals. If your case requires hard disks and optical drives to be fitted on runners, look for these in an accessory box either inside the packaging or the case itself.

If you're installing a graphics card, look inside its box carefully. Here you'll probably find DVI-to-VGA adaptors, which you'll need if you have a monitor with analogue inputs only; Molex-to-PCI Express power adaptors, which you'll need if your power supply doesn't have the necessary power connector; and, if your card supports it, DVI-to-HDMI adaptors. In the case of ATI graphics cards, this last item is really important. You have to use the ATI DVI-to-HDMI adaptor in order to get the sound working correctly; a standard adaptor will only deliver the picture.

Look inside all the component boxes for driver CDs. You can use these to get your hardware installed, although it's best to follow our guide on downloading the latest drivers on page 12 before you start building.

OPERATING THEATRE

A computer is useless without an operating system, so make sure that you've got your Windows or Linux disc handy before you begin building your computer.

A Windows install CD is made by Microsoft, bears a holographic Microsoft logo and has all the files needed to install the operating system. You can also use this CD to recover damaged Windows installations if you have trouble later on.

Your software box should also contain the licence key that you'll need to install Windows. You'll need this key when you install your operating system and if you ever have to reinstall Windows or contact Microsoft for support. It's critical, therefore, that you keep this key somewhere safe; without it, you'll need to buy a new copy of the software. Our complete guide to installing Windows Vista (page 78), XP (page 90) and Windows 7 (page 98) explains everything.

You will have to create a Linux installation CD before you build your computer. This is easy to do, and our guide to installing Linux on page 94 explains everything you need to know.

SAVE IT FOR LATER

When you build your PC, you'll find that you may be left with some spare parts, such as blanking plates for expansion cards and extra drive rails for more hard disks. We recommend that you keep these parts somewhere safe, as you may need them should you decide to upgrade your computer in the future. It's also worth keeping any spare screws, as you never know when they'll come in handy.

TOOL UP

Building a PC isn't a particularly complicated procedure, and you'll need only a few tools to complete the job successfully. The picture opposite shows you the most common tools that you'll need, and you shouldn't need anything more specialised. Our guide to essential building skills on page 10 will show you how to use these tools, and our guide to your workspace on page 8 shows you the kind of area in which you should work.

ESSENTIAL TOOLS	
No 2 crosshead screwdriver	£1.50
Long-nose pliers	£4.50
Multi-head screwdriver	£9
Total	**£15**
www.screwfix.com	

OPTIONAL TOOLS	
Torch	£6
Cable ties	£3
www.screwfix.com	
4GB flash drive	£9
www.pcnextday.co.uk	
Thermal paste	£3
Anti-static wristband	£3
www.lambda-tek.com/componentshop	
Total	**£24**
TOTAL AMOUNT	**£39**

toolkit

RECOMMENDED
Hardware tools

MULTI-HEAD SCREWDRIVER A ratchet or electric screwdriver with a wide range of fitments should cover anything that a standard crosshead screwdriver can't. Choose one with a range of hex sockets that includes at least 5, 6 and 7mm sizes.

CABLE TIES (not pictured) Great for tidying the inside of your PC, or to clip groups of wires or loose components out of the way while you work. Longer ties are more expensive but more versatile, and you can snip off any extra length.

ANTI-STATIC BAG Use a large anti-static bag as a safe surface for working on any sensitive components. Smaller bags are ideal for storing or transporting components. Most PC parts arrive in anti-static packaging, so don't throw them away.

MEDIUM CROSSHEAD SCREWDRIVER This can be used for almost every screw inside a PC, allowing you to fit or adjust all the major components. Choose one with a long shaft so that you can reach recessed screws.

TORCH This can be particularly useful when connecting a PC under a desk or making adjustments inside its case. A torch will also help you to read text on those components inside your PC that are labelled with small text or simply stamped with information.

FINE PLIERS You can use these to remove and fit jumpers, hold parts in tight spaces and help extract bits that are reluctant to move. You can also use them to cut wires or cable ties, and twist out metal blanking plates from a drive bay.

ANTI-STATIC WRISTBAND Wearing this reduces the chances that static electricity will damage sensitive components such as your expansion cards, motherboard, memory or processor.

STORAGE DEVICE A simple USB flash memory device lets you transfer any drivers or patches you need from another PC. A larger hard disk device is perfect for taking full backups if you're transferring data and programs from another PC.

THERMAL PASTE You may need this for the trouble-free installation of a new processor or graphics card heatsink, or when transferring a processor to a new motherboard. Make sure that you don't buy thermal adhesive by mistake.

Your workspace

1 DESK
You need a clear desk or table to work on your PC. As cases can have sharp edges, put down a cloth before you start work to prevent scratches. If you haven't got a suitable cloth, lining your desk with paper should do the job.

2 PLASTIC CUP
Screws and clips from inside your case can easily get lost. A plastic cup is a handy way of storing everything so you don't lose them.

3 RADIATOR
It's good to work near a radiator, so you can touch an unpainted part of it to discharge static. Alternatively, wear an anti-static wristband.

4 LAMP
A desk lamp will help make sure that you have enough light inside your PC.

5 MANUALS
Keep any manuals that came with your kit handy, as they'll help you build your PC correctly.

6 COMPONENTS
Keep your components in or on top of their anti-static bags until you're ready to use them.

Essential skills

BEFORE YOU UNWRAP all the shiny new components you've bought and start shoving them into your case, there are some safety lessons to learn, along with some key skills that will make building your PC much easier. Without these, you run the risk of damaging your computer before you've even turned it on. The worst part is that most of the time, you'll be unable to tell that you've caused any damage until you turn on your PC for the first time. At this point, tracking the problem down can be a real nightmare. We'll take you through the main pitfalls you'll face when building a new computer and, more importantly, how to avoid them.

STATIC

We all know about static electricity: it's the charge that builds up when we walk across a carpet and discharges when we touch someone else. This little flash of electricity may not seem very powerful, but it's potentially fatal for sensitive electronic components. Get a build-up of static and touch your processor, and you may have destroyed one of the most expensive parts of your computer before you've even started.

Fortunately, avoiding problems isn't that hard. If you've got one, wear an anti-static wrist strap. This will prevent static electricity from building up, making it safe to touch any component in your computer. If you haven't got one, don't panic, as there are other ways around the problem. Try to work near a radiator. To discharge any build-up of static, simply touch the unpainted part of the radiator. You're then safe to work.

Finally, all computer components come in anti-static bags to protect them. Don't remove any component from its bag until you're ready to fit it.

MAGNETIC SCREWDRIVER

Inside your PC, you'll find that there are lots of parts of your case that are awkward to reach to screw components into place. The easiest way to deal with this problem is to use a magnetic screwdriver. Simply place the screw into the screwdriver and then manoeuvre the screw towards its destination. The opposite is true when removing screws, as a gentle action should mean that a screw comes away attached to the screwdriver, rather than dropping to the floor.

Don't worry about magnetically sensitive devices inside your PC. A magnetic screwdriver isn't powerful enough to cause any damage or wipe any data.

THE RIGHT SCREWS

While the right screwdriver can make your job easier, it's essential to use the right screws to prevent damage. Put a screw that's too long into a hard disk, for example, and you could damage a circuit board and break the whole thing. Where possible, you should use the screws that come with the device, as these are guaranteed to work. Failing that, if your case has special fittings for devices, such as rails for hard disks and optical drives, the correct screws should have been fitted.

Of the different types of screws that are used, the small stubby ones are for hard disks and optical drives, the long screws are for holding expansion cards in place, while the screws with the flat heads are for fitting the motherboard and for some case panels. At all times, make sure that you don't overtighten screws, or you could cause damage. The idea is to tighten screws to the point where your components are held snugly in place.

⬆ Prevent the build-up of static by wearing an anti-static wrist strap

↑ Choose the right screw for the right job

↑ Check that the cables are all plugged in

THE RIGHT AMOUNT OF FORCE

When you plug components such as expansion cards, memory and a processor into your motherboard, it can be difficult to know how much force you should apply. Our tips should help you get it right. First, make sure that you've lined up your components correctly with the slot or socket – our step-by-step guide to building your PC on pages 42 to 67 will show you how to do this.

Next, make sure that you're applying equal pressure across the device to move it into position. Processors should drop into place with little pressure, memory needs a firm push to click it into place, while expansion cards need a fair push. If you're getting a lot of resistance, stop what you're doing and start over again.

POWER CABLES

When building a PC, it's important to remember you're dealing with an electrical device. Before you plug the power in and turn on your computer, check that you've plugged in all the power cables properly, particularly on the motherboard. Loose connections can cause problems.

The fans inside a PC can cause problems, too, particularly if you've got power cables near them. Make sure that all power-carrying cables are clipped out of the way of fans so that you don't cut through them. Power connectors plug in only one way, so if you can't get one in make sure that it's

the right way round. Forcing a connector in the wrong way will damage your devices irreparably.

Before you plug in your power cable, make sure that your power supply is set to the correct voltage. Some supplies, although rarely seen today, have a switch that changes the input voltage from 110V (US) to 230V (UK). If you've accidentally set it to 110V, the supply will be damaged and your motherboard may be affected, too.

TAKE YOUR TIME

The best tip that we can give is to follow each step carefully and take your time. Building a PC isn't a race and, as you're dealing with lots of expensive components, it's best to get it right the first time around. Our step-by-step help will guide you through every step you need to take, while our troubleshooting guides on pages 140 to 157 will help you fix any problems that you may run into.

→ A magnetic screwdriver is a PC builder's best friend

Finding and installing drivers

ANY NEW HARDWARE that you buy will come with a driver disc, so that you can install it easily. Some motherboards even have fancy installation wizards that automatically detect which drivers you need and install them automatically. However, while this sounds straightforward, the drivers that you get on the disc are usually out of date.

If you've already got a computer, then your first job is to go on to the internet and download the latest driver files, saving them to a USB key or external hard disk. If you haven't got access to a PC, don't worry. Simply use the drivers that came on the disc until you've got a working computer, and then follow these instructions to download the latest drivers and install them afterwards. Thanks to the internet, getting drivers is incredibly easy and shouldn't take too long.

MOTHERBOARDS

The motherboard is the main part of your PC and it comes with plenty of built-in features, including onboard sound, networking, storage drivers and potentially even graphics. Windows, particularly Vista, will have drivers for many of these things, but if you want the best performance and the best range of features, you'll need the latest drivers.

You can get everything for your motherboard from the manufacturer's website: you'll find the address in your motherboard's manual. If not, then use a search engine to find the URL.

Once you're on the website, there should be a link for Support. Just keep following the links for motherboards and drivers. Eventually, you'll get to a point where you'll need to enter the details of your motherboard to locate the driver download page for your model. It's vital you get exactly the right model in order to get the correct drivers for your computer. If you can't find the details on the box or in the manual, then the motherboard's name is usually written on the board itself.

After you've entered your motherboard's details, you'll be presented with a long list of drivers divided by type, such as graphics or networking. For each heading, download one driver, making sure that you select the latest version. Most driver packages cater for all versions of Windows, but check the details to ensure that you download the correct driver.

GRAPHICS CARDS

If you're using onboard graphics, you'll be able to find the latest drivers on the motherboard

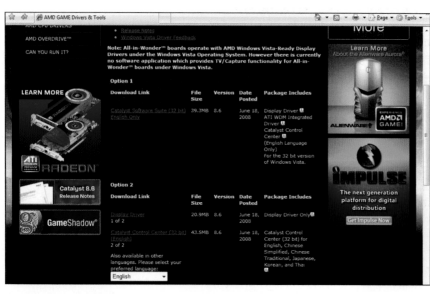

↑ ATI gives you a choice of files to download, but the full Catalyst Control Suite is the best choice for new computers

↑ You'll need to perform several file downloads to get the latest motherboard drivers

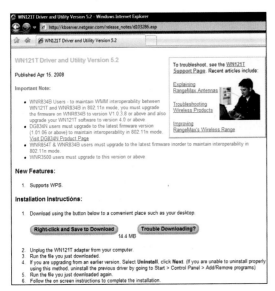

↑ You can find the latest drivers for all your devices on the internet

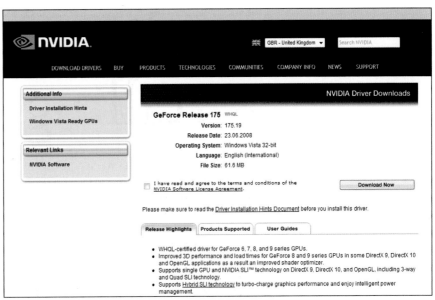

↑ Nvidia has a unified driver architecture, so a single download is all you need

manufacturer's website. If you're using a dedicated graphics card, you should download the drivers directly from ATI's or Nvidia's sites. This will ensure that you get the best performance and stability from your graphics card.

NVIDIA

Nvidia uses a unified driver package, so one download will work for most of its graphics cards. This makes installation simple. Visit *www.nvidia.com* and select Download Drivers from the Download Drivers menu in the top-left of the screen. Select the type of card (GeForce for consumer graphics cards) and the series of card that you have, such as 9xxx series for a GeForce 9600 GT. Select your language as English (UK) and click Search. Tick the box to accept the licence agreement and click Download.

It's important to select your graphics card model, as not every driver package has the driver for every graphics card. If you download the wrong package, your card won't install.

ATI

ATI has a similar unified driver architecture to Nvidia. Visit *http://support.amd.com/us/Pages/ AMDSupportHub.aspx* and click the Download graphics drivers link under Support & Drivers. On the next page, select which operating system you'll be installing, select Radeon from the list (consumer graphics cards are all Radeon models), and then select your card. Click Go to be taken to the driver page. The Catalyst Software Suite includes the driver and the Catalyst Control Panel for configuring settings. Make sure you select your

model from the list, or you may get a version of the driver that doesn't support your card.

OTHER DEVICES

If you're installing other hardware, such as a wireless network adaptor, TV tuner, sound card or printer, you'll need to download the latest drivers for these, too. In a similar way to the procedure we've described above, you'll need to visit the manufacturer's website and follow the links until you get to where you can select which device you want to download drivers for. Check a device's manual for full details on the manufacturer's website. If you can't find any information, a Google search for the manufacturer's name should bring up the details you need. Remember to make sure that you get the right driver for your device and for the OS that you require.

REGULAR CHECKS

Once you have the latest drivers, your job isn't done. You should regularly check manufacturers' websites and see if updates are available. Typically, graphics card drivers are updated monthly, while other devices are updated less regularly.

Driver updates fix known problems and can help your PC become more stable and perform better. It's worth going back to a manufacturer's site to check for updates if you're suffering a problem, as a new driver can often fix this.

Manufacturers' websites are also useful if you want help with a product. You can also find manuals for download, which can be really helpful if you lose your printed version and need to check a detail or plan an upgrade.

TIP
New versions of drivers can sometimes fix problems with your computer. If you're having trouble with a particular device, look for a newer driver before doing anything else.

CHAPTER 2

CHOOSING AN OPERATING SYSTEM

WHILE THE CHOICE of hardware may seem the most important decision when building a PC, it's the operating system that dictates how you'll use your computer. Depending on the type of PC you want, there's a choice between Windows and Linux. Here, we'll take you through the different options so that you get a system you're happy with.

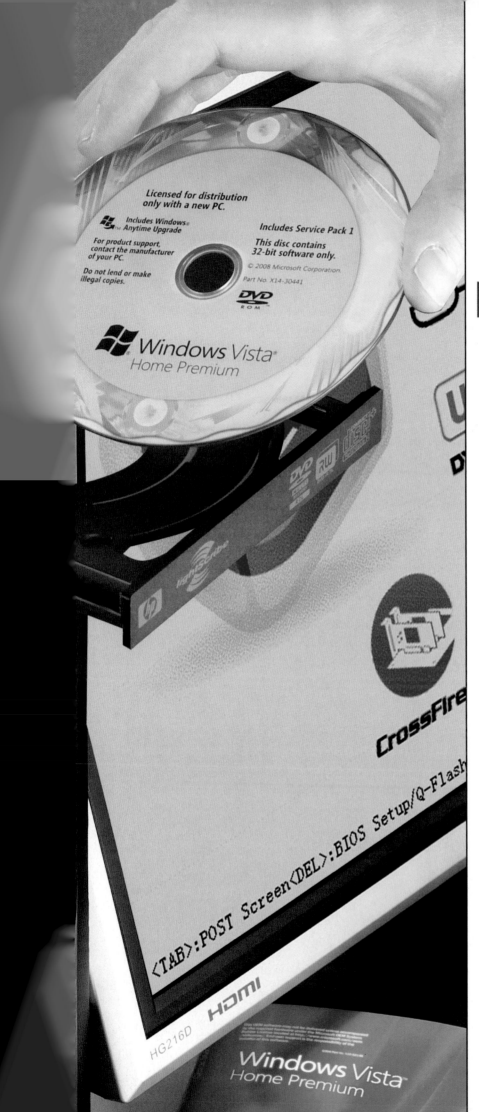

IN THIS CHAPTER

Windows 7

WINDOWS 7 IS Microsoft's latest operating system, and the early impressions of it are that it's everything that Windows Vista should have been. This makes it the ideal choice for any new PC, to the point where we now feel comfortable recommending that you shouldn't bother with Vista or XP unless you have an old copy of either of these two operating systems that you really want to use. With Windows 7 you're buying an operating system that's going to enjoy Microsoft's full support for the next few years.

When Windows Vista was first released, it had several compatibility problems. In particular, some hardware didn't have drivers for Vista, and some older software refused to run on the operating system. With Windows 7, this isn't the case: everything that worked on Vista – which is practically everything now – will work on Windows 7, so you can buy it safe in the knowledge that you won't have any compatibility problems.

Security has been beefed up, and Windows 7 also loads much faster and is less sluggish than Windows Vista. All round, it's a much better operating system. You're sure to be happy with your choice if you choose Windows 7.

FRIENDLY FIRE

Not all the new features are hidden under the surface. A lot of work has been put into making Windows easier to use and better to look at. This shouldn't be underestimated, as Windows 7's look and flash graphics mean it's a lot friendlier and make XP and even Vista look dated.

The new Windows management interface lets you quickly resize windows, see your desktop and choose which application you want to switch to.

Vista's sidebar has gone, but you can still run the same Gadgets (small applications for a specific job, such as showing the current weather, displaying post-it notes and showing you the current time). There are loads of Gadgets to choose from, with both official Microsoft and third-party applications available.

Those used to Vista will be pleased that there's still the built-in search, which makes it easier to find your files and programs. Simply click on the Start menu and start to type, and you'll be presented with a list of files and programs that contain your search terms. This search integrates with email (Windows Mail in Vista), so all your important information is incredibly easy to find. If you want Vista to search other email clients, such as Mozilla's Thunderbird or scan new file types, you can download iFilters (*http://ifilter.org*) to add these capabilities.

Windows 7 adds a lot more features besides, including Homegroups for easier networking, Blu-ray disc burning and full image-based backup in every edition. For more information, see our full guide to Windows 7 on page 98.

VERSION THERAPY

While Windows Vista had a relatively simple choice of just two versions – Home and Professional – Windows Vista comes in three major retail versions: Home Premium, Professional and Ultimate. The main benefit over Vista is that each edition contains the same features as the lower version, plus some more options. You can even use Windows Anytime Upgrade to upgrade your existing edition without having to reinstall the operating system.

↑ You can upgrade your version of Windows 7 without having to reinstall all your programs and files

↑ Media Center is the easy way to view photos, videos and pictures, and record TV programmes

We think that Windows 7 Home Premium is the best version for home users. Professional, as the name implies, has extra features for businesses, while Ultimate has all the features of both other editions plus the BitLocker drive encryption feature. Both versions are relatively expensive compared to Windows 7 Home Premium, though, and we don't think that they're worth the extra cash. You can use Microsoft's website to make sure that the version you've chosen has all the features you need (*http://windows.microsoft.com/ en-US/windows7/products/compare-editions*).

Finally, you also get a choice between the 32-bit and 64-bit versions of Windows. The 64-bit version of Windows can handle more system memory (the 32-bit version is limited to using a maximum of around 3.5GB). However, there are fewer drivers for it and not all software is guaranteed to work with the 64-bit version. Unless you're intent on sticking tons of memory in your new PC, stick with the 32-bit version.

UNDER CONTROL

One of the key benefits of Windows 7 is that it comes with Windows Media Center. This application lets you watch and control you music, videos and photos using a remote control (which costs around £15) using a TV-friendly interface. If you add a TV tuner (from around £15), you can even turn your PC into a hard disk recorder, complete with the best and completely free electronic programming guide (EPG).

It's incredibly easy to configure and the updated version supports the Red Button for interactive digital TV and Freesat HD broadcasts; two things that Vista's Media Center didn't support.

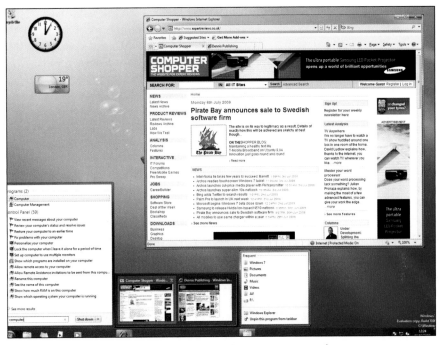

⬆ Windows 7's new interface makes the operating system even easier to use

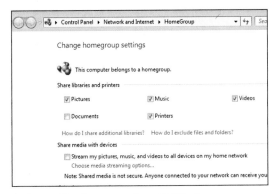

⬆ Networking is even easier with Windows Homegroups

GOING STREAMLINE

Microsoft stuffed Vista full of extras such as the Windows Photo Gallery for organising photos. While some of these applications were useful, they just added to the general bloat of the operating system. With Windows 7, Microsoft has gone for a more streamlined operating system and any extra applications are optional: you can either download similar applications to Vista's from Windows Live or install other third-party applications instead.

POWER UP

Windows 7 will work with any computer on which Windows Vista would run. It needs a fairly decent specification and we strongly recommend that you have a PC with at least 2GB of memory in order to get the best experience. This means that Windows 7's not ideal if you want to build a budget PC; you may want to consider using Linux instead.

You may also find that some older hardware such as printers and scanners won't have drivers for Windows 7, but this is unlikely to be a problem for most people. If you have a particular bit of kit that you want to keep using and you can't find Windows 7 or Vista drivers, then XP could be a better choice if you've got a copy. For everyone else, Windows 7's the operating system we've all been waiting for.

TIP

The Original Equipment Manufacturer (OEM) version of Windows 7 can be bought with any new bit of hardware and is designed for people building a new computer. You don't get any telephone support, but the OEM versions are considerably cheaper than the full boxed products, and cheaper than the upgrade version.

Windows Vista

NOW THAT WINDOWS 7 is available, there probably doesn't seem much point in buying Windows Vista. To an extent, that's true. However, it doesn't mean that Windows Vista is a bad choice. If you already have a copy of Windows Vista and don't want to buy a new operating system, then it's still a reasonable choice. There's also a good chance that you'll be able to pick up a copy of Vista at a discounted price now that everyone wants to buy Windows 7.

The good thing about Vista now is that support for it is widespread and there are drivers for just about every new bit of hardware. It supports the latest gaming technologies, DirectX 10 and DirectX 11, so you'll definitely be able to play the latest games. As Vista is basically a slightly more sluggish version of Windows 7, it supports all the same software, such as Office 2007, which was written specifically for Vista.

The release of Service Pack (SP2) means that most of Vista's bugs and flaws have been ironed out, and the operating system is now more secure than Windows XP ever was. For the most part, Vista is a robust environment, and Microsoft has boosted the firewall's capabilities over that of Windows XP's. We still recommend dedicated internet security software, but a more secure operating system from the start is a good reason to opt for Vista over Windows XP.

LOOKING GOOD

A lot of work was put into making Windows Vista easier to use and better to look at than its predecessor. This seemingly cosmetic improvement shouldn't be underestimated, as Vista's look and feel and impressive graphics make it a lot easier to use and make XP look dated. The Sidebar sits down the side of the screen and holds Gadgets, which are small applications for a specific job, such as showing the current weather, displaying post-it notes and showing you the current time. There are lots of official and third-party Gadgets available.

One of Vista's big changes was its built-in search, which makes it easier to find your files and programmes. Simply click on the Start menu and start typing and you'll be presented with a list of files and programs that contain your search terms. This search integrates with email (Windows Mail in Vista), so all your important information is incredibly quick to find. If you want Vista to search other email clients, such as Mozilla's Thunderbird,

DETAILS

Microsoft Windows Vista

WEB

www.microsoft.com

PRICE (OEM VERSIONS)

Home Basic	£55
Home Premium	£60
Business	£86
Ultimate	£120

GOOD FOR

Mid-range or faster PC, Media Center computer

MINIMUM REQUIREMENTS

800MHz processor, 512MB memory, 40GB hard disk, DirectX 9-compatible graphics card for Aero interface

PROS Easier to use than XP; more stable; Media Center is built in
CONS Needs a lot of memory to run smoothly; doesn't support all old hardware and software; Windows 7 is better

VERDICT

Easier to use, more secure and with better support than Windows XP, Vista is a good choice for new PCs if you've got a copy that you can use. For all other new computers, we recommend Windows 7 instead.

↑ Media Center is the easy way to view photos, videos and pictures, and record TV

↑ New Gadgets can be added easily

↑ Vista's integrated search locates files and programs

or scan new file types, you can download iFilters (*http://ifilter.org*) to add these capabilities.

VERSION AVERSION

While Windows XP had a relatively simple choice of just two versions (Home and Professional) Windows Vista comes in four retail versions – Home Basic, Home Premium, Business and Ultimate – so choosing the right one can seem rather daunting. Microsoft has a feature-comparison table on its website (*http://tinyurl.com/mseditions*) to help you make the right decision.

For most people, Vista Home Premium offers the best combination of price and features. Home Basic doesn't give you much for your money, and misses out a number of important features including Media Center and the Aero desktop interface. The Business edition is really designed for work use only, and has some extra networking features at the expense of Windows Media Center. Finally, Windows Vista Ultimate has all the features included in the Business and Home Premium versions, but it's considerably more expensive. It also gives you access to the Ultimate Extras download site, but there's little here that makes the Ultimate edition worth £60 more than Home Premium.

Finally, you also get a choice between the 32-bit and 64-bit versions of Windows. The 64-bit version of Windows can handle more system memory, while the 32-bit version is limited to using a maximum of around 3.5GB. However, there are fewer drivers for the 64-bit version, and not all software is guaranteed to work with it. Unless you're bent on sticking lots of memory in your new PC, we'd advise you to stick to the 32-bit version.

MEDIA CENTER

One of Windows Vista Home Premium's key benefits is that it comes with Windows Media Center. This application lets you watch and control you music, videos and photos using a remote control (which costs around £15) using a TV-friendly interface. If you add a TV tuner (from £15), you can even turn your PC into a hard disk recorder, complete with the free electronic programming guide (EPG).

Vista wasn't the first version of Windows to include Media Center, but with XP Media Center was an optional version of the operating system and not built in as standard. With Windows Vista,

↑ Vista's Aero interface makes it look much better than its predecessors

as it's part of the operating system, Media Center is easier to configure and more reliable. For this reason alone, if you're looking to build a PC for your living room, Windows Vista Home Premium is an excellent choice.

PICTURE PERFECT

You probably have lots of digital photographs on your PC, and possibly no simple way to organise them. Vista includes the Windows Photo Gallery, a useful utility that enables you to organise and categorise your photos by assigning simple tags to them. Using Photo Gallery, you can either look through your photos by directory or view them by tags, choosing to see all photos that contain a pet, for example.

POWER PC

The biggest problem with Vista is that it requires a fairly meaty computer to run it smoothly, and we strongly recommend that you have a PC with at least 2GB of memory in order to get the best experience. This means that Vista isn't ideal if you want to build a budget PC. You may also find that some older hardware such as printers and scanners won't have drivers. If you have a particular bit of kit that you want to keep using and you can't find Vista drivers for it, then XP could be a better choice. For everyone else, Vista's a big improvement over its predecessor and a reasonable choice for a new PC.

TIP

The Original Equipment Manufacturer (OEM) version of Windows Vista can be bought with any new bit of hardware and is designed for people building a new computer. You don't get any telephone support included, but the OEM versions are considerably cheaper than the full boxed products, and cheaper than the upgrade version.

Windows XP

ALTHOUGH WINDOWS VISTA was launched with much fanfare in January 2007, it didn't quite make the impact that Microsoft had hoped for. In part, this is because it requires a much higher specification than Windows XP. For this reason, XP has had something of a resurge recently, with netbooks such as Asus's Eee PC available with XP installed. However, Microsoft has since withdrawn XP from sale and says it will only provide security updates, not bug fixes, until 2014.

For most new PCs we recommend that you buy Windows 7, but if you have a copy of Windows XP, it's not a bad choice, especially for a low-power computer. Alternatively, you may be able to find a second-hand copy of the operating system on eBay or a similar auction site.

Unlike Vista, with its many versions, XP's choices are simple: Home and Professional. XP Professional is in effect the 'full XP' edition, with Home essentially a stripped-down – and less expensive – version. Because Home is targeted towards non-work use, options necessary in a corporate environment such as Terminal Services (which allows access to central server data and applications), as well as additional networking features, are disabled in Home. Similarly, because Professional users benefit from more configurable user groups and administration options, such features are thinned out in Home. Finally, remote desktop, which lets you control your computer over a network, is missing altogether from Home.

The only other advantage that Professional has is that it's available in 64- and 32-bit versions, while Home is available only as 32-bit. The main difference is that the 64-bit version can handle memory capacities over 4GB, while the 32-bit version can only accept 4GB of RAM (although only around 3.5GB is usable in practice). The downside of the 64-bit version is that it suffers from poor driver support, and not all software will run on it. For that reason, we recommend sticking to the 32-bit version. We'd also recommend XP Home, as you're unlikely to need the more advanced features of XP Professional.

COST CUTTER
As well as the more plainly targeted editions of XP Home and Professional, the pricing of Windows XP is less than that of Vista, making the older OS even more tempting in terms of putting a system together on a tight budget; saving money on your operating system means you'll have more to spend on the components. So while the two ends of Windows Vista's scale, Ultimate and Home Premium, cost around £120 and £60 respectively, XP Professional and Home's Service Pack 1 editions can be found for around £85 and £50.

SPEED RUNNER
Pricing isn't the only area in which XP seriously challenges Vista. Based purely on the speed of a system running each OS, XP leaves Vista behind on startup, shutdown and in the opening of applications and programs, which ultimately translates into a faster computing experience.

The reason XP is quicker has a lot to do with the required specifications of the systems on which they were designed to run. When XP was

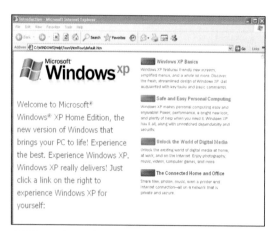

↑ XP may be getting old, but it's quick to run and has lower hardware requirements than Vista

↑ XP's familiar interface, stability and reliability still make it a good choice for a new computer

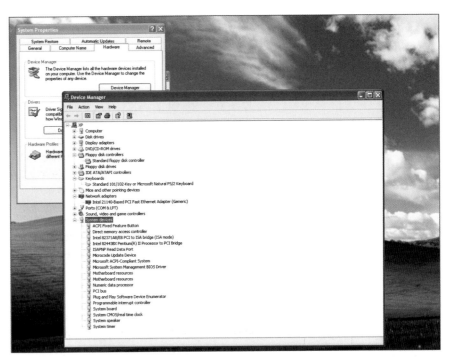

↑ You'll have no problems getting hardware or software to work with XP

launched in 2001, both the Home and Professional editions were designed to run on a PC with a 233MHz processor, 64MB of RAM and just 1.5GB of hard disk space. Compared to Vista – even the entry-level Home Basic edition – the difference is gargantuan. Vista Home Basic requires an 800MHz processor, 512 MB of RAM and 15GB of disk space. Vista's Home Premium, Business and Ultimate editions increase the requirements to 1GB of RAM and a sizable 40GB of free hard disk space. Frankly, Vista is highly resource-intensive and sluggish compared to XP.

SUPPORT GROUP

Although the cost and speed may be tempting you to consider using XP, you may be concerned about the support now offered to the older operating system by Microsoft. Such fears aren't unreasonable, as with the release of any new product Microsoft has to prioritise resources – and developers – towards the newest arrival. Microsoft has said that it will provide security updates until 2014, but you won't get any other bug fixes or updates to fix other problems.

There's no free support for XP any more, although there is a paid-for support number that you can use. However, the chances are that if a problem has been found with XP, there's a fix for it on the internet. But for the best levels of support and the knowledge that your operating system will be kept up to date, it's best to choose Windows 7. If you really want to stick with XP, however, then at least the security updates until 2014 will give you some peace of mind.

STABLE INFLUENCE

The final reason that Windows XP is still a good choice for a new system is its stability and reliability. XP benefits from three service packs, as well as extensive driver support for hardware across the board, including older peripherals that Vista and Windows 7 don't currently support. Obviously Vista and Windows 7 are still relatively young compared to their predecessor, and the latest version of Windows looks to be a relatively stable and reliable operating system, but XP has had many years of work and support put in to it, helping to make it the number one operating system worldwide. Given the amount of user support that Windows XP still retains, hardware and software developers will continue to support it as they have done with previous operating systems, probably at least until 2014 as well.

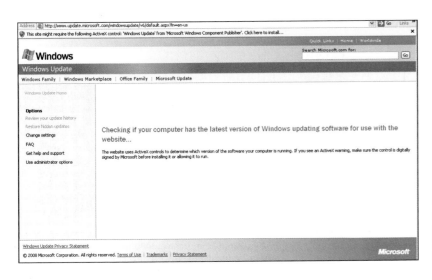

← Support is a key concern for older applications, but Microsoft has announced it will support XP until 2014

💡 **TIP**

The Original Equipment Manufacturer (OEM) version of Windows XP can be bought with any new bit of hardware and is designed for people building a new computer. You don't get any telephone support included, but the OEM versions are much cheaper than the full boxed products, and less expensive than the upgrade version.

Linux

LINUX HAS A reputation for being tricky to use and something that only those that like to mess around with command lines should even bother with. While to a certain degree this reputation is justified, Linux has come on leaps and bounds in the past few years, and is now arguably just as easy to install as Windows. It's also being used by many companies in mainstream laptops. The current bunch of netbooks, including Asus's Eee PC and Acer's Aspire One, all run a version of Linux with a simplified menu stuck on top.

Linux, then, can be just as good a choice as Windows. Here we'll examine why you might want to install Linux on your new PC.

OPEN BORDERS

The main benefit of Linux is that it's free. As an open-source product, Linux costs nothing no matter what you use it for. The result has been that different companies have taken Linux and modified it to create their own versions, or distributions (distros), of the operating system.

The downside is that there are lots of different versions to choose from, each with its own slightly different installation routine and slightly different way of working. While this can be confusing, we recommend Ubuntu (*www.ubuntu.com*). This manages to strike a good balance between ease of use and power, and is a popular choice within the Linux community.

A FAMILIAR ENVIRONMENT

If you decide to install Linux, you'll find that you end up with a desktop that doesn't look a million miles away from Windows. In fact, from the

desktop you can select Computer from the Places menu and browse through your files using a Windows Explorer-style file manager. All the familiar drag-and-drop functions are available, and you can even create files and folders in the same way as with Windows. Using Linux from this point of view, therefore, is just as easy as using Windows.

As well as sharing a similar way of managing files, you'll find that Linux also shares a lot of applications with Windows, such as the free OpenOffice office suite and the Firefox web browser. What you may find surprising, though, is that using Ubuntu to install these applications is actually easier than it is with Windows. Using the Add/Remove Programs application you can browse additional software to install from an easy-to-use menu. Ubuntu then automatically downloads any applications you want to install. Try to do that with Windows.

That said, there's no getting away from the fact that your Windows applications won't install on Linux. While you'll be able to find free open-source equivalents for most of your Windows applications, not every type of application will be listed. You may be lucky enough to find an application to download from the web, but there's no standard installation routine for Linux, so installing a new application can sometimes be difficult.

STAYING UP TO DATE

Just as with Windows, Ubuntu is at risk from malicious hackers looking to exploit security vulnerabilities in the operating system. Fortunately, Ubuntu also has its own free updates. A message

DETAILS

Ubuntu Desktop Edition

WEB
www.ubuntu.com

PRICE
Free

GOOD FOR
Budget PC, mid-range PC

MINIMUM REQUIREMENTS
700MHz processor, 384MB RAM, 8GB hard disk space

PROS Free; simple application installation
CONS Hardware support not as good as in Windows; poor games support

VERDICT
As it's completely free, Ubuntu is an attractive choice where cost is a primary concern. Even where this isn't the case, if you want a PC for the internet and office work, Ubuntu's great.

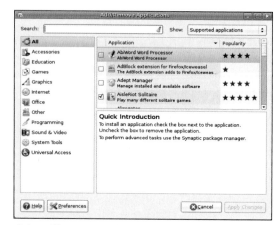

↑ The Linux desktop is similar to Windows

↑ Installing new applications is incredibly easy

pops up when new updates are ready to be installed. Clicking on it lets you select the updates you want to install, which are then downloaded automatically from the internet and installed on your computer. Ubuntu is therefore just as easy to use and keep updated as Windows is.

HARDWARE COMPATIBILITY

While you'll find that Ubuntu will install flawlessly on most computers, there are times when you'll have hardware that won't work properly as there aren't any drivers for it. Wireless network adaptors are a good example of hardware with which you can have problems. A fair number of hardware manufacturers make Linux drivers available on their websites. What you don't get, though, is a simple installation file to run. Instead, installing drivers can be a real pain. Fortunately, if you search the internet for help, you'll find lots of friendly sites and forums that can talk you through installation.

In general, before choosing to install Linux, you may be best off running Ubuntu from a CD first to see if you like the look and feel of the operating system. If you do decide to use it on your new PC, check that drivers are available for the hardware and peripherals that you'll want to use.

CONFIGURE IT OUT

Finally, although Linux has improved in leaps and bounds, there will be the odd times when it proves to be a bit tricky to deal with. Installing drivers is one such area, but there are other things that are difficult. Trying to troubleshoot problems in Linux can become very difficult, and sometimes there's no choice but to revert to a command line to get

⬆ **Familiar applications such as Firefox are the same in Linux as in Windows**

something done. This shouldn't put you off, however, and if you're interested in tinkering with your new computer and want to learn some new skills, Linux is a good way to go.

CHARMED LIFE

It's hard not to be taken in by Linux's charms, especially as it's free. With Firefox and OpenOffice being so easy to install from within Ubuntu, it's a great choice for a budget or mid-range PC whose primary job is going to be browsing the internet, sending email and using office documents.

If you want a wider choice of applications, have lots of peripherals and other hardware, then Windows works out better. If you're building a higher-end PC, particularly if gaming is a consideration, you should also use Windows.

⬆ **Linux's file browser is similar to Windows Explorer**

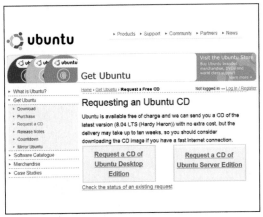

⬆ **Linux is free, so it's great for a budget PC**

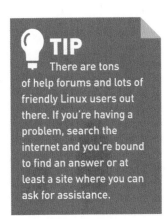

TIP
There are tons of help forums and lots of friendly Linux users out there. If you're having a problem, search the internet and you're bound to find an answer or at least a site where you can ask for assistance.

CHAPTER 3

CHOOSING YOUR HARDWARE

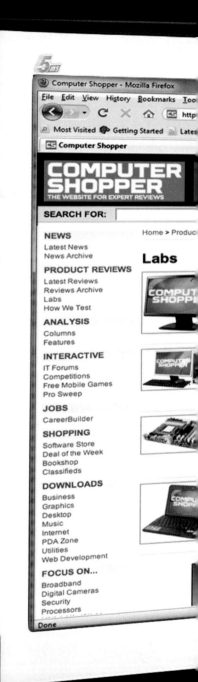

CHOOSING THE RIGHT components for your PC can be daunting. Here we'll explain the ins and outs of the latest peripherals, and we've also put together recommended specifications and upgrade advice for different budgets and PC use.

Choosing an
AMD processor

AMD'S PROCESSORS CAN'T match Intel's processors for speed at the high end, but for normal computers they strike a great balance between performance and price. Its processors are easier to understand and upgrade, as there are two main types of processor socket to choose from: socket AM2+ and socket AM3.

First, we need to explain processors cores. A core is essentially a processor on a single chip. All modern processors have at least two cores (known as dual-core), so each processor really acts like two processors. This is brilliant for running multiple applications or for applications written to use multiple cores, such as video-editing suites. High-end processors have four cores (quad-core) and are even faster in video-editing applications and at running multiple programs. AMD also has some processors with three cores (tri-core).

SOCKET AM2+
Socket AM2+ processors are common AMD processors, but are being replaced by AM3 processors. There's still a vast range from which to choose and all will work in any AM2+ motherboard. They'll also work in older AM2 motherboards, but won't run at full speed because AM2 boards only

support a slower HyperTransport speed (the bus the processor uses to communicate to system devices such as the graphics card). Unfortunately, they won't work in AM3 motherboards because of a new pin configuration of that socket.

They're good value, but choice is limited to the Phenom and Phenom II ranges, which comes in tri- and quad-core models. Currently, the best choice is the Phenom X4 9950 Black Edition (around £92). This processor is incredibly fast and its Black Edition moniker means that it's easy to overclock if you want a free speed boost. If you want lots of power, the Phenom II X4 940 quad-core processor (around £126 including VAT) is a brilliant choice.

SOCKET AM3
Socket AM3 processors give you the widest range of options. These processors can be used in older AM2+ motherboards, which are currently quite cheap, and newer AM3 motherboards. If you buy an AM3 motherboard, you'll also need to buy DDR3 memory, which is more expensive than DDR2 memory (see page 29 for more information on different memory types).

The AM3 processor range includes the Phenom II range and Athlon II X2 (which are essentially Phenom processors with two cores) ranges. For a budget computer, we recommend an Athlon II X2 240 (around £44). If you want a bit more power, the Phenom II X2 550 Black Edition (around £80) is hard to beat, and this dual-core processor can also be easily overclocked.

For the best performance going, the Phenom II X4 955 Black Edition processor (around £146 including VAT) is very hard to beat. It's incredibly fast at every job and a perfect choice for a high-end computer.

LOW POWER
AMD currently doesn't have any Atom-equivalent processors that you can buy, so if you want to build a low-power entry-level computer or network storage device, you're out of luck. Intel's excellent dual-core Atom 330 processor is the best choice for these types of computer.

↘ AMD's quad-core Phenom II X4 processor offers masses of power for around £126 including VAT

Choosing an Intel processor

YOUR CHOICE OF Intel processors is defined by your motherboard's socket type (see page 28 for more information on choosing a motherboard). Choosing the processor is fairly straightforward, and there are three types of socket available: LGA775, LGA1366 and LGA1156. We'll explain each socket type in turn.

Again, it's important to understand processor cores. A core is essentially a processor on a single chip. All modern processors have at least two cores (known as dual-core), so each processor really acts like two processors. This is brilliant for running multiple applications or for applications written to use multiple cores, such as video-editing suites. High-end processors have four cores (quad-core) and are even faster in video-editing applications and at running multiple programs.

LGA775 PROCESSORS

LGA775 processors are more widely available, cheaper and the best choice for most people. Processors that fit into these sockets include the Core 2 Duo, Core 2 Quad, Pentium Dual-Core and Celeron Dual-Core chips.

The most important thing that you need to be aware of is that you'll require a motherboard that supports your processor's external bus speed. Depending on your choice of processor, this will be either 200MHz, 266MHz, 333MHz or, rarely, 400MHz. Confusion can arise because this number is often multiplied by four to give the front-side bus speed (which is used by the processor to communicate with every other component in your PC). You may see motherboards quoted as supporting 800MHz, 1,066MHz, 1,333MHz or 1,600MHz FSB speeds instead.

For a budget computer, we recommend the Pentium Dual-Core E5200 processor, which costs around £46 including VAT. It's powerful, and great value. If you want a bit more power, the Core 2 Duo E7400 processor costs around £82 including VAT. For the ultimate power, the quad-core Core 2 Quad Q9400 (around £139 including VAT) is a brilliant choice. Unless money is no object, we'd advise you to ignore the Extreme processors: these are easier to overclock – in other words, adjusting the

processor's settings to get a free speed boost – but they're incredibly expensive.

LGA1366 PROCESSORS

Older Core i7 processors use the LGA1366 socket. These are all quad-core processors, but a technology called HyperThreading makes the processor act like an eight-core processor. These are the fastest processors you can buy, but look set to be replaced by LGA1156 processors. We don't recommend them.

LGA1156 PROCESSORS

The new quad-core Core i5 and Core i7 processors are based on the LGA1156 socket. Both processors support TurboBoost, which increases the processor's speed when it's under load, improving performance. So far, the only Core i5 processor is the 750. It doesn't have Intel's Hyper-Threading technology, but it's still very fast and great value at around £150 including VAT. For the best performance, try the Core i7 860 (around £220 including VAT). With LGA1156 set to be the new socket of choice, either of these processors are the best bet for a high-end system.

ATOM PROCESSORS

Finally, Intel's Atom processors are low-powered models and perfect for entry-level computers or for network storage. The Intel Desktop Board D945GCLF2 (around £55 including VAT) is the best choice as it's a motherboard and dual-core Atom 330 processor in one.

↖ The Core 2 Quad processor is, as the name suggests, a quad-core chip, and provides the ultimate in power

TIP Processor prices are always changing, so hunt around for a bargain. You may be able to find the models we've recommended for less.

Choosing a Motherboard

THE MOTHERBOARD IS arguably the most important part of your computer, as it defines which processor, memory, graphics card and other components you can install.

SOCKET TO 'EM

The first choice is the socket type, as this defines which processors you can fit. For Intel Pentium Dual-Core, Celeron Dual-Core and Core 2 processors, you need a motherboard with an LGA775 socket. Motherboards with Intel's P43 or P45 chipset are a good choice, and there are also 'G' variants that have onboard graphics.

For the new Core i5 and Core i7 processors, you need a motherboard with the LGA1156 socket. Currently only Intel's P55 chipset supports this. For old Core i7 chips, you need an LGA1366 socket. Intel's X58 chipset is currently the best choice.

For AMD processors an AM2+ motherboard can take every current AM2+ or AM3 processor. However, some will require a BIOS update to work with the latest processors. This can be tricky, as you'll need a processor that will work with the motherboard to perform the upgrade. Our advice is to check the manufacturer's website to see if a BIOS upgrade is necessary to install your chosen processor; if it is, you can either choose a different model or ask your supplier to upgrade it for you.

AMD's AM3 motherboards can only take AM3 processors, but will have the maximum upgrade potential in the long run. The only downside to these boards is that they require DDR3 memory, which is a little more expensive than the more popular DDR2. For either motherboard, AMD's 790 or 785 chipsets are great choices.

SIZE MATTERS

Motherboards come in two common sizes: ATX and microATX. ATX motherboards measure a maximum of 305x244mm and will fit in ATX cases only. MicroATX motherboards measure a maximum of 244x244mm and will fit in ATX and microATX cases. The main difference between the two types is that microATX motherboards have fewer expansion ports. Mini-ITX motherboards are designed for tiny cases, although the motherboards will also fit in most standard cases.

↑ Make sure your chosen motherboard has enough spare ports

Intel's destop Atom processors typically use Mini-ITX motherboards.

EXPANDING OPTIONS

Make sure that the motherboard you choose has enough SATA ports for hard disks, IDE ports for optical drives, and PCI and PCI-E slots for any additional expansion cards that you want to install, such as a TV tuner.

Look for onboard graphics (not currently available on Intel P55 motherboards) if you want to save money and aren't interested in playing games. If you want to play games and want the best-quality output for Blu-ray movies, then you should buy a dedicated graphics card. You'll need a PCI-E x16 slot to fit a dedicated card.

You can also buy motherboards with multiple graphics slots, which are certified for Nvidia's SLI or ATI's CrossFire technologies.

RECOMMENDED CHOICES

If you want an AM2+ motherboard, Gigabyte's GA-M720-US3 (around £45 including VAT) is a good ATX board; Asus's M4A78-HTPC/RC (around £64 including VAT) is a decent AM2+ microATX board. If you want an AM3 motherboard, we recommend Gigabyte's GA-MA785GMT-UD2H (around £69 including VAT).

For Intel systems, Asus's P5QL/EPU (around £54 including VAT) is a good choice for LGA775 processors, while the Foxconn G45M-S is an excellent microATX board. For LGA1366, Gigabyte's P554-UD4 (around £116 including VAT) is a great choice.

TIP
After choosing your motherboard check the manufacturer's website to see if it needs a BIOS update before you can use your chosen processor; if it does, pick a different motherboard instead, as you may have trouble turning your computer on to perform the update if your processor is not recognised.

Choosing
Memory

MEMORY IS one of the most important components in your computer. The more you have, the better Windows will run, as it can keep all its data and applications in system memory; when Windows starts to run out of physical memory it begins using the hard disk as virtual memory, which is incredibly slow.

It's not quite as easy as buying the right type of memory and plugging it in, though, as you need to consider how much RAM you want and the configuration of it. Here, we'll explain your options.

MEMORY TYPE

The first thing you need to know is the type of memory that your computer needs, which will be dictated by the slots in your motherboard. Memory will be either DDR2 or DDR3: the types aren't interchangeable, so you need to make sure you buy the right one. You motherboard's manual and its manufacturer's website will let you know which memory you need to install.

A further clue is that Intel Core i5 and i7 and AMD AM3 motherboards all require DDR3 memory. Intel Core 2, Pentium Dual-Core and Celeron Dual-Core, and AMD AM2 motherboards all require DDR2 memory.

SPEED DEMONS

It's not just a simple case of buying the right type of memory, but also getting the right speed. We'll look at DDR2 memory first. This comes in speeds of PC2-6400 (800MHz) and PC2-8500 (1,066MHz). For Intel systems, you need to buy the memory that is the closest match to the processor's front side bus (FSB) speed. You can fit PC2-8500 RAM in a system with an 800MHz FSB, but it will simply run a bit slower. For AMD systems that require DDR2 memory, you can fit PC2-8500 memory. You can expect to pay around £25 including VAT for 2GB of PC2-8500 RAM.

For computers that require DDR3 memory, there's a choice of PC3-6400 (800MHz), PC3-8500 (1,066MHz), PC3-10600 (1,333MHz) and PC3-12800 (1,600MHz). PC3-10600 memory is currently the best value and will work with all DDR3

processors. You can expect to pay around £37 including VAT for 2GB of this memory.

MEMORY BANK

Once you know which type of memory you need, you can choose how much RAM you want to install. We recommend a minimum of 2GB, but you should get more for better performance. Remember, there's a limit on the memory you can install. This is both set by the motherboard (check its specifications carefully) and by Windows.

If you have a 32-bit edition of Windows, it can only access around 3.5GB of memory (fit 4GB maximum); 64-bit versions of Windows have no practical limit, so you can fit more. That said, 4GB should be enough for most people.

CONFIGURATION

All modern motherboards and processors support at least dual-channel memory. This works by sending memory data over two channels, and thus increases performance. For this to work, you have to install memory in even numbers of modules: so, for a dual channel system with 2GB, you'd need two 1GB modules.

LGA1366 Core i7 processors use triple-channel memory, so you need to install memory in multiples of three. Most memory manufacturers will sell packs of memory with the required number of modules.

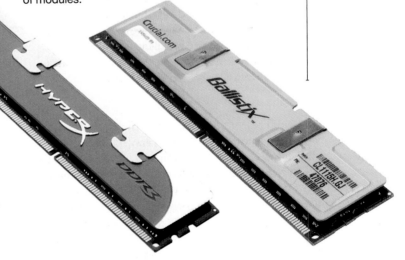

↑ Make sure you get the right memory for your chosen motherboard

Choosing a
Graphics card

↑ For the best games performance, you'll need a dedicated graphics card

MANY MOTHERBOARDS HAVE built-in graphics, but these deliver only basic games performance. For something a little more, you need a dedicated graphics card.

SIZE AND FEATURES
If you're building a media centre PC, a graphics card can be used to decode Blu-ray movies, leaving the processor free for other jobs. The chances are that you'll have a tiny case that accepts only a low-profile graphics card. There aren't many of these available; Sapphire's Radeon HD 4550 (around £32 including VAT) is the best choice.

The other factor you'll need to consider is how many slots a card takes up. The most powerful cards take up two expansion slots, so you can only fit them in large cases.

All modern graphics cards support HDCP, so you can plug them into an HD TV and watch Blu-ray movies. To do this you'll probably need a DVI-to-HDMI adaptor. For ATI cards you need to use the official ATI adaptor, or sound won't be transmitted over the connection. To make sure you get the necessary adaptor and cables, buy the full version of any card you want, not the OEM editions.

Be warned, though, that most modern graphics card (except ATI's Radeon HD 5870) don't currently support PAP, so HD sound from Blu-ray discs will be downsampled to a lower quality. To get round this, it's best to use analogue outputs and let the PC decode the sound.

Finally, the most powerful modern graphics cards require an eight-pin PCI Express connector on your power supply.

RECOMMENDED CHOICES
For general high-performance gaming, Asus's EAH4870/HTDI/512M (around £91 including VAT), which uses ATI's Radeon 4870 graphics chip, is the best choice. If you want no-holds-barred performance, Sapphire's HD5870 (around £320 including VAT) is the best choice.

Choosing a
Power supply

↑ Make sure your power supply has the right connectors for your PC

YOUR POWER SUPPLY brings your PC to life and ensures that there's enough power going to each component. Cheap power supplies are available, but in our experience they're unreliable, can break easily and often deliver unstable voltages that can crash a computer. Pick branded, more expensive models and it will save you money in the long run.

POWER UP
Your main choice when picking a power supply is getting one with the right power output, which is measured in Watts. For a basic entry-level PC, look for a 500W supply; for a mid-range or high-end PC, you'll need a 650W supply. For very powerful computers with lots of hard disks and powerful graphics cards, you should buy an 800W supply or higher.

The other thing to consider with power supplies is the number of power connectors that they have. Make sure that the supply you choose has enough SATA and Molex connectors for your computer.

Check that the supply supports your chosen graphics card; powerful modern graphics cards have eight-pin PCI Express connectors, and your power supply must have the matching connector for this to work. If you want to use ATI's CrossFire or Nvidia's SLI, look for a supply with multiple six- and eight-pin PCI Express connectors.

RECOMMENDED CHOICES
OCZ's ModXstream Pro 500W (around £52 including VAT) is a good entry-level power supply. For a more powerful computer, try Be Quiet!'s 650W DarkPower Pro (around £104 including VAT). For very powerful computers, FSP's 1,200W Everest Pro (around £207 including VAT) is a great choice.

Choosing a
Hard disk

YOUR HARD DISK stores your operating system, applications and all your data. Getting the right model is therefore incredibly important. The choice should be fairly simple, but here we'll explain what features to look out for.

FULL CAPACITY

All modern hard disks and computers use SATA interfaces. This makes your choice infinitely easier. Your primary consideration when buying a hard disk is to get a drive with the highest capacity that you can afford. However, small and extremely large hard disks usually cost more per gigabyte, so aren't especially good value. Unless you're on a particularly tight budget, it's worth

spending a few pounds more to get a larger, better-value disk.

Finally, if you're planning to use RAID – where you use multiple hard disks to create one virtual disk with better performance, data protection or both – you should buy identical drives.

RECOMMENDED CHOICES

Hard disks have fallen a lot in price recently, so large disks are comparatively cheap. The smallest hard disk we would recommend is Seagate's 500GB Barracuda 7200.12, which costs around £37 including VAT; a 160GB hard disk will cost only a few pounds less and isn't worth it. For more capacity, Samsung's

↑ When choosing a hard disk, look for the highest capacity you can afford

750GB F1 DT (around £54 including VAT) or Seagate's 1TB Barracuda 7200.12 (around £60 including VAT) are good value.

If you think you'll need lots of storage space, Seagate's 1.5TB Barracuda 7200.11 (around £90 including VAT) is an excellent choice.

Choosing a
Case

YOUR CASE DEFINES what your computer looks like, how many components you can fit inside and even the size of motherboard and type of graphics card that you can fit. Making the right choice is therefore incredibly important. Here's what to look out for.

SIZE OF THE PRIZE

The most important factor is the size of motherboard that you can fit. Most cases can take a full-sized ATX motherboard (see page 28 for more information). However, some cases can accept only microATX motherboards, while some specialist cases are designed for tiny Mini-ITX motherboards.

Larger cases can take smaller types of motherboard, but not the other way round, so make sure that you buy a case big enough for your motherboard.

COMPONENTS

Another thing you'll need to consider when choosing a case is the number of components that you can fit inside. Look for a case that has enough 3½ in drive bays for hard disks and enough 5¼in drive bays for optical drives.

The size of the case can also play an important part in deciding which expansion cards you can fit: media centre cases often have only enough room for low-profile graphics cards, which aren't very common.

RECOMMENDED CHOICES

More expensive cases are generally quieter, better looking and also easier to build. Choose a decent-quality case and you'll be happy, but pick a cheap and nasty model and it could ruin your new build.

↑ Good-quality cases are quieter and better-looking than cheap models

Akasa's Zen AK0ZEN-01 BK (around £35 including VAT) is a good choice for a budget computer. For something a bit sturdier, Antec's mini P180 (around £65 including VAT) is a great choice. For a high-end computer, Antec's P182 (around £104 including VAT) is excellent. For a media centre PC, try ThermalsTake's Xaser Bach (around £120 including VAT).

BUDGET PC

This budget computer will be good enough for basic computing tasks, such as photo editing and surfing the web. You can add a faster processor, install Windows 7 and add a better graphics card if you want a better PC.

SHOPPING LIST
Recommended minimum specifications

PROCESSOR	
Intel Pentium Dual-Core E5200	£46
(AMD Athlon II X2 240	£44)
MOTHERBOARD	
Intel: Gigabyte GA-EG41MF-S2H	£54
(AMD: MSI KA790GZ	£64)
CASE	
Akasa Zen AK-ZEN-01 BK	£35
HARD DISK	
500GB Seagate Barracuda 7200.12	£37
MEMORY	
2GB Corsair Value Select DDR2 PC2-5300	£22
OPTICAL DRIVE	
Samsung Super-WriteMaster SH-S202J	£14
OPERATING SYSTEM	
Ubuntu Linux 9.04	Free
POWER SUPPLY	
OCZ ModXStream Pro 500W	£52
TOTAL	**£260**

MID-RANGE PC

This powerful computer will be able to cope with any application and its dedicated graphics card means that it can also play games. Look for a bigger hard disk and quad-core processor if you want more from your PC.

SHOPPING LIST
Recommended minimum specifications

PROCESSOR	
Intel Core 2 Duo E7400	£82
(AMD Phenom II X2 550 Black Edition	£80)
MOTHERBOARD	
Intel: Asus P5QL/EPU	£54
(AMD: Gigabyte GA-MA785GMT-UD2H	£69)
CASE	
Antec Mini P180	£63
HARD DISK	
750GB Samsung F1 DT	£54
MEMORY	
Intel: 4GB Corsair TwinX DDR2 XMS2 PC2-8500	£50
(AMD: 4GB Corsair TwinX XMS3 DDR3 PC3-10666)	£58)
OPTICAL DRIVE	
Samsung Super-WriteMaster SH-S202J	£14
OPERATING SYSTEM	
Windows 7 Home Premium	£70
GRAPHICS CARD	
Asus EAH4870/HTDI/512M	£91
POWER SUPPLY	
Be Quiet! DarkPower Pro 650W	£104
TOTAL	**£582**

HIGH-END PC

This is a stunning PC that will be more than good enough for any job. There's little need to upgrade here, but a larger hard disk and faster graphics card could boost performance.

SHOPPING LIST
Recommended minimum specifications

PROCESSOR	
Intel Core 2 Quad Q9400	£139
(AMD Phenom II X4 955 Black Edition	£146)
MOTHERBOARD	
Intel: Asus P5QL/EPU	£54
(AMD: Gigabyte GA-MA785GMT-UD2H	£69)
CASE	
Antec P182	£104
HARD DISK	
1TB Seagate Barracuda 7200.12	£60
MEMORY	
Intel: 4GB Corsair TwinX XMS2 DDR2 PC2-8500	£50
(AMD: 4GB Corsair TwinX XMS3 DDR3 PC3-10666	£58)
OPTICAL DRIVE	
LG GGC H20L	£84
OPERATING SYSTEM	
Windows 7 Home Premium	£70
GRAPHICS CARD	
Asus EAH4870/HTDI/512M	£91
POWER SUPPLY	
Be Quiet! DarkPower Pro 650W	£104
TOTAL	**£756**

EXTREME PC

This PC is incredibly fast, but you're paying a lot of money for it. The graphics card will deliver the best games performance. If you want an even faster computer, look to buy an Intel Core i7 Extreme Edition processor.

SHOPPING LIST
Recommended minimum specifications

PROCESSOR	
Intel Core i7 860	£220
(AMD Phenom II X4 955 Black Edition	£146)
MOTHERBOARD	
Intel: Gigabyte P55M-UD4	£116
(AMD: Gigabyte GA-MA785GMT-UD2H	£69)
CASE	
Antec P193	£126
HARD DISK	
1.5TB Seagate Barracuda 7200.12	£90
MEMORY	
4GB Corsair TwinX XMS3 DDR3 PC3-10666	£58
OPTICAL DRIVE	
LG GGW H20L	£132
OPERATING SYSTEM	
Windows 7 Ultimate	£120
GRAPHICS CARD	
Sapphire HD4870	£320
POWER SUPPLY	
FSP Everest Pro 1200W	£207
TOTAL	**£1,389**

MEDIA CENTRE PC

This system will give you plenty of disk space for digital TV recording, and the optical drive is capable of playing Blu-ray films. Arcsoft's TotalMedia Theatre 3 Blu-ray playback software costs around £70.

SHOPPING LIST
Recommended minimum specifications

PROCESSOR	
Intel Core 2 Duo E7400	£82
(AMD Phenom II X2 550 Black Edition	£80)
MOTHERBOARD	
Asus P5QL/EPU	£54
CASE	
ThermalTake Bach Media Lab	£116
HARD DISK	
1.5TB Seagate Barracuda 7200.11	£90
MEMORY	
4GB Corsair TwinX DDR2 XMS2 PC2-8500	£50
OPTICAL DRIVE	
LG GGC H20L	£84
OPERATING SYSTEM	
Windows 7 Home Premium	£70
OTHER	
Hauppauge WinTV Nova TD500 dual digital tuner	£55
GRAPHICS CARD	
Sapphire Radeon HD 4550	£32
POWER SUPPLY	
OCZ ModXStream Pro 500W	£52
TOTAL	**£685**

MINI PC

This small PC won't take up much room on your desk, but it'll be powerful enough for most tasks. The PCI-E x16 slot is quite short, so you may find that it's hard to fit a dedicated graphics card for games.

SHOPPING LIST
Recommended minimum specifications

PROCESSOR	
Intel Core 2 Duo E7400	£82
(AMD Phenom II X2 550 Black Edition	£80)
CASE	
Intel: Asus T3-P5945GCX (includes motherboard and 300W power supply)	£75
(AMD: Asus T3-M2NC51PV (includes motherboard and 300W power supply)	£87)
HARD DISK	
500GB Seagate Barracuda 7200.12	£37
MEMORY	
2GB Corsair Value Select DDR2 PC2-5300	£22
OPTICAL DRIVE	
Samsung Super-WriteMaster SH-S202J	£14
OPERATING SYSTEM	
Windows 7 Home Premium	£70
TOTAL	**£300**

LOW-POWER PC

This tiny and cheap computer is absolutely great value. It'll cope with everyday tasks well and its low-power processor and integrated graphics chip means it'll cost very little to run. Look at one of the other PCs here for better performance.

SHOPPING LIST
Recommended minimum specifications

MOTHERBOARD	
Intel Desktop Board D945GCLF2 (includes Atom 330 processor)	£56
CASE	
Antec Minuet 350 (includes 350W PSU)	£68
HARD DISK	
500GB Seagate Barracuda 7200.12	£37
MEMORY	
2GB Corsair Value Select DDR2 PC2-5300	£22
OPTICAL DRIVE	
Samsung Super-WriteMaster SH-S202J	£14
OPERATING SYSTEM	
Linux	Free
TOTAL	**£197**

HOME STORAGE

The case may not be as small as a NAS, but this low-power computer will be perfect for sharing files over your network. The motherboard has only two SATA ports, so you'll need to add a SATA card if you want more hard disks.

SHOPPING LIST
Recommended minimum specifications

MOTHERBOARD	
Intel Desktop Board D945GCLF2 (includes Atom 330 processor)	£56
CASE	
Akasa Zen AK-ZEN-01 BK	£35
HARD DISK	
2x 1.5TB Seagate Barracuda 7200.11	£180
MEMORY	
2GB Corsair Value Select DDR2 PC2-5300	£22
OPTICAL DRIVE	
Samsung Super-WriteMaster SH-S202J	£14
OPERATING SYSTEM	
FreeNAS	Free
POWER SUPPLY	
OCZ ModXStream Pro 500W	£52
TOTAL	**£359**

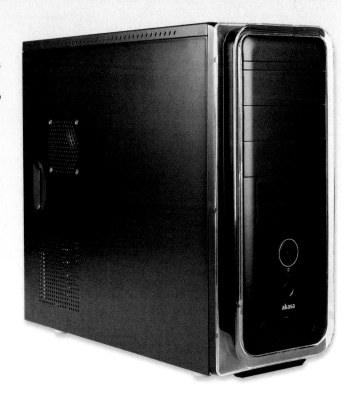

dabs●com

ULTIMATE PERFORMANCE

ASUS™ **P6T SE** Motherboard

Rock Solid · Heart Touching

P6T SE Motherboard

OFFER

Only £134*

Compatible with Windows®7

/ISUS RoHS Compliant

GREEN

Usually £139.99 Inc Vat   *Offer ends 19/11/09

With Heat Pipe cooling system

This motherboard supports the latest Intel Bloomfield processors (LGA1366) which have a memory controller integrated to support 3-channel (6 DIMMs) DDR3 memory. The Intel Bloomfield processor is one of the most powerful and energy efficient CPUs in the world. The Intel X58 Express Chipset is the latest chipset designed to support the latest Intel Core i7 Processors and Intel's next generation system interconnect interface - Intel QuickPath Interconnect (QPI) - providing improved performance by utilizing serial point-to-point links, allowing increased bandwidth and stability. It also supports up to 36 PCI Express 2.0 lanes providing better graphics performance.

| INTEL X58 EXPRESS | X12 USB 2.0 PORTS | ATX FORM FACTOR | SUPPORTS DRR3 SDRAM | LGA1366 PERFORMANCE SOCKET | CROSSFIRE SUPPORT ON VGA PORTS |

Bringing you low prices on all the latest technologies for over 20 years!

- Cameras & Camcorders
- Storage
- Memory & Upgrades
- Gaming & Gadgets
- Desktop PCs
- PC Components
- Cables & Accessories
- Printers & Multifunctions
- TFT Displays
- Laptops & Netbooks
- TV & Audio
- Networking & Communications
- Software
- Telephones & Mobiles
- In-Car & Sat-Nav

Buy online today at www.dabs.com/buildpc

Essential peripherals

ALTHOUGH GETTING THE base specifications for your PC and choosing the right operating system is incredibly important, you should also start thinking about the other peripherals you want to use. If you're sitting in front of your computer all day, buying a decent monitor and a comfortable keyboard and mouse is incredibly important. Don't scrimp and save on the extra peripherals, as you'll end up not enjoying using your new PC. Here, we'll talk you through the options that are available to you.

MONITORS

The monitor is your window into your computer. When you use your PC, it's this display that you'll be staring at all the time. Getting one that produces a decent image and fits your needs is, therefore, incredibly important.

If you haven't bought a monitor for a while, you'll be surprised at the increased choice available. For starters, regular 'square' monitors are pretty much a thing of the past, and have been replaced by widescreen monitors. These make watching films more pleasant and make working with things such as large spreadsheets much easier. With wider resolutions than standard monitors, things such as Windows Vista's Sidebar fit more comfortably on the screen and still leave plenty of rooms for documents.

Widescreen monitors, like standard displays before them, come in a range of different sizes and resolutions. At the bottom of the pile are budget 17in and 19in models, which have a 1,440x900 resolution. These typically start at less than £100. However, in our eyes they're not worth it. Instead, 22in monitors, such as BenQ's G2220HD, are larger and easier on the eye than 19in models and cost only a little more from around £130. The main benefit, however, is that most models have a resolution of 1,920x1,280, so you get a lot more information onscreen, and can watch Full HD video. If you'd like something a little bigger, 24in models such as Samsung's 2494HM have the same resolution and cost around £200.

If you want to take the next step up, you'll need a 26in monitor, such as LG's W2600H-PE. These have a resolution of 1,920x1,200, so are capable of displaying full 1080p HD video. For standard Windows use, this large desktop is a pleasure to use.

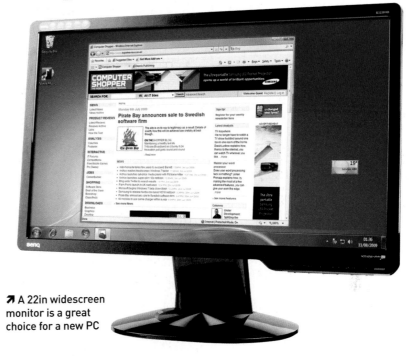

↗ A 22in widescreen monitor is a great choice for a new PC

If money's no object, you can opt for an even bigger screen with an even larger resolution. Dell's 3008WFP is a massive 30in monitor with an incredible 2,560x1,600 resolution, although at £1,033 it's also incredibly expensive.

When choosing a suitable monitor, it's worth being able to decipher the specifications to make sure you get one suitable for your needs. The viewing angles (horizontal and vertical) describe how far from straight on you can get before the picture deteriorates. Higher viewing angles are better, particularly if you want to use your monitor to show films to more than one person.

The brightness of a monitor is measured in candela per square metre (cd/m^2). The higher the number, the brighter the picture, so the easier your monitor will be to see. Brightness levels from $300cd/m^2$ should be chosen.

The contrast ratio of a monitor tells you the difference between the darkest shade (black) and the lightest shade (white) that the monitor can produce. Many modern monitors use dynamic contrast ratios, where the backlight is dimmed to increase the range of shades that can be produced. Typically, a monitor with a contrast ratio of 1,000:1 or higher should be able to produce dark blacks and bright whites.

The final specification that you'll come across is the response time. This measures how long it

TIP
If your PC has two graphics outputs – most graphics cards do – you can run two monitors together and split the Windows desktop over both.

↑ A 24in monitor has a high resolution, which is perfect for Windows applications and movies

takes the monitor to change a pixel from black to white and back to black, although some manufacturers 'cheat' and quote a grey-to-grey time. High response times imply that the picture will take a long time to change, so fast-moving action, as in games, could end up with ghosting and smearing. In our extensive tests we've noticed that as long as a monitor has a response time of 25ms or lower, you won't get any problems. Don't get drawn into paying more money for a monitor just because it has an incredibly quick advertised response time.

The only other option to consider is the type of inputs you want on your monitor. If the PC you're building has a digital DVI output, look for a monitor with a matching input. This will give you the best-quality picture. If you want to watch HD movies, then look for a monitor with an HDMI connection or HDCP support on its DVI input. If your PC only has an analogue D-sub output, you'll need a monitor with one of these. Most monitors that support DVI also have an D-sub input, too. If you want to connect a games console or regular

DVD player, you'll need a monitor with SCART, S-video, composite or S-video inputs. These are a lot rarer, though.

KEYBOARDS AND MICE

The keyboard and mouse remain the main way that we interact with our computers. Buying the right set is crucial if you want to make your computer easy to use. The most cost-effective way to buy a new keyboard and mouse is to get a set that includes both.

Most sets will include wireless peripherals. These are reliable and generally have long battery lives. With no cables to clutter up your desk, we highly recommend these products. The main choice you'll have to make is whether you want a regular keyboard or an ergonomic model.

Regular keyboards, such as Logitech's Cordless Desktop LX710 Laser (around £27 including VAT), are easiest for most people to use, as they place the keys in a straight line. For touch-typists, ergonomic keyboards can be better, as the keys are placed more naturally for the typing position. However, we've never got on very well with the full-on ergonomic models with the 'split' in the middle of the board. We've found that Logitech's Cordless Desktop Wave (around £42 including VAT) provides a decent balance

↘ The Desktop Wave's curved keyboard fits perfectly under your hands and makes typing easier

between comfort and ergonomic design. It has a slight 'smile' to it and each key is at a slightly different height to match the differences in finger length. It's a great keyboard if you're going to be doing a lot of typing.

Although wireless mice are fine for using Windows, if you play a lot of games a wired mouse is a much better option. This is because they don't have as much lag in them, so each mouse movement is replicated instantly in your game – essential if you want to get that accurate head shot. In this case, we'd recommend buying a dedicated gaming mouse, such as Razer's Death Adder (£40 including VAT).

If you love playing the latest games, you should think about buying a mouse mat, rather than using the surface of your desk. With the right mat, such as the ICEmat 2nd Edition (around £30), you'll get a low-friction surface, so your mouse will glide around effortlessly.

SPEAKERS

To get the best out of your computer, you need to invest in a decent set of speakers. Don't rely on those built into your monitor, as they'll never be able to produce the clean balanced sounds of a

↗ These surround-sound speakers can connect to your DVD player as well as your PC, making them ideal for use in a home-entertainment setup

dedicated set. Fortunately, buying speakers doesn't have to be expensive.

First, work out what kinds of speakers you want. Standard 2.1 sets have two stereo speakers and a sub-woofer, which produces rich, thumping bass. If you primarily use your computer for music or games, then these kinds of speakers will suit your computer. The best set we've reviewed, Logitech's X-230, costs only £30. For this, you'll get incredibly rich and detailed sound.

Next, you've got the choice of surround-sound speakers. These are ideal if you want immersive sound around you when you're watching films and want to enjoy the full soundtrack, for example. Surround-sound speakers typically come in 5.1 or 7.1 speaker configurations, where the .1 is the bass sub-woofer and the 5 and 7 refer to the number of satellite speakers. To be honest, 7.1 sets aren't worth it unless you'll be using your computer in a massive room. Besides, the extra two speakers and cables mean that you're just adding clutter to your home. A 5.1 set will suit most people.

Again, there's a choice of sets to consider. Standard 5.1 PC speakers, such as Logitech's X-540 (around £52), use analogue mini-jack plugs

↑ A decent set of 2.1 speakers will produce rich sounds in games and music

that connect to the sound card's outputs at the rear of your PC. To enjoy surround sound on your DVDs and HD movies, you'll need software capable of decoding the sound to analogue outputs. Windows Media Center will decode Dolby Digital soundtracks, but not DTS; CyberLink's PowerDVD will do all formats, but you'll need to upgrade to the full version from any 'lite' version that came bundled with your optical drive.

Alternatively, buying 5.1 speakers with a built-in decoder, such as Logitech's Z-5500 Digital (around £200), means that you can connect your computer digitally to the speakers and let them do the hard work of decoding. For this to work, you'll need to

have an S/PDIF output from your PC. The Z-5500 speakers have optical and coaxial S/PDIF inputs and can decode Dolby Digital and DTS soundtracks. They also have 5.1 channel analogue inputs, so you could still let your PC do the audio decoding. The benefit of this system is that you can also connect your regular DVD player to the speakers, so you can use them for your home cinema setup, too.

TV TUNERS

With Media Center now built into Vista Home Premium and Windows 7, turning your PC into a fully fledged hard disk recorder simply requires you to add a TV tuner. With Media Center's excellent free programme guide, you'll find a PC the easiest hard disk recorder to use. When you make your choice, there are a few things to consider.

First, it's not worth buying an analogue-only tuner. The analogue TV service is being turned off over the next few years, leaving only digital TV. That said, if you can't get a very good reception for digital TV, look to get a hybrid tuner with both digital and analogue capabilities; this way you can use the best signal but still switch over to digital when the time comes.

The best choice for most people is a digital tuner. As Media Center can handle two tuners at once, allowing you to record one channel while watching another, it makes sense to buy a TV card with dual tuners. This doesn't have to be expensive, as Terratec's Cinergy DT USB XS Diversity (£60) shows. This USB tuner plugs into a spare USB port, but you can also get internal tuners that plug into a spare PCI or PCI Express slot for similar money. The Diversity tag means that the card can use both tuners to improve the quality of your TV reception. However, using it in Diversity mode means you can only watch a single channel, as with a single-receiver TV tuner.

Finally, Freesat now means that you can get HD TV for free, and some cards give you this ability on your PC. To use the service, you'll need a satellite dish, such as those provided by Sky. The downside to Freesat at the moment is that Vista Media Center doesn't currently support the service, so you'll have to use the software bundled with the card. Fortunately, Windows 7 supports it, so use this OS if you want Freesat.

↑ A dual tuner allows you to watch one TV channel while recording another

McAfee®
Family Protection

Keep them safe from the bad things on the web.

Bolt on McAfee Family Protection to your existing security product and keep your children safe online.

Its fast and its simple, just add McAfee Family Protection to your existing security software and start protecting your children in minutes.

Giving you complete peace of mind, that whatever age your children are and wherever they surf, they will be completely safe.

McAfee Family Protection works with McAfee VirusScan Plus, McAfee Internet Security, McAfee Total Protection as well as security products from other brands.

✓ Peace of Mind

✓ Perfect for Children of All Ages

✓ Instant Message Reporting

✓ Email Alerts

✓ YouTube Filtering

✓ Peer-to-peer File Sharing controls

On sale now for only
£29.99! RRP

Available from **www.mcafee.co.uk**, PC World and other good retailers.

CHAPTER 4

BUILDING YOUR PC

THE MAIN TASK you have when building a PC is making sure that you put all the components together correctly so that your new computer works first time. Our detailed step-by-step advice will help you put any PC together from start to finish.

IN THIS CHAPTER

Taking the case apart

TIP
If you're having trouble taking your case apart, look out for hidden screws that may be holding it together.

REMOVE THE FRONT Many cases require you to remove the front panel. Some simply lift off, but check for screws and clips inside.

SCREWS Most cases are held together by screws that need to be removed. Thumbscrews such as these can be undone without a screwdriver.

HOW TO...
Take the case apart

1 REMOVE THE SIDES
Start by taking off the side panels to get inside the case. As noted on the diagram opposite, you may need to take the front panel off first to get at the screws to remove the side panels. Some cases, like the one pictured, have thumbscrews, so you don't even need a screwdriver. If your case has a second panel, make sure that you remove this, too, so that you can work on both sides of the case when you're inside it.

2 TAKE OUT INNARDS
Once you're inside your case, you need to check it for accessories. It's common for manufacturers to put spare screws, proprietary drive rails and instruction manuals inside. Take out everything that isn't screwed into place. Look for silica gel taped to the side as well. Remove any packaging so that you're left with a bare interior.

3 REMOVE OPTICAL DRIVE BLANKING PLATES
In order to fit your optical drive later, you may need to remove some plastic and metal blanking plates. At this point, if you haven't had to already, it's probably helpful to take the front of the case off. Your case's manual will tell you how to do this, but most cases simply unclip from the inside.

Look for the 5¼in drive bay into which you'll fit your optical drive. Match this up to the front panel. On some cases this will be the top one, which will have a flap to hide the optical drive from view, so you don't have to get a drive the same colour as your case. On other cases, you'll have a plastic blanking plate on the front panel that should unclip.

Inside the case, you'll find a metal blanking plate that you'll need to remove. By gently rocking it backwards and forwards, you should be able to break the connection. Be careful not to cut yourself doing this.

4 REMOVE FLOPPY DRIVE BLANKING PLATES
If you're planning to fit a memory card reader or floppy disk drive, you'll need to follow the same steps you did for the optical drive. Find the 3½in drive bay you want to use and break off the metal blanking plate. Next, pop out the corresponding plastic blanking plate on the front panel.

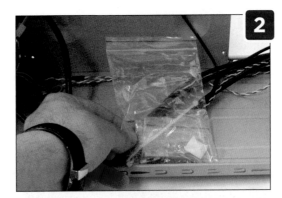

TIP
The inside of the case can have sharp edges, so be careful when you remove any blanking plates.

Installing the power supply

The ATX connector provides power to your motherboard

The SATA connector is for hard disks and optical drives

A standard PCI Express graphics card connector

The newer 8-pin PCI-E power connector

TIP
Tuck any unwanted cables out of the way inside the case to improve airflow and keep your PC tidy.

The secondary motherboard power connector

A connector for floppy disks and memory card readers

The Molex connector is for hard disks

HOW TO...
Install the power supply

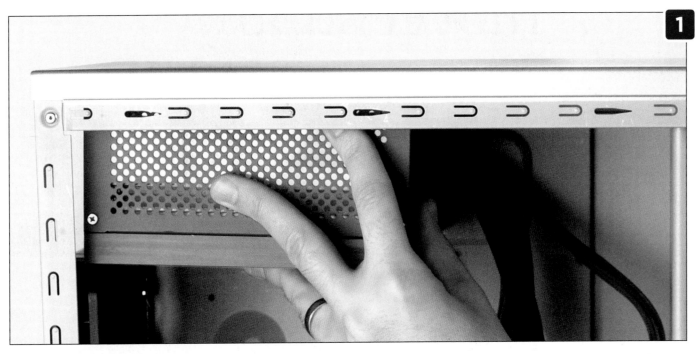

1 **FIT SUPPLY ON TO SHELF**
If your power supply fits at the top of your case (some cases have space at the bottom), you'll see a small shelf for it to rest on. Slide the power supply on to this shelf and push it backwards until it makes contact with the back of the case.

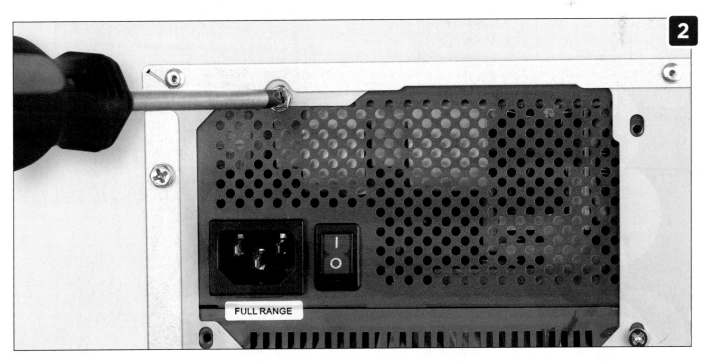

2 **SCREW IN SUPPLY**
If your power supply is the correct way round, its screw holes will match up with those in the back of the case. If they don't, remove the supply and rotate it 180°. Use four screws to attach the power supply securely to the case.

Installing the motherboard

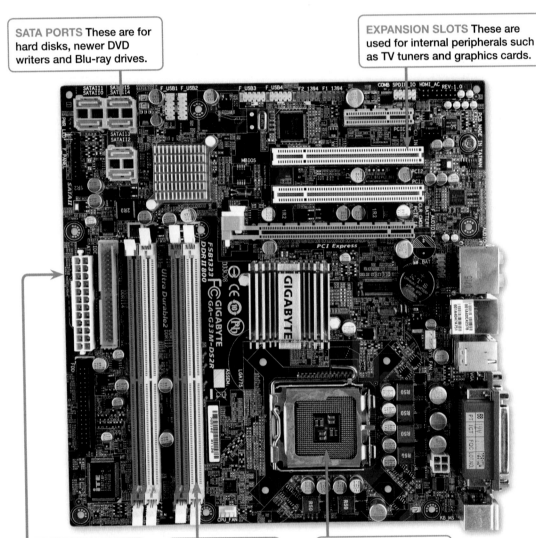

SATA PORTS These are for hard disks, newer DVD writers and Blu-ray drives.

EXPANSION SLOTS These are used for internal peripherals such as TV tuners and graphics cards.

IDE PORT This is for attaching a DVD writer or old hard disk.

MEMORY SLOTS These are for your PC's memory.

PROCESSOR SOCKET For your processor.

TIP Blanking plates can be difficult to fit. Push them in until they click, but don't worry if they're not entirely level around the sides.

REAR PANEL CONNECTORS These ports are fixed on your motherboard.

HOW TO...
Install the motherboard

1 UNPACK THE BOARD
Open your motherboard's box. You'll see lots of cables, a driver CD, a metal blanking plate with holes cut out and a manual. Take these components out and put them to one side, as you'll need them later on.

The motherboard will be inside an anti-static bag and resting on top of anti-static foam. Slide the motherboard out of the bag, but leave it attached to the foam for now. Place the motherboard and foam on top of the anti-static bag, and take out the metal blanking plate.

2 MEASURE BLANKING PLATE
The blanking plate fits into the case, and gives you access only to the ports that your motherboard has. However, some motherboard manufacturers use generic blanking plates that fit their entire range of boards. With these, you may need to remove some metal covers to give access to your motherboard's ports.

The easiest way to see is to hold the blanking plate up to the motherboard until the cutouts match the ports on your board. The blanking plate should be pushed against the motherboard with the ridge pointing out, so any text is readable. It will only fit one way, so manoeuvre it until it's the right way. Make a note of any ports that are covered.

3 REMOVE UNNECESSARY BITS
If you need to remove any parts of the blanking plate, you should do that now. You'll have two options for doing this. First, you may have to remove a bit of metal, in a similar way to the metal blanking plates on your case. These should be rocked gently out until the metal snaps.

Second, some ports may be covered by a flap. In this case, the flap should be bent inwards (towards where the motherboard will be). Make sure that you bend it far enough for the motherboard's port to be given enough clearance to pass underneath.

4 INSTALL THE BLANKING PLATE
From the inside of the case, you need to take the blanking plate and push it into the gap at

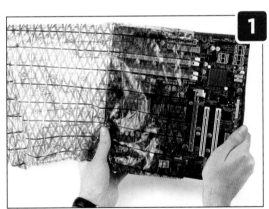

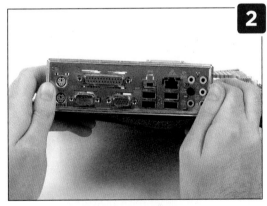

TIP
Motherboards can require a bit of force to be inserted. Push from the sides of the board; don't force any components, as this could cause damage.

the rear of the case. Remember to align it so that it's the same way up as when you measured it against your motherboard.

The ridge round the outside of the plate should clip into the hole. Be warned that this can be really fiddly and the blanking plates don't always fit perfectly. It should, however, clip into place and remain stable without any support.

5 MEASURE WHERE THE MOTHERBOARD GOES

Next, you need to see where the screw holes for the motherboard will go. Lie the case flat on the desk and make sure that all the internal cables are out of the way. When you've got a clear case, take the motherboard off its foam backing and slide it gently into the case. Make sure that its rear ports are pushed up against the blanking plate correctly. Take a note of where the screw holes in the motherboard go, and remove the board. Place it back on its foam.

6 FIT THE RISERS

You need to fit risers where you noted the screw holes. These will be included with the case and look like tall copper screws. Their job is to hold the motherboard off the bottom of the case, so it isn't shorted out when its contacts touch the metal. The risers simply screw into the pre-drilled holes in

the case. Use as many risers as there are screw holes in the motherboard, making sure that you screw them tightly into position with your fingers.

7 SLIDE THE MOTHERBOARD INTO PLACE

Put the motherboard back in the case, making sure that all its screw holes have risers underneath. If some are missing, check to make sure that you haven't screwed the risers into the wrong place. You'll probably notice that the motherboard has a tendency to be slightly off from the risers. This is normal, and is caused by pressure from the backplate pushing against the motherboard. Simply line up the motherboard's ports with the backplate and push the motherboard towards it until the screw holes line up. This will take a bit of gentle force.

8 SCREW THE MOTHERBOARD DOWN

With the motherboard in place, you can start to screw it in. Start with the corners, holding the motherboard firmly, so that its screw holes line up with the risers that you put in.

When screwing the screws in, don't use too much pressure as you don't want to break the motherboard. Ideally, you want the screws tight enough for the board to be secure, but not so tight that it feels as though the board is going to start cracking.

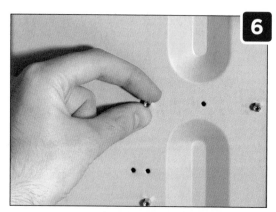

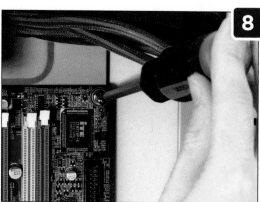

Once you've done the corners, you can put screws in the other holes. How many you put in is up to you, but you shouldn't need to do all of them to make the motherboard secure. Keep going until the motherboard is firmly in place.

9 IDENTIFY ATX CONNECTORS

With the motherboard in place, you're ready to connect it to the power supply. There are two connectors that you'll need to plug in. The first is the ATX connector. On modern motherboards, you need a 24-pin connector. There's only one of these on the power supply. However, as older motherboards only required a 20-pin connector, there's usually a four-pin connector that can be detached. Make sure that this is connected and that you have an unbroken 24-pin connector.

10 PLUG IN ATX CONNECTOR

You need to plug this 24-pin connector into the matching connector on the motherboard. This should be easy to find, but it's usually located by the IDE ports on the right-hand side of the motherboard.

The ATX connector will only plug in one way, so you can't get it wrong. Once it's lined up, the connector should plug in smoothly. There's a clip on it to hold it in place. This will require gentle pressure to get it to clip in, but no more. If you're

having to force the cable, then the chances are that you've got the connector the wrong way round. Once the cable is in place, give it a gentle tug to make sure that it's secure.

11 IDENTIFY SECONDARY CONNECTOR

Modern motherboards also have a secondary power connector. On most boards this is a single four-pin connector, but some require eight-pin connectors. Check to see what your power supply has, as you may need to buy an adaptor.

In a similar way to the 24-pin connector, the eight-pin connector on power supplies can be split into two. If your motherboard has only a four-pin connector, you'll have to split it into two halves. Only one of these will plug into the motherboard.

12 CONNECT SECONDARY CONNECTOR

Locate the secondary motherboard power connector. Your board's manual will tell you exactly where it's located, but on most motherboards it's near the processor socket. Next, plug the power supply's secondary connector into it. This plug will only go in one way, so there's no chance of getting it wrong. The connector should slide gently into the plug. You'll need to apply a bit of force in order to get the clip to lock into place, and you should hear it click when it's in properly.

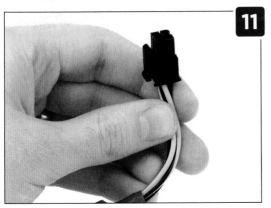

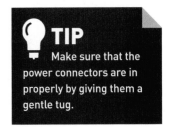

TIP
Make sure that the power connectors are in properly by giving them a gentle tug.

HOW TO...
Install an Intel processor

1 LIFT THE PROCESSOR CAGE
Intel's processor sockets are covered by a cage. A new motherboard will also have a plastic cover on top. First, remove this cover. It should easily unclip. To access the socket, unclip the handle that runs down the side of the socket and lift it up. This releases the retaining clip for the main cage.

Lift the main cage up and out of the way to expose the socket. Be careful not to touch any of the pins inside the socket, as bending them will stop the processor from working correctly.

2 INSTALL THE PROCESSOR
The processor has two cut-out notches in its sides, which line up with the ridges in the socket. This prevents the processor from being put in the wrong way round. You'll also notice an arrow on the processor. This should line up with the corner of the socket that has its pins arranged diagonally.

Line the processor up and sit it gently in the place. If it doesn't sit properly, then you've got it the wrong way round. Once you're happy with the processor's position, close the drive cage and pull the retaining handle down. This should take a bit of force, but if it feels like there's too much resistance, check that the processor is seated properly.

3 THERMAL PASTE
Thermal paste fills in micro-cracks in the surface of the processor and the surface of the cooler, ensuring that there's efficient heat transfer between the two. Some fans come pre-coated with thermal paste, in which case you can skip this step.

If it doesn't, you'll need to apply your own. This is easy to do. First, squeeze a tiny blob of thermal paste into the middle of the processor. Take a thin bit of card and use this to spread it, so that the surface of the processor is coated. Don't spread it over the side of the cage, and add more thermal paste if you don't have enough.

4 ATTACH THE FAN
Most Intel coolers clip into the four round holes on the outside of the processor socket. If you're not using an Intel reference cooler bundled with your processor, check the cooler's instructions; some need a backplate screwed to the motherboard.

For all other coolers, you'll see four feet. Make sure that all the feet are rotated away from the direction of the arrow. Line up the cooler so that the four feet touch the holes in the motherboard. It's best to try to get the power cable pointing towards the header on the motherboard marked CPU (we'll cover this later).

Starting at diagonally opposite sides, push the four feet into the place. You'll need some force, and the feet should click into position. When done, check the cooler is seated properly and that it isn't wobbly. If it is, make sure the feet are properly in position.

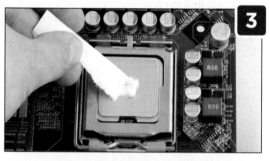

TIP
The plastic clips on Intel coolers can be annoying to fit. Make sure the black plastic clips are raised before fitting the cooler, and push diagonally opposite clips in together.

HOW TO...
Install an AMD processor

1 OPEN THE SOCKET LEVER
AMD's processors fit into AM2, AM2+ or AM3 sockets. The sockets are very similar, so the installation instructions are the same.

To fit the processor in the socket, first lift the lever. This unclips to one side and rises vertically above the board. This will move the socket very slightly, aligning the holes in the plastic socket with the connectors beneath. The processor should drop into place with no force, hence the socket's type: zero insertion force (ZIF).

2 FIT THE PROCESSOR
The processor can fit only one way into the socket. Make sure the arrow on top of the processor is aligned with the arrow on the processor socket. Gently push the processor into place. You should feel it click into position when it's all the way in. If it feels like you have to use too much force, stop and check that the processor is correctly aligned.

Once the processor is all the way in, check round it to make sure that it's sitting flush against the plastic socket. If it's not, push gently down on the sections that aren't flush. Push the lever down and clip it back into place to secure the processor.

3 THERMAL PASTE
Thermal paste fills in micro-cracks in the surface of the processor and the surface of the cooler, ensuring that there's efficient heat transfer between the two. You may find that your fan comes pre-coated with thermal paste, in which case you can skip this step.

If it doesn't, you'll need to apply your own. This is simple to do. First, squeeze a tiny blob of thermal paste into the middle of the processor. Take a thin bit of card and use this to spread it, so that the surface of the processor is coated. Don't spread it over the side of the processor, and add more thermal paste if necessary.

4 FIT THE COOLER
If you're using a third-party cooler, check its instructions for how to fit it. If you're using an AMD cooler that came with your processor, fitting it is simple. Around the processor socket is a plastic cooler mount, with two nodules sticking out. These are designed to hold your cooler's clips.

Take your cooler and open its handle. Fit the metal clip without the handle on it over one nodule and push it snugly against the mount. Place the cooler flat across the top of the processor. Push the cooler's remaining metal clip over the second nodule and close the handle. This will require a bit of force to get the handle all the way down. We'll cover connecting the fan's power connector later.

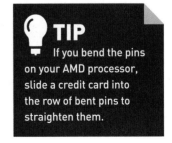

TIP
If you bend the pins on your AMD processor, slide a credit card into the row of bent pins to straighten them.

Installing memory

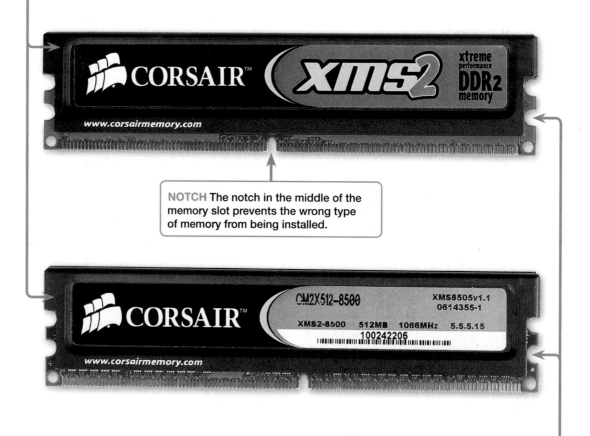

DUAL MEMORY Motherboards have dual memory channels. Installing two memory modules – one in each channel – can increase performance. The slots to use are usually the same colour, but check your motherboard's manual first.

NOTCH The notch in the middle of the memory slot prevents the wrong type of memory from being installed.

CLIPS The clips at the side of the memory slot hold the RAM in place. You open them to install memory, and they close automatically when the RAM is installed.

TIP
Make sure your memory is lined up properly before you insert it to prevent damage.

HOW TO...
Install memory

1 IDENTIFY WHICH SLOTS TO USE
Presuming that you've bought memory in a kit with two sticks of RAM, you should now identify the slots in which you're going to install the memory. As noted opposite, the slots to use are usually the same colour, but you should check your motherboard's manual carefully to make sure that you're using the right ones.

To be doubly safe, the slots will also be numbered to make it easier to follow the motherboard manual's instructions.

2 OPEN THE RETAINING CLIPS
To install your memory, you need to open the clips on either end of the slot into which you're going to insert your memory stick. Pick the first slot and push open these clips; they should open gently without any force, clicking as they open. The clips should open to around 45°, but don't force them further open when you feel resistance.

3 LINE THE MEMORY UP
To fit the memory, you need to slide it into the slot. Make sure that the notch in the memory lines up with the ridge in the socket. If it doesn't, then you've got the memory the wrong way round.

If the memory still doesn't fit, then you're using the wrong type of memory. Check the memory's instructions and motherboard's manual to see what type you need.

4 CLIP THE MEMORY INTO PLACE
Once the memory module is lined up, press firmly on both sides to push it into place. The clips should spring back and click into position. Check the clips are in place and nestled against the notches in the side of the memory module. If they're not, try pushing the memory down a bit further. You can also push the clips up to help them lock into place.

Once your first module is in place, repeat these steps for any remaining modules.

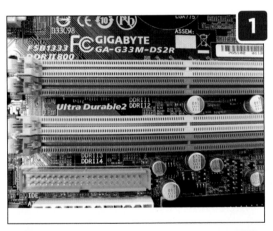

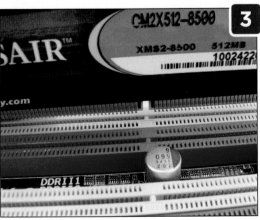

TIP
Push down evenly on both sides of the module, or you'll find it hard to get the retaining clips to lock into place.

HOW TO...
Fit the internal cables

1 POWER

To get your PC to turn on when you push the power button, you need to connect the power switch to the motherboard. Among the loose cables in your case, you'll find a two-pin connector. This will usually be marked PWR SW, but check the case's manual if you're not sure.

This needs to be connected to the power jumpers on the motherboard. Typically, these will be located on the bottom-right of the motherboard and will be marked, although you should double-check your motherboard's manual to make sure. The connector will just plug over the two pins and should connect easily.

2 RESET

If your case has a reset switch – not all do – then there will be a similar connector to the power switch, with RESET SW written on it. Connecting this to your motherboard lets you restart your PC after a major crash, as it resets the hardware and forces your computer to reboot.

To connect it, you need to find the reset jumpers on the motherboard. These will be near the power switch, but you should read your motherboard's manual for an exact location. Simply push the connector over the two pins

to connect the switch. It doesn't matter which way round this connector goes.

3 POWER AND HDD LEDS

The HDD connector connects to an LED on the front of the case and lights up when the hard disk is in operation. This is useful, as you can see whether your PC's working or if it's crashed.

As this connects to an LED, it must be connected correctly. The cable should be marked as positive and negative (this is usually written on the plug). The motherboard HDD jumper will also have a positive and negative port. Check your motherboard's manual carefully to make sure you get this right, and then connect the cable.

Do the same thing for the power LED, which will have a similar connector. This must be connected the right way round, so make sure you get the positive and negative connectors aligned.

4 USB

If your case has front-mounted USB ports or a card reader, you'll need to connect these to spare headers on your motherboard. In all likelihood, the cable in the case will be marked USB.

Your motherboard will probably have spare connectors marked USB, but the manual can tell

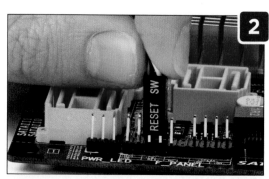

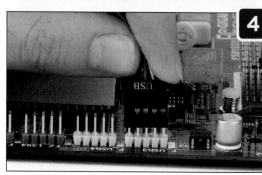

you exactly where these are. USB connectors take power, so you need to plug the cable in the right way round. Fortunately, the USB ports on most cases have a single plug that can only be connected to the motherboard in one way. If it doesn't, you'll need to check the case's and motherboard's manuals carefully to make sure that you install the connectors correctly.

Assuming you're using a block connector, plug it into a spare USB header on the motherboard. We'd recommend using the closest header to the cable to avoid draping cables everywhere.

5 FIREWIRE

Front-mounted FireWire cables plug in much the same way as USB cables. Again, look for a spare FireWire header on the motherboard (the manual will explain where these are), and then connect the FireWire cable to it. The cable may be marked as 1394, as FireWire is also known as i1394.

6 AUDIO

Front-mounted audio ports also need to be connected to the motherboard if you want to be able to plug in your headphones and a microphone. Fortunately, most motherboards and cases have a single block connector that plugs into the front audio connector on the motherboard.

Your motherboard's manual will have full details of where this is connected, but it's usually located by its back panel. Again, there's only one way to connect this cable, so just slide it gently into place. If your case has a Speaker header, plug this into

the appropriate connector on the motherboard. This is used to give warning beeps.

7 FANS

It's common for modern cases to have extra fans pre-fitted. These help increase airflow through the case and keep your PC cool. While fans can be connected directly to the power supply, it's better to connect them to spare fan headers on the motherboard. This way, the motherboard can automatically control the fan speed and keep your PC running as quietly as possible.

If your fans end in three- or four-pin connectors, you can plug them into your motherboard. Look at the manual to find a spare fan connector and then plug in the fan's power connector. Three-pin connectors can plug into four-pin ports and vice versa. The cables can also plug in only one way, so it's easy to get it right.

8 CPU FAN

The processor fan, which we installed earlier, can now be connected to the motherboard. In the same way as system fans, the processor's fan speed is controlled by the motherboard based on the processor's temperature. This keeps your computer as quiet as possible.

There's a special connector for the processor fan on the motherboard, which is often called CPU FAN. Check your motherboard's manual for its location. This is likely to be a four-pin connector, but three-pin processor fans can also plug in. The connector can go in only one way, so just plug it in.

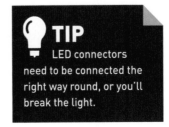

TIP
LED connectors need to be connected the right way round, or you'll break the light.

Installing a hard disk

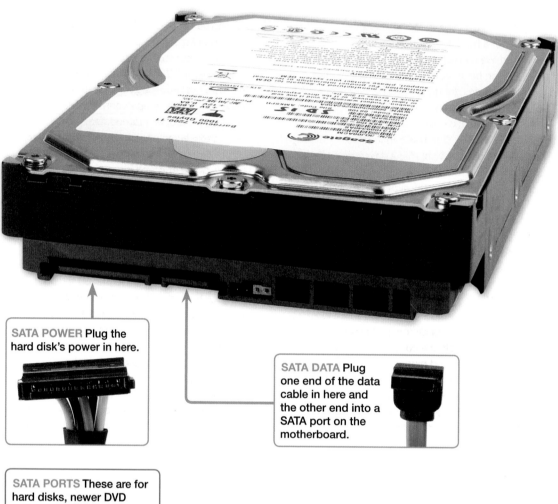

SATA POWER Plug the hard disk's power in here.

SATA DATA Plug one end of the data cable in here and the other end into a SATA port on the motherboard.

SATA PORTS These are for hard disks, newer DVD writers and Blu-ray drives.

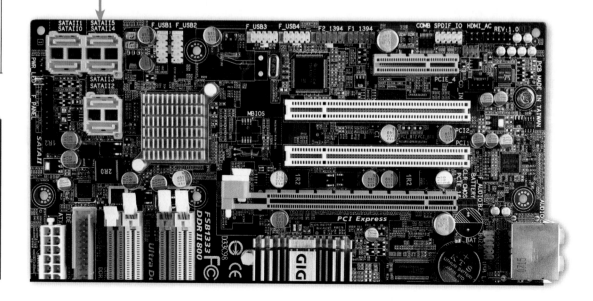

TIP
If you're installing more than one hard disk, plug the one from which you want to boot in the lowest-numbered SATA port. The BIOS will pick this hard disk as the boot drive by default.

HOW TO...
Install a hard disk

1 FIT HARD DISK INTO A BAY

To fit a hard disk, you need to find a 3½in drive bay. Be careful not to use one of the external bays, which have a cutout on the front of the case, as these are designed for memory card readers and floppy disk drives.

If your case has drive rails or screwless fittings, you'll need to read the case's manual for instructions on how to fit these drives. For other cases, slide the hard disk into a spare drive bay until the screw holes in the side of the drive line up with the holes in the drive bay. The disk should then be secured with four screws: two either side of the case. Suitable screws should have been provided with the hard disk or case. Screw these up tightly to prevent the drive wobbling.

2 PLUG IN SATA POWER

In the main picture opposite, you can see the SATA power connector on the hard disk and on the power supply. Locate the correct connector from your power supply and plug it into the back of your hard disk. It goes in only one way and clicks when it's connected. Be extremely careful when plugging it in, as downwards pressure can break the clip surrounding the power connector. If you do this, the power plug won't stay in place.

3 PLUG IN SATA DATA CABLE

Unlike IDE, SATA uses a simple and thin connector to carry data. Your motherboard will ship with several SATA cables, so take one of these from the box. Plug it gently into the rear of the hard disk. It will plug in only one way and will click when it's properly connected.

Be careful when you plug it in, as downwards pressure can break the connector and prevent the SATA cable plugging in.

4 PLUG SATA DATA CABLE INTO MOTHERBOARD

Next, you need to find a spare SATA port on your motherboard. These are usually located at the bottom-right of the board and are numbered. The lower the number, the higher up the boot chain your hard disk is. If you're installing more than one hard disk, therefore, make sure the drive from which you're going to boot is plugged into the lowest-numbered port. Check the motherboard's manual to ensure that all the ports do the same thing; some boards have ports reserved for RAID.

Connecting the SATA cable is easy, as it will plug in only one way. It will click when the cable is connected properly.

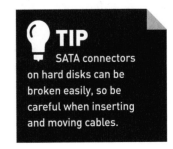

TIP
SATA connectors on hard disks can be broken easily, so be careful when inserting and moving cables.

Installing an optical drive

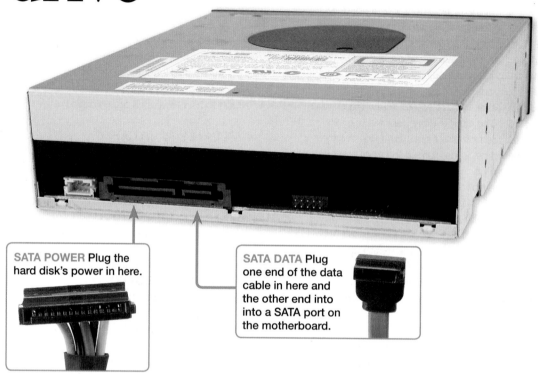

SATA POWER Plug the hard disk's power in here.

SATA DATA Plug one end of the data cable in here and the other end into into a SATA port on the motherboard.

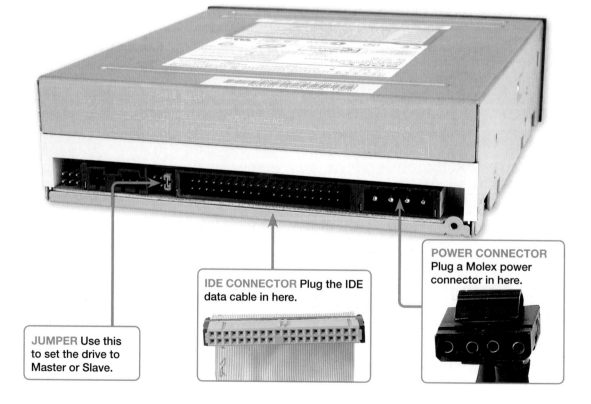

IDE CONNECTOR Plug the IDE data cable in here.

JUMPER Use this to set the drive to Master or Slave.

POWER CONNECTOR Plug a Molex power connector in here.

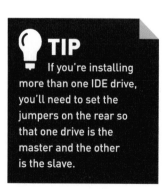

TIP
If you're installing more than one IDE drive, you'll need to set the jumpers on the rear so that one drive is the master and the other is the slave.

HOW TO...
Connect an optical drive

1 FIT THE DRIVE

First, fit the optical drive into a spare 5¼in drive bay in the case. Some cases have flaps at the front to hide the optical drive from view. If you have a screwless case or your drives need to be fitted on runners, consult your case's manual for full instructions.

Other cases require you to screw the drive into place. The optical drive needs to be slid into the case from the front. This often means that you need to have the front of the case removed, if you haven't done that yet. Slide the drive into the bay. The front of it needs to be flush with the case where there's no flap, and slightly further back if your case has a drive flap.

To tell where the drive should be, push it in until the screw holes in its side match up with the round screw holes inside the case. Now use the four screws (provided with the optical drive or case) – two either side – to hold the drive in place.

2 FIT THE IDE CABLE

Most optical drives use the older IDE data connector. If yours uses SATA, follow the instructions for fitting a hard disk (page 58). An IDE cable is a wide ribbon cable. It's harder to plug in than a SATA cable, but shouldn't cause any problems if you know what to look out for. First, the cable can plug in only one way due to a blocked-off connector in the cable. Second, the coloured cable (red or white depending on the cable provided with your motherboard) goes to the right of the connector closest to the power connector. Plug the cable in gently and as straight as possible so as not to bend any pins on the drive.

3 FIT THE POWER CABLE

Optical drives tend to use a Molex power connector. This is the large four-pin connector on your power supply. Locate a free one and push it into the drive's power connector. Use a bit of force to get it to connect properly. Once you think it's in, give it a gentle tug to make sure it's secure.

4 FIT THE IDE CABLE INTO THE MOTHERBOARD

Now you're ready to plug the cable into the motherboard. Don't get the connector confused with the floppy disk connector; check your motherboard's manual for its location. The IDE connector can plug in only one way, thanks to a notch in the motherboard's connector. Plug in the cable gently as straight as possible to avoid bending any pins.

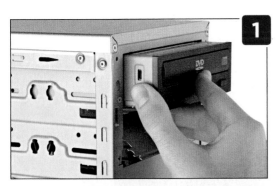

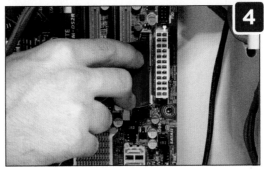

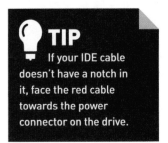

TIP
If your IDE cable doesn't have a notch in it, face the red cable towards the power connector on the drive.

Installing a graphics card

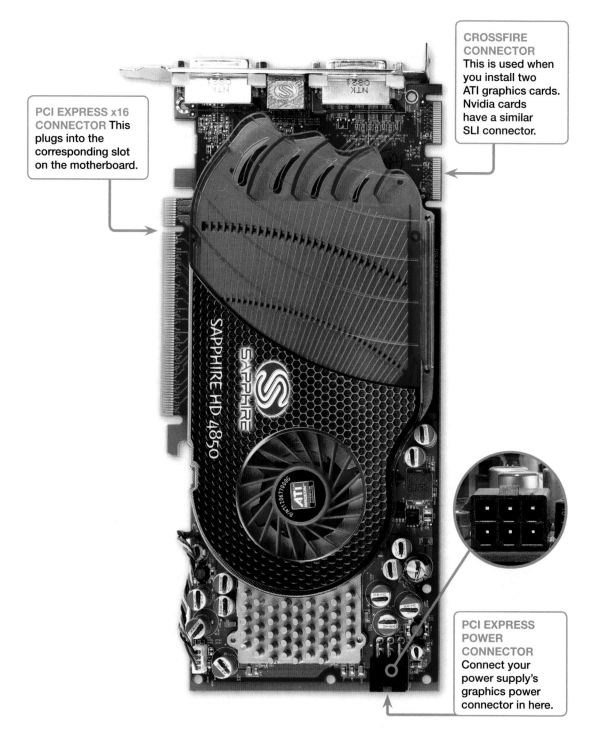

CROSSFIRE CONNECTOR This is used when you install two ATI graphics cards. Nvidia cards have a similar SLI connector.

PCI EXPRESS x16 CONNECTOR This plugs into the corresponding slot on the motherboard.

PCI EXPRESS POWER CONNECTOR Connect your power supply's graphics power connector in here.

TIP
PCI Express x16 slots typically have retaining clips. You'll need to use this clip if you have to remove a graphics card later.

HOW TO...
Install a graphics card

1 REMOVE BLANKING PLATE
To fit a graphics card, you'll need to locate the PCI Express x16 slot and remove the associated blanking plate. If you're going to fit a double-height card, then you'll need to remove the blanking plate for the next expansion slot as well.

The steps will differ according to your case, so check its manual for full details. Typically, blanking plates are either screwed in place individually, or a single retaining bar holds them all in place. Remove whatever's holding the blanking plates in place. Some blanking plates just lift out, while others are attached to the case and need to be rocked backwards and forwards to snap them out.

2 PLUG CARD INTO SLOT
With the blanking plates free, you can put your card into the case. This is easy to do: simply line up the graphics card's connector with the slot in the case. The card should look like it's upside down, with the fan pointing towards the bottom of the case.

Pressure on both sides of the card should be enough to make sure that it ends up seated in the expansion card slot properly. You should check the card when you think it's in place to ensure that you've made proper contact. If you can still see some of the card's slot sticking out, then push the offending side in a bit further.

3 SCREW CARD IN PLACE
How you remove the blanking plate will depend on how you attach your card securely, so check the case's manual for full details. In most instances, you'll need to screw the card into place. Line up the top of its connector with the screw hole in the case and screw it into place so that the card can't move in its slot.

4 CONNECT POWER ADAPTOR
Most modern graphics cards require a secondary power source to run. These will need a dedicated PCI Express six-pin power connector. This is on most modern power supplies, but if yours doesn't have one, a Molex-to-PCI Express adaptor is often bundled with graphics cards. The PCI Express power connector can plug in only one way and can be pushed easily into place.

TIP
Don't forget to plug in the PCI Express power connector (if required), or your PC may not turn on.

Installing expansion cards

PCI SLOTS An older type of expansion slot, but there are plenty of cards that will fit them.

PCI EXPRESS x1 SLOT The newest type of expansion slot. Also look out for x4 slots, which look similar but are longer.

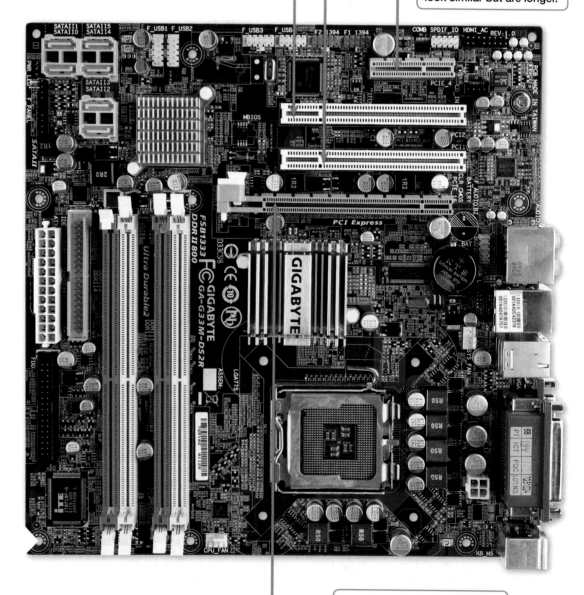

PCI EXPRESS x16 SLOT If you don't install a dedicated graphics card, this slot can be used for expansion cards.

TIP
PCI Express cards can fit in a higher socket type, so an x1 card can fit in an x4 slot and so on.

HOW TO...
Plug in expansion cards

1 LOCATE SPARE SLOT

Before you start, carefully read the instructions that came with your expansion card as some require you to install software first. If yours does, you'll need to finish building the PC and install the operating system and necessary software before fitting the expansion card.

When you're ready, find a spare slot (PCI or PCI Express) on your motherboard. Ideally, leave a gap between other expansion cards, such as your graphics card, to increase airflow and keep your PC running cool.

2 REMOVE BLANKING PLATE

To fit an expansion card, you'll need to remove the expansion slot's blanking plate. The steps will differ according to your case, so carefully check its manual for full details. Typically, blanking plates are either individually screwed in place or held in place by a single retaining bar. Remove whatever's holding the blanking plates in place. Some plates just lift out, while others are attached to the case and need to be rocked backwards and forwards to snap them out.

3 FIT THE CARD

PCI and PCI Express cards are fitted in the same way. Line up the connector on the bottom of the card with the slot in which you want to put it. Slots have notches part of the way along, which you need to line up with the gap in the card's connector. When you've done this, push the card into place. It will take a bit of force to get the card to slide home properly. If the card doesn't feel like it's going to go into the slot, remove it and make sure it's lined up and that you're trying to install it into the correct slot. When the card is in place, check round it to make sure the connector is firmly in the slot. If the card doesn't look level, apply pressure to the part of the card sticking up until it clicks into place.

4 SCREW IT IN

When your card is firmly in place, you need to secure it in its slot. As some cases use proprietary fixing methods, check your case's manual for instructions on how to do this. If you need to use a screw, line up the screw hole in the card's blanking plate with the screw hole in the case. Tighten the screw up to the point where the card feels firm and doesn't wobble in the slot.

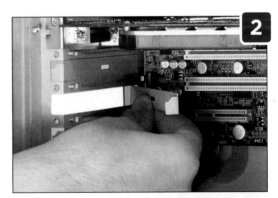

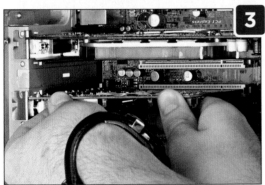

TIP
Try to use alternate slots in order to improve airflow and stop adjacent cards from heating one another up.

HOW TO...
Put the case back together

1 CABLE TIDY

If the inside of your computer is neat and tidy, you'll get better airflow and keep it cooler. A neat PC is also easier to work on should you need to install an upgrade later on.

One way to keep your case tidy is to fit cable ties. Simply locate loose cables that are running in the same direction and loop a cable tie around the bunch. Slide the strap through the buckle and pull it tight. The ratchet should click into place and stop the cable becoming undone. If it doesn't, you've inserted the strap the wrong way into the buckle. You can clip the long strap off when you're done. For extra neatness, loop the strap through drive bays in the case. This will anchor your cables out of the way.

2 KEEP CABLES OUT OF FANS

It's worth double-checking that none of your power cables is in the way of the fans inside your PC. If they are, you run the risk of severing your cables when you turn your PC on for the first time. Pull any loose cables out of the way of fans and secure them with cable ties if necessary. The processor fan (particularly on Intel's designs) is often the worse culprit for snagging cables, so check this one carefully.

3 ATTACH FRONT

Check your case's manual for the exact fitting instructions. If you removed its front, now is the time to fit it again. Line its clips up with the holes in the case and push firmly to reattach it. If you find that your optical drive sticks out too far, you've probably fitted it incorrectly. Undo its screws (or fixings if your case is screwless) and slide it further into the case. Screw it back in and fit the front of the case.

4 ATTACH SIDES

Check your case's manual carefully for full fitting instructions. For most cases, fitting the side panels is a matter of lining up their clips with the grooves on the inside of the case. Take each panel in turn, slide it into place and attach it firmly with a screw.

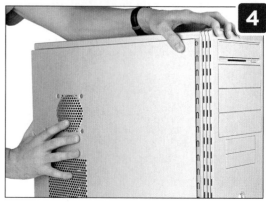

5 CONNECT NETWORK CABLE

If you want to connect your PC to a broadband router via an Ethernet cable, now's the time to plug it in. Vista's and Windows 7's installations can use a the internet to search for updated drivers, to make your installation smoother. Even if you're not using Windows 7 or Vista, being able to connect straight to the internet after installing an operating system is really useful.

6 CONNECT KEYBOARD AND MOUSE

To install an operating system, you'll need to connect a mouse and keyboard. Most motherboards support older PS2 keyboards and mice as well as newer USB models. PS2 keyboards plug into the purple port and mice into the green one. Simply line up the notch in the plug with the one in the port in the back of your computer and push.

For USB keyboards and mice, plug the connector into a free USB port; it will go only one way. For other USB devices, check their manuals before plugging them in. Many devices require you to install drivers first, so you'll have to install an operating system before you can plug them in.

7 CONNECT SPEAKERS

You can connect your speakers to your PC now. This is useful, as after installing an operating system you'll be able to check instantly whether the sound is working properly. How you connect your speakers will depend on how many you're plugging in. Generally speaking, surround-sound speakers have colour-coded cables, so you just need to match the cable with the same-coloured port on the back of your PC. For stereo speakers, plug a 3½mm jack into the green port on the back of the PC. Headphones generally connect to the green port on the front of the case.

8 PLUG IN MONITOR

Finally, you need to connect your computer to a monitor. This is simple. If your screen has a DVI input and your graphics card has a DVI output (pictured), you need a DVI-to-DVI cable. These are D-shaped, so they will plug in only one way. Line up the cable with the graphics card's connector and push the cable straight in. Screw it in place using the thumbscrews on either side of the connector. Repeat this on job on the monitor.

If your monitor has a blue analogue D-sub connector, you have two options. For graphics cards with DVI outputs, you'll have to plug in a DVI-to-D-sub connector first. You can then plug the D-sub cable into this and the monitor. If you're using onboard graphics with a D-sub output, plug the cable directly into this and the monitor. Just like DVI connectors, D-sub connectors are D-shaped, so they'll plug in only one way.

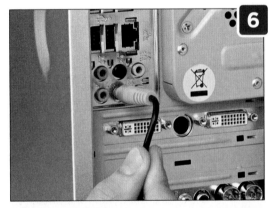

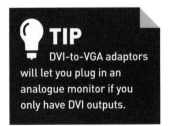

TIP
DVI-to-VGA adaptors will let you plug in an analogue monitor if you only have DVI outputs.

BEFORE YOU CAN install an operating system on your newly assembled PC, you'll need to change a few settings in the BIOS. The BIOS is where you can configure the speed of your processor and memory, make settings such as a system password and choose the time at which the PC boots up every day. In this chapter, we'll show you how to access the BIOS and make the appropriate changes.

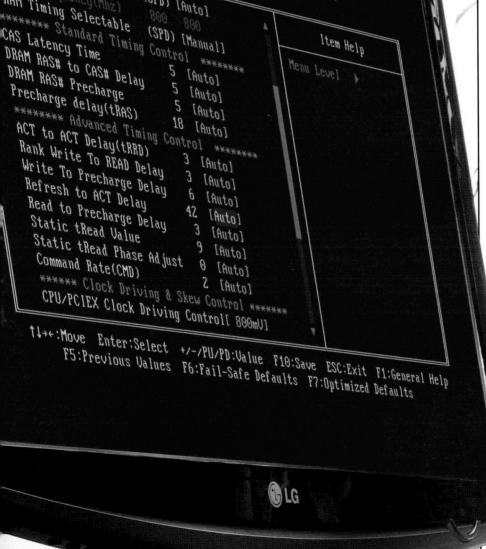

IN THIS CHAPTER

Into the BIOS

THE BIOS IS part of the motherboard, and is arguably one of its most important components. If it gets physically damaged or corrupted by a virus, there's a good chance that you won't be able to use your computer at all.

Thankfully, the chances of either of these things happening is minimal: it's much more common that the wrong settings will have been made in the BIOS. Fortunately, the BIOS is simple to use, and relatively easy to understand.

BIOSes have a limited amount of memory, which is used to store the settings. This memory keeps the settings – including the date and time – as long as the motherboard's battery is charged. However, despite huge advances in almost every other aspect of a computer, the BIOS has

remained virtually unchanged in the way it looks and works for around 25 years.

There are only a few major BIOS makers, including Award and Phoenix, and most BIOSes look very similar. However, you need to bear in mind that yours may have different options to those shown over the next few pages. So, while the following steps may not match up with the options you have, it shouldn't be too difficult to work out how to modify our instructions to apply them to what you see on your screen.

Initially, you may find that you don't need to make many changes to get to a stage where you can install your operating system. Here, we'll show you what all the options are for, so you can come back later and tweak everything to your liking.

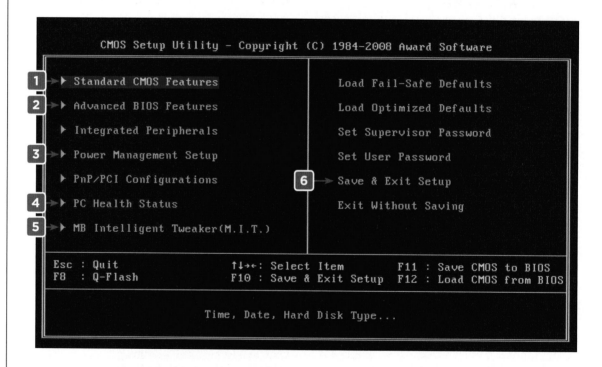

1 Contains settings for date, time, hard disks, optical and floppy drives

2 Here you can set the boot order, passwords and processor features

3 Head for power settings, including sleep mode and devices that can wake up the PC

4 Information on temperatures, fans and voltages

5 Here is the place to make advanced processor and memory settings

6 When you've made changes, choose this option to save and reboot

HOW TO...
Edit the BIOS

1 GET INTO THE BIOS
Many of the latest motherboards feature graphic splash screens, which hide the traditional black and white text. We've used a Gigabyte motherboard here. As with most other boards, you press the Delete key to access the BIOS. While a minority of BIOSes use alternative keys, such as F1, F2 or F10, it should be easy to spot which you need to use, as it will be shown somewhere obvious onscreen. Push the power button, wait for the Power-On Self Test (POST) screen to appear and press the appropriate key to enter the BIOS. If you miss the POST screen, press Ctrl-Alt-Del to restart the computer.

2 THE MAIN SCREEN
The main BIOS screen will now appear. Even if yours doesn't look like this, the menu options should be similar. To navigate around, use the cursor keys. On most BIOSes, you can select an option by pressing Enter or the right cursor key. Pressing Esc will return you to the POST screen, while F10 jumps to the Save & Exit confirmation prompt.

3 SET DATE AND TIME
Let's work through the main menu options in order. One of the first things you need to do is to set the correct date and time, as Windows uses this information. Standard CMOS Features should already be selected – it's highlighted in red – so you simply need to press Enter.

Again, you navigate through the settings using the cursor keys. All changeable settings are shown in yellow, while those that aren't will be in light blue. Set the correct time and date by highlighting the part you want to change, and alter its value by pressing the + or – key. Alternatively, you can use the Page Up and Page Down keys.

4 CONFIGURE HARD DISK
In the IDE listing, you should see your hard disk and optical drive. Most motherboards don't differentiate between PATA and SATA drives, simply referring to them as IDE. All the entries marked None are the PATA and SATA ports, to which no drives are connected. During the POST, all of these are checked to see if there's anything connected, but to save a few seconds of boot time you can disable the unused channels.

To do this, highlight a channel, press Enter, then select the name of the channel in the screen that appears – in this case IDE Channel 0 Slave. Press Enter again and a window will appear with the options None, Auto or Manual. Change the setting

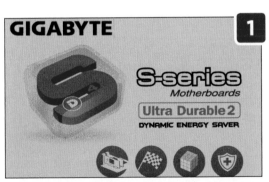

TIP
If you make a mistake or your settings aren't working, use the Load Fail-Safe Defaults option to reset the BIOS.

from Auto to None, and this channel will no longer be checked at boot time. If you ever want to connect a drive to this channel, remember to re-enable it by changing it back to Auto.

5 CONFIGURE FLOPPY DISK

Press Enter to accept the change and return to the Standard CMOS Features menu. It's unlikely that you'll have fitted a floppy drive in your PC, so highlight Drive A and press Enter. This will open a window where you can select the type of floppy drive. Here, you can see proof that the BIOS hasn't changed for a long time, as there are entries for 5¼in floppy disk drives, despite the fact that this motherboard was brand new in summer 2008. Select None or 1.44M, 3.5" if you've installed a drive, and press Enter to Accept.

On the right-hand side of the Standard CMOS Features screen, you'll see contextual help, which provides terse information on the setting you've highlighted. Usually, this is fairly unhelpful, so it's a good idea to have your motherboard's manual handy in case you need to refer to it.

6 SET UP BOOT DEVICE

Press Esc to return to the main BIOS menu, and go to the second heading: Advanced BIOS Features. Depending on your particular BIOS, you may find processor and memory settings here, but we'll get to those in Step 13, as they're under a different heading in our BIOS. The most important settings in this menu are the Boot Device options. You need to ensure that the first

boot device is set to CD-ROM, since the operating system is most likely to be on a CD. The BIOS doesn't differentiate between types of optical drive, so CD-ROM refers to all types, including DVD and Blu-ray drives. Press Enter to accept your choice, and then ensure that the second boot device is set to hard disk. This is necessary since, once you've installed an operating system, the hard disk becomes the bootable device.

7 MORE ADVANCED FEATURES

The rest of the Advanced BIOS Features vary from motherboard to motherboard, but you may want to check the rest of the options to make sure you're happy with their default values. The CPU Thermal Monitor, for example, can be disabled if you don't want the BIOS to keep tabs on the processor's temperature. However, it's advisable to enable this to prevent overheating and possible damage to your processor.

Other options include the ability to disable the POST splash screen, and also which graphics card is initialised first – either an integrated chip or a graphics card in the PCI Express slot.

8 CONFIGURE PORTS

Press Esc to return to the main menu, then choose Integrated Peripherals. This will show a list of the main components on your motherboard, including SATA and RAID ports, USB ports, audio, FireWire, network adaptors and legacy ports such as serial and parallel. It's good practice to disable anything you know

you're not going to use. Notable here is that, like many modern motherboards with Intel chipsets, the audio chip is somewhat mysteriously called Azalia Codec – this is a case where the motherboard manual may be useful.

9 POWER MANAGEMENT

Next, go into Power Management Setup. It's crucial that you make the right choice for ACPI Suspend Type, as this will determine whether Windows' Sleep mode works correctly or not. Usually, you'll see two options: S1 and S3. You want S3, which is the Suspend-to-RAM option.

S1 provides little in the way of power saving, and doesn't power down all the main components. S3, by contrast, turns off everything apart from the memory, so the processor, graphics card and other power-hungry components are switched off.

When you tell Windows to go into Sleep mode, the current state of open programs is saved to memory, enabling Windows to restart in just a few seconds when you push the power button.

10 POWER ON CONTROL

Other settings in Power Management Setup include Soft-Off by PWR-BTTN. This sets how long you have to hold down the PC's power button before it switches off. The options usually range from instant to four seconds. We'd advise setting this to the latter to avoid losing work if you accidentally knock the power button.

Other options include Resume by Alarm, which lets you specify when you want your PC

to switch on either every day, on weekdays or at weekends. Usually, you can choose only one option and can't set a different power-on time for weekdays and weekends.

Finally, there are options that determine which devices can wake up the computer, including the mouse, keyboard and network adaptor. The latter is often called Power On by Ring.

11 PC HEALTH

Return to the main menu and then choose PC Health Status. This is where you can view voltages, temperatures and fan speeds. For most, voltages won't be of interest, but temperatures will be. There may be more than two, but you will certainly have at least CPU Temperature and System Temperature. The former will usually be quite a lot higher than the latter; 30°C to 60°C is a normal idle temperature for a processor. System temperature is the ambient temperature inside the computer's case, and if it's significantly higher than 30°C, you may want to install an extra case fan or two.

Fan speeds aren't particularly useful or interesting, but you may find Smart FAN options, which can be used to vary the fan speed according to temperature. Usually this leads to a quieter PC when you're not doing anything demanding.

12 MONITOR TEMPERATURES

One of the most useful settings in PC Health Status is the CPU Warning Temperature. Press Enter when this is highlighted and you'll see a

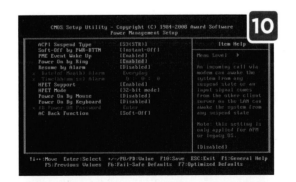

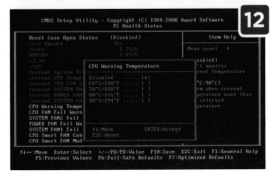

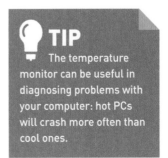

TIP
The temperature monitor can be useful in diagnosing problems with your computer: hot PCs will crash more often than cool ones.

window with a selection of temperatures. The one you choose will need to be based on the processor you have, as some run much cooler than others and you don't want a buzzer going off when it's running at a normal temperature. Our processor's idle temperature is around 55°C, so 80°C is a sensible warning temperature.

13 EXAMINE PROCESSOR SPEED

Somewhere in the main BIOS menu, there should be an item for processor and memory settings. Names vary, but it shouldn't be hard to find. Options for altering settings will also vary from those you see here, but the essential ones are always present. Check that your processor's speed is correctly set. Here, our Core 2 Duo E8500 is correctly showing under CPU Frequency as 3.16GHz (333x9.5). The part in brackets is the front side bus speed (also known as CPU Host Clock or Frequency) and the multiplier (also known as CPU Clock Ratio). Multiplying the two gives you the processor's speed. If you know the frequency at which your processor should run and this figure matches what you see on this screen, you don't need to worry about the figures in brackets.

14 ADJUST PROCESSOR SPEED

If your processor's speed isn't showing correctly, set it manually by altering the CPU Host Frequency (MHz). Highlight this field, which represents the front side bus speed, and press Enter (you may first have to enable this field by choosing Enabled under CPU Host Clock Control).

Type in the speed, which will either be 333 or 400 for Intel processors, and 200MHz for AMD processors. If you're not sure, check the specification of your particular model. Press Enter and the change should be reflected in the CPU Frequency field.

15 ADJUST PROCESSOR MULTIPLIER

If the CPU Clock Ratio is showing the wrong value, you may be able to change it. Highlight this field and press Enter. You'll either see a list of the available multipliers, or a box in which to type the ratio number. Enter the right one for your processor. If the value you want isn't shown, your motherboard may not fully support the processor and run at a slower speed. It's worth noting that it isn't normally possible to alter the multiplier, since most Intel and AMD processors have locked clock ratios. Only enthusiast processors such as AMD's Black Editions and Intel's Extreme Editions tend to have unlocked multipliers. Some Intel motherboards also force you to type an integer into the ratio box, and if you need a 0.5 multiplier, you have to select this in the next field down.

16 BIOS VERSION

You may be able to upgrade your BIOS to a newer version to add support for newer processors. Visit the website of your motherboard manufacturer to find out if there's a new version. This is often listed in the Downloads section under Firmware. To check which BIOS version your motherboard is currently running, save and exit the BIOS, and

restart the PC. When the POST screen shows, look for a version number; it's usually at the top or bottom of the screen – we've highlighted it in the picture. Version numbers aren't shown on graphical splash screens; hit Tab to show the POST screen.

17 SET MEMORY SPEED

It's unlikely that you'll have a problem with your processor's speed being detected incorrectly. More common is that memory speeds are wrongly set. The BIOS usually defaults to Auto settings to ensure overall system reliability, but this can often lead to the memory running slower than it should. Memory has a headline speed figure, in MHz, such as 667, 800 or 1,066. But there are other speed ratings that can affect performance, including those shown here: CAS Latency; RAS-to-CAS Delay; RAS Precharge and Precharge Delay (tRAS).

18 SET MEMORY TIMINGS

Many memory modules have these timings printed in that order on stickers, so look to see what yours is rated at. It'll be something like 4-4-4-12 or 2-2-2-5. If the values in the BIOS are higher than these, change them manually. Highlight each in turn, press Enter and change it from Auto to the value you want. Higher numbers indicate slower performance, as they relate to times.

As with all advanced BIOS settings, we'd advise changing only one setting at a time and rebooting to see if everything is working correctly. If you make several changes and the PC doesn't boot, you won't know which change caused it.

19 OVERCLOCK YOUR PC

Scroll down the list of processor and memory options, and you should find voltage settings. We'd recommend leaving these at their default values, as changing them can damage your hardware. They're here for those that want to overclock some components, primarily the processor and memory. Overclocking makes components run faster than their stated speed, which can give extra performance for free, but it usually comes with the trade-off of reliability. When you overclock a component, you'll usually need to increase its voltage slightly to increase stability. Many motherboards have automatic overclocking options, so you don't need to change frequency and voltage settings yourself. Look for a menu that has options such as 2%, 5%, 10% or Standard, Turbo, Extreme.

20 SAVE YOUR SETTINGS

The rest of the options in the main menu are self-explanatory and let you set passwords – for the BIOS or the whole PC – and exit the BIOS having saved your settings. The other menu items are Load Fail-Safe Defaults and Load Optimized Defaults. The first sets all BIOS options to their original values, which should ensure that the PC will boot and avoid stability problems. You should use this option if you made changes to the BIOS that caused your PC to stop booting. Optimized Defaults loads settings to run the PC at optimal performance, but if you've followed these steps, you'll have the optimal setup.

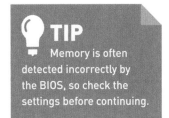

TIP
Memory is often detected incorrectly by the BIOS, so check the settings before continuing.

CHAPTER 6
INSTALLING AN OPERATING SYSTEM

IT'S INCREDIBLY IMPORTANT that you install your PC's operating system and drivers correctly if you want a reliable and stable computer. Whether you've chosen Windows 7, XP, Vista, Linux or you want a Media Center PC for the living room, we'll show you how to install and configure your operating system.

IN THIS CHAPTER

HOW TO...
Install Windows 7

1 START YOUR COMPUTER

Turn on your PC and put the Windows 7 DVD into its optical drive. If you have a new hard disk, the installation routine will load automatically. If you're using an old hard disk with an operating system already on it, you need to press any key when prompted. If you don't, your old operating system will start and you'll have to reset your PC to start the setup wizard. If the new Windows installer doesn't appear, you'll need to access your PC's BIOS. Check the boot options here to make sure your optical drive is listed first.

2 CHOOSE YOUR LANGUAGE OPTIONS

The first screen that appears will ask you which language you want to use. Select English from the drop-down menu. It should change the next drop-down box, but select English (United Kingdom) as the time and currency format if it doesn't. Your keyboard or input method should be set to United Kingdom automatically when you set the language. If it isn't, select United Kingdom from the third drop-down menu. Click Next to continue.

3 INSTALL WINDOWS 7

On the next screen, click 'What to know before installing Windows' if you want additional information about Windows 7. The 'Repair your computer' link starts the repair console, which can fix problems with a current Windows 7 installation. To install Windows 7, click the 'Install now' button.

4 ACCEPT THE LICENCE TERMS

You'll now be prompted to accept the terms. These are long and wordy, but read through them if you want to know what your licence allows. Tick the 'I accept the license terms' box when you're done. Click Next to continue to the next stage.

5 CHOOSE TYPE OF INSTALLATION

On the next screen, you'll be asked which type of installation you want to perform. Upgrade will upgrade your existing version of Windows. It can also be used to repair a damaged Windows 7 installation. However, this option can be run only from inside Windows. For a fresh installation, select Custom (advanced).

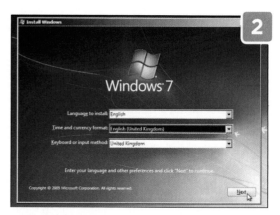

6 SELECT HARD DISK

Your hard disk should automatically be detected by Windows 7. If it isn't, click on the Load Driver button and insert the CD, USB key or floppy disk with the relevant driver. You should need to do this only if you're using RAID or you have a new motherboard that Windows doesn't recognise.

If you're using an old hard disk, it's best to start afresh. Select the partition that contains your old operating system, choose Advanced and click Delete. You can also delete any other partitions this way. You're now ready to continue.

For a fresh disk, or an old disk where you've wiped the existing partitions, you can just select Unallocated Space and click Next. Windows will automatically create the necessary disk partitions and perform the installation. We recommend that you have at least two partitions: one for Windows, and a smaller one for storing backups, drivers and other files you want to keep permanently.

Select the Unallocated Space and click Advanced and then New. You have to select the size of the partition in megabytes (where 1,024MB

is equal to 1GB). Generally, we'd recommend leaving at least 40GB (40,960MB) for the second partition. Subtract the size of second partition you want from the figure in the box, and enter this. Then click Apply. Select Disk 0 Unallocated Space, click New and then Apply. You'll get a warning that Windows may create extra partitions, but click OK.

You'll now have two partitions: the one you created, and a 100MB System Reserved partition. Click Disk 0 Unallocated Space, New, and then Apply. You now have all the partitions you need.

7 FORMAT DISKS

To make things easier once you've started Windows, you should format your partitions now. Select Partition 2 (the installation will deal with Partition 1 automatically) and click Format. Click OK in the warning box. You'll get a spinning cursor for a few moments while the disk is formatted. Repeat these steps for the second partition and any others you have that you want to wipe (leave all partitions or disks with important data on them alone). When done, click Partition 2 and then Next.

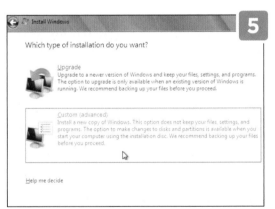

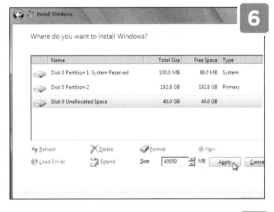

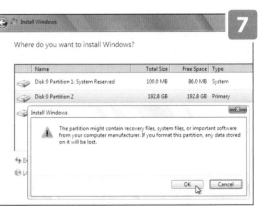

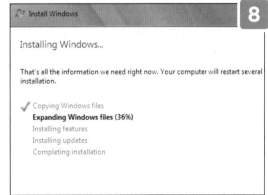

TIP
You can use the back arrow in the installation screens to go back and change a previous setting if you've made a mistake.

8 INSTALL WINDOWS FILES
Windows will automatically copy system files and install the necessary drivers to get your PC working on the first partition you created.

9 SET UP USERNAME AND PASSWORD
After the installation files have finished copying, you'll be prompted to type in a username for yourself (you can create more for other users later) and a name for your computer. Enter this information and click Next. On the next screen, you're asked to enter a password.

The password is optional, but if you want to protect your files and ensure that only authorised users can access your PC, it's vital that you have one. Finally, enter a hint that will remind you of your password in case you forget it and click Next.

10 ENTER PRODUCT KEY
You will now be prompted to type in your product key, which is inside the box in which your copy of Windows came. Leave the 'Automatically activate Windows when I'm online' and click Next.

11 TURN ON WINDOWS UPDATES
Windows now asks whether you want to turn on Windows Updates automatically. The best option is to select 'Use recommended settings'. Next, set the date and time of your computer.

If you chose your location as UK in the Windows installation routine, the time will be set to GMT by default. Then click Next. If Windows picked up your network adaptor correctly and found that your computer was connected to a network, you'll be asked to choose the type of network – for most people, this will be Home network. Windows will then start for the first time.

12 INSTALL MOTHERBOARD DRIVERS
Although Windows is now working, you still need to install all the relevant drivers to make sure that everything will run smoothly. The trick here is to install any drivers that are for Windows 7; only install Windows Vista drivers if a component isn't working, such as your network adaptor.

Start with your motherboard's drivers. If you downloaded these earlier, insert the USB key or disc to which you saved them. If you couldn't do this, insert the driver disc that came with your motherboard and follow the onscreen instructions. You'll need to download the updated drivers later, and then follow these instructions.

For each driver you downloaded, run the associated file. It's best to start with the chipset driver, but the order afterwards doesn't matter. If Windows displays any warning messages, just click OK. Be careful, as some files you download are just archive files that extract the actual driver

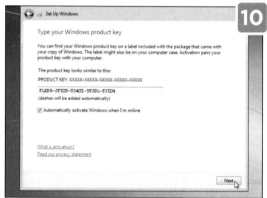

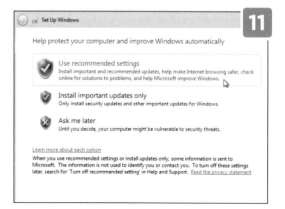

files on to your hard disk. If this is the case, go to the folder to which the files were extracted and run the Setup program. You'll probably need to restart your PC after each driver installation.

13 INSTALL GRAPHICS CARD DRIVERS

Windows will install its own graphics drivers for any onboard or dedicated cards you have. These are fine for running Windows, but you won't be able to play games properly. For this, you'll need to install the graphics drivers.

Both ATI and Nvidia provide a single driver package. Simply run the file you downloaded. If you couldn't download the drivers earlier, you should do it now. (Follow Step 14 if you need to install a wireless adaptor to get online and then come back to this step.) Restart your computer after the graphics drivers have been installed. Right-click on the desktop, select Screen Resolution and adjust the resolution to match your monitor's native resolution.

14 INSTALL OTHER PERIPHERALS

You can now install your other peripherals. Install the relevant driver files for each device that's plugged into your motherboard. For USB devices, install the driver file first and, when prompted, connect the device to a USB port. If you're in any doubt, you should read the manual that came with

your peripheral. If you've installed a wireless adaptor, make sure you connect it to your wireless network and follow the provided instructions.

15 RUN WINDOWS UPDATE

Click on the Start menu, type Windows Update and click the entry that appears. Click the Check for Updates button, and Windows will connect to Microsoft's update server and detect which updates you need.

Click on View available updates and look at the list. Some will have been preselected as important updates, but there are also some optional ones, including even newer drivers for your hardware. Select what you'd like to update, then click install.

When they've finished downloading and installing and your PC has restarted, you'll have a working copy of Windows 7 that's up to date.

16 CREATE A SYSTEM REPAIR DISC

Windows 7 has an option to let you create a disc to repair problems with the operating system. It's worth doing this now while you've got a working PC. To do this, click on the Start menu and type repair, and click on Create a System Repair Disc. Put a blank CD or DVD into your optical drive and click Create disc process. This will take a few minutes. When it's done, take the disc out, label it clearly and put it somewhere safe.

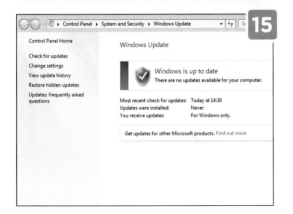

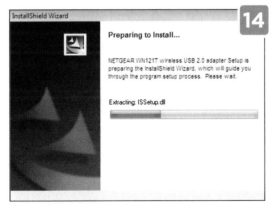

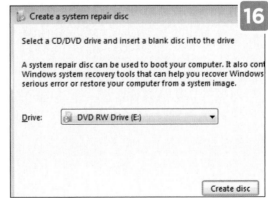

TIP Copying the installation files can take more than an hour, so you'll need to be patient while Windows installs.

HOW TO...
Install Windows Vista

1 START YOUR COMPUTER
Turn your PC on and put the Windows Vista DVD into the optical drive. If you have a new hard disk, the Vista installation routine will load automatically, but if you're using an old hard disk with an operating system already on it, press any key when prompted. If you don't, your old operating system will start and you'll have to reset your PC to start the setup wizard.

Your computer will take a few minutes to start the installation routine, so don't worry if you've got a blank page to look at for a bit.

2 CHOOSE YOUR LANGUAGE OPTIONS
The first screen that appears will ask you to choose which language you want to use. Select English from the drop-down menu. Select English (United Kingdom) as the time and currency format. This should automatically change the keyboard or input method to UK. If it doesn't, select UK from the third drop-down menu. Click Next to continue.

3 INSTALL VISTA
On the next screen, click 'What to know before installing Windows' if you want additional information about Windows Vista. The 'Repair your computer' link needs to be used only if you've already installed Vista and are having problems with the installation. Everyone else should just click the Install now button.

4 ENTER YOUR PRODUCT KEY
Windows will now prompt you to type in your product key, which is inside the box in which your copy of Windows came. Leave the 'Automatically activate Windows when I'm online' box ticked to let Windows activate itself when you connect to the internet. Unlike previous versions of Windows, you don't have to enter your product key now, and can proceed with the installation. However, after 30 days you'll be prompted for a key. If you don't enter one, you'll only be able to access a few of Vista's features. It's therefore easier to enter the key now. Click Next, and click the tickbox on the next screen to confirm that you've read the licence agreement and click Next.

5 CHOOSE TYPE OF INSTALLATION
You'll be asked to choose if you want to upgrade an old copy of Windows or run a new

Custom installation. As you're installing to a new PC, it's likely that the Upgrade option will be disabled. If you're using an old hard disk and a version of Windows that can be upgraded has been detected, select the Custom option. A clean installation of Vista is always the best bet and we don't recommend using the Upgrade option.

6 SELECT HARD DISK
Your hard disk should automatically be detected by Windows Vista. If it isn't, click on the Load Driver button and insert the CD, USB key or floppy disk with the relevant driver. You should need to do this only if you're using RAID or if you have a brand new motherboard that Windows doesn't recognise.

From the list of disks, select the one on which you want Windows to be installed. This is usually Disk 0. If you click Next, Windows will format the entire disk automatically. However, it's best to create at least two partitions: one for Windows, and a smaller one for storing backups, drivers and other files you want to keep permanently.

Click Advanced options and then New to add a new partition. You have to select the size of the

partition in megabytes (1,024MB = 1GB). Generally, we'd recommend leaving at least 40GB (40,960MB) for the second partition. So subtract the size of second partition you want from the figure in the box, and enter this. Click Apply. Select Disk 0 Unallocated Space, click New and click Apply. You now have two partitions.

7 FORMAT DISKS
To make things easier once you've started Windows, you should format your partitions now. Select Partition 1 and click Format. Click OK in the warning box. You'll get an hourglass for a few moments while the disk is formatted. Repeat these steps for the second disk. When that has been formatted, click Next.

8 INSTALLING WINDOWS FILES
Next, Windows will automatically copy system files and install the necessary drivers to get your PC working on the first partition that you created. The process can take up to 30 minutes and your computer will restart several times during the operation. There's nothing for you to worry about at this point, and you can just sit back and

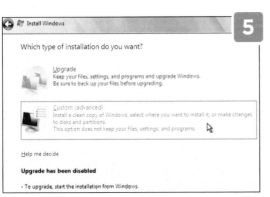
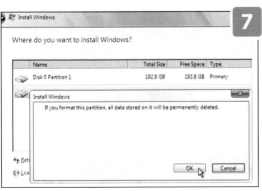
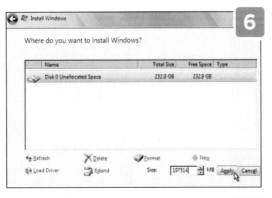

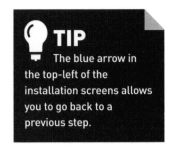
TIP The blue arrow in the top-left of the installation screens allows you to go back to a previous step.

let Windows do its job until the operating system starts for the first time.

9 SET UP USERNAME AND PASSWORD

When your computer starts Windows Vista for the first time, you'll be asked to type in a username and password. Although the password is optional, if you want to protect your files from unwanted attention and ensure that only authorised users can access your PC, it's vital that you have one. So type in a username and password, and then click Next.

Give your computer a meaningful name and then choose which desktop background you'd like. Click Next to continue.

10 PROTECT WINDOWS

Windows now asks whether you want to turn on Windows Updates automatically. The best option is to select Use recommended settings. Click that box. Next, set the date and time of your computer. Make sure that your time zone has been set correctly. If you chose your location as the UK in the Windows installation routine, the time zone will be set to GMT by default. Click Next and then Start to launch Windows.

11 START WINDOWS

Windows will now perform some tests on your computer's performance. These will take around five minutes to complete. Once it's

finished, you'll be presented with the login screen. If you set a password, you'll have to enter it now and press Enter. Windows will prepare your desktop for its first use and log you on. You'll see the Welcome Center, which gives you quick access to information about Vista and also short cuts to common tasks such as adding new users. The next time you start Windows, you'll see a box, which you can tick if you don't want to see the Welcome Center again. You can now remove the Windows Vista installation DVD.

12 INSTALL MOTHERBOARD DRIVERS

Although Windows is now working, you still need to install all the relevant drivers to make sure that everything will run smoothly. The first place to start is with your motherboard's drivers. If you downloaded these earlier, insert the USB key or disc to which you saved them. If you couldn't do this, insert the driver disc and follow the onscreen instructions. You'll need to download the updated drivers later, and then follow these instructions.

For each driver you downloaded, run the associated file. It's best to start with the chipset driver, but the order afterwards doesn't matter. If Windows displays any warning messages, just click OK. Be careful, as some files you download are actually just archive files that extract the actual driver files on to your hard disk. If this is the case, navigate to the folder to which the files were extracted and run the Setup program you find

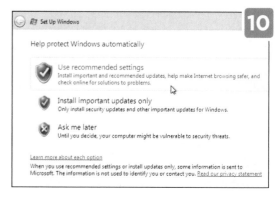

there. You'll probably need to restart your computer after each driver installation.

13 INSTALL GRAPHICS CARD DRIVERS

Windows will install its own graphics drivers for any onboard or dedicated cards that you have. These are good enough to run Windows, but you won't be able to play games properly. To do this, you need to install the graphics drivers.

Both ATI and Nvidia provide a single driver package. You simply have to run the file that you downloaded. If you couldn't download the drivers earlier, you need to insert the bundled CD, but remember to download newer drivers later on.

Restart your computer after the graphics drivers have been installed. Right-click on the desktop, select Personalize, then Display Properties and change your display resolution to match your monitor's native resolution.

14 INSTALL OTHER PERIPHERALS

You can now install the other peripherals that you've added to your PC. Install the relevant driver files for each device that's plugged into your motherboard. For USB devices, you need to install the driver file first and, when prompted, connect the device to a USB port. If you're in any doubt, you should read the manual that came with your peripheral. If you've installed a wireless adaptor, make sure that you connect it to your wireless network and follow the provided instructions.

15 INSTALL SERVICE PACK 2

When everything else is installed, you should install Windows Vista Service Pack 2, unless the installation disc you used included this, in which case you can skip to the final step.

To install Service Pack 2, first connect to the internet. The easiest way to force it to install is to go to *http://tinyurl.com/vista32sp2* (for the 32-bit version) and *http://tinurl.com/vista64sp2* (64-bit). Click Download and save the file to your hard disk. When it's finished, run the file and follow the wizard. Service Pack 1 will take around an hour to install and will restart your PC when necessary.

16 RUN WINDOWS UPDATE

Click on the Start menu, type Windows Update and click the entry that appears. Click the Check for Updates button, and Windows will connect to Microsoft's update server and detect which updates you need.

Click on View available updates and have a look at the list. There will be some that have been preselected as important updates, but there are also some optional ones, including even newer drivers for your hardware. Select what you'd like to update and then click Install.

When they've finished downloading and installing and your computer has restarted, you'll have a working copy of Windows Vista. You can now install our recommended free software (see page 128).

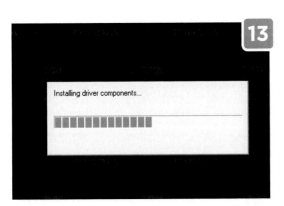

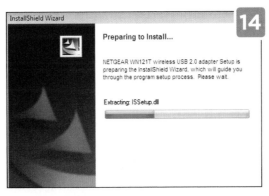

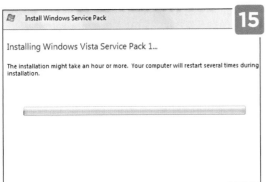

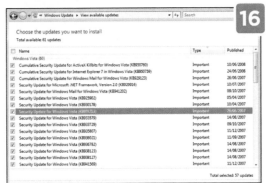

TIP Windows Update is essential on all new computers, as it will make sure that you've got the latest patches and drivers.

Improve Windows Media Center

The default installation of Media Center doesn't let you do much, and you can't play downloaded media such as DivX files very easily. Fortunately, it's easy to tweak – here we show you how

WINDOWS MEDIA CENTER is a brilliant application once you've tweaked it to get rid of all of its minor annoyances and added new features with free software. In this guide we'll show you how to turn Media Center from a useful bit of kit into the best media player you'll ever own.

To make the most of these instructions, you'll need an official Microsoft Media Center Remote (around £30 including VAT from *www.kikatek.com*). We've found that third-party remote controls don't work very well with some of the third-party software we've recommended.

QUICK FIXES
Once you've installed extra software on your computer, we've found that Media Center can often lose screen priority and let the Start menu reappear. Not only is this annoying, but it can actually cause a crash if you're in the middle of watching a video.

This is easy to fix using Media Center. Go to the Tasks section of the main menu and select Media Only and select Yes when prompted. This will force Media Center to run in full-screen mode,

preventing other applications from taking control. To revert to the standard Media Center mode, select the Media Only option again.

If you're using Media Center just for its media capabilities, you should dispense with some of Windows' more irritating automatic features. First, disable automatic updates, otherwise Window may automatically restart your computer. Open Control Panel and select Security (System and Security in Windows 7). Click Turn automatic updating on or off. Select Never check for updates and click OK. You should still update your computer at regular intervals, but use Windows Update in the Start menu manually.

Finally, we recommend disabling the indexing service, which periodically scans your hard disk for Windows Search, but isn't used by Media Center. To do this, right-click on Computer in the Start menu and select Manage. Expand the Services and Applications section on the left-hand panel and click Services. Double-click Windows Search and change the Startup type from Automatic to Disabled and click Apply. Click the Stop button and then click OK.

⬇ Put Media Center into Media Only mode to make sure that it's always the most important application

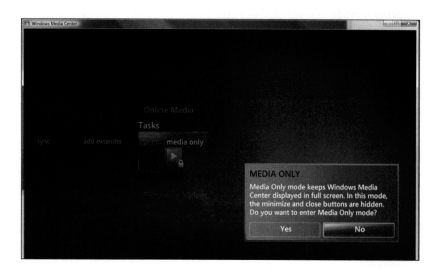

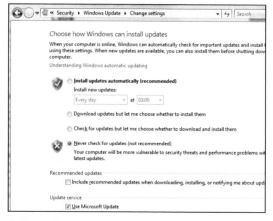

⬆ Turn off automatic updates to prevent Windows from restarting your PC automatically

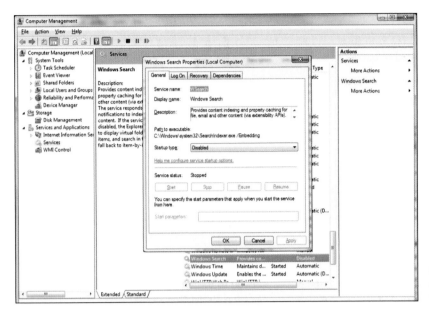

← Disable Windows Search to prevent your computer from thrashing the hard disk

PLAYING ALL MEDIA FILES

Media Center's handling of videos, with the exception of WMV files, is incredibly poor, and you'll find that even if you install the necessary codecs to play other files, you can't even fast-forward them. Fortunately, it doesn't have to be this way, and with some free software you'll be able to do all of these things.

First, uninstall any video codecs that you've already installed, such as QuickTime and DivX, as you won't need them. Then downloaded and install ffdshow tryouts (*http://ffdshow-tryout.sourceforge. net*) using the application's default settings. This is a free audio and video decoder that will handle pretty much any video format you'll throw at it.

It still won't let you fast-forward videos, though, so you also need to download the Media Center Control Plugin version 6 (*http://damienbt.free.fr*). Make sure you get the right version for your operating system (32- or 64-bit). This application lets you fast-forward all videos, add bookmarks and resume from the last point at which you stopped watching.

Before you install it, download and install Microsoft Visual C++ 2008 SP1 (*http://tinyurl.com/ C2008SP1*). Then install Media Center Control Plugin. When the installation has finished, select the option to launch the Media Control Configuration. Click on the Remote control & keyboard tab. There's currently no option to stop a video from fast-forwarding, so click Add command. In the first drop-down menu, select Stop Fast Forward/Rewind. The next two options can be used to set a keyboard short cut for the action, but skip this and select Play from the Remote button drop-down menu. Click Commit changes.

To complete the basic configuration, click on the ffdshow configuration tab. Click on Apply minimal configuration and then OK, then on Apply recommended configuration and then OK. Click Commit changes and OK, then restart your computer to apply the changes.

After your PC has restarted, you'll find that you can play any video format in Media Center, and be able to fast-forward and rewind them. Coming back to a video at a later date will pop up an option that asks if you want to resume the video. Press 'i' on the remote control and select More, then Media Control. You can use the menu options to set Bookmarks for programmes you're watching, so that you can jump to your favourite scenes later.

IMPROVE VIDEO PICTURE QUALITY

The picture quality of many downloaded videos isn't very good, but fortunately, you can fix this. With a DivX video playing take Media Center out of Media Only mode, use your mouse to put the application into windowed mode (the middle icon

↓ You need to configure remote commands in the Media Control window

when you move the mouse to the top right). In the Notification Area you'll see two new icons: a blue ffdshow audio decoder and a red ffdshow video decoder. Double-click the audio one first.

First, set the correct audio settings. Put a tick in the Mixer box and then click Mixer. Select the Output speakers configuration from the drop-down menu. For most PCs with surround sound this should be 3/0/2 – 5 channels, but for 7.1 speakers select 3/2/2. If you have surround sound, you also need to tick the LFE box to send the subwoofer its own signal. Next, click Dolby decoder and select Apply Dolby Pro Logic II decoding to all stereo sources. This will upsample stereo soundtracks to use all of your speakers. Click OK.

Double-click the video icon. For every setting that we show you how to adjust, make sure that Process whole image is selected. Put a tick in the Deinterlacing box and select Cubic interpolation from the drop-down menu. This will deinterlace TV shows to match your TV's progressive mode. Put a tick in Postprocessing, and a tick in Picture Processing and adjust the sliders until you're happy with the picture's colour, brightness and contrast. Downloaded video can look harsh, so put a tick in the Blur & NR (Blur and Noise Reduction)

box. We find that setting Soften to 40 or less and Gradual denoise to 40 or less helps reduce noise and produce a better image.

You can bring out the detail in a video by ticking the Sharpen box. Select unsharp mask and adjust the Strength bar until you're happy (around 25 should do it). Now to make sure that the picture looks as good as possible, you can force ffdshow to upscale video to match your TV's resolution.

Put a tick in Resize & aspect, select Specify horizontal and vertical size, and type in the size of your display in the box below, such as 1,920x1,080 for 1080p TVs. By default the video will maintain its aspect ratio, so old TV shows will have black bars down the side of the picture. If you don't like this, select No aspect ratio correction, to fill the screen. Click Apply. You can now maximise Media Center and use it as normal.

There are a couple of problems with Media Control. First, it will also work when you try to play a DVD, prompting you to launch ffdshow. The idea is that ffdshow can take over the picture processing, increasing quality. However, we've yet to get this to work successfully and have found that it stops DVD menus from working. Just wait for the option to disappear.

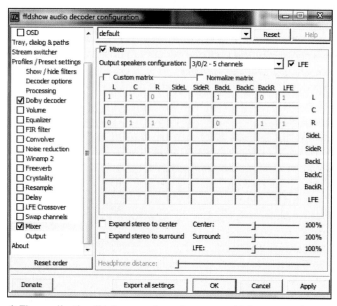

↑ The application ffdshow can turn stereo sound into surround

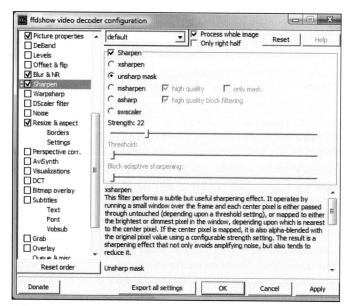

↑ You can also improve the quality of your video with ffdshow

Second, when you stop watching a video, pressing fast-forward later on – when you're watching a DVD, for example – will cause your old video to start playing again. To get round this, when you've stopped watching a video, select Media Control from Media Center's main menu and select Restart Media Center. You'll have to put Media Center back into Media Only mode.

TV EVERYWHERE
Media Center can also be used to catch up with TV shows that you may have missed with the free TunerFree MCE application (*www.milliesoft.co.uk/ tunerfree.php*). This provides a single interface for all the major catch-up services, including the BBC's iPlayer and Channel 4's 4oD. Download the application for your operating system (Vista or Windows 7), quit Media Center and install TunerFree using the Typical settings. The process will take several minutes as the database of available programmes is downloaded.

Before you can use the software you need to make sure that your computer has all the necessary codecs to play the files. Visit each service using Internet Explorer (see below) and play a sample video, downloading extra software when prompted.

SERVICE	ADDRESS
BBC	www.bbc.co.uk/iplayer
ITV	www.itv.com/ITVPlayer
Channel 4 On Demand	http://www.channel4.com/4od
Five	http://demand.five.tv

When done, you can start Media Center. TunerFree MCE is installed into the TV + Movies section of the main menu. When you launch the application, you can either browse through the individual channels, or use the options at the top to browse by date or search by keyword.

The default installation also lets you select Hulu, which is a US-only service. To fix this, select Preferences and select Get Hulu so that it has a grey box next to it. Click Save, and then Back. You'll now have access to every TV-on-demand service in the UK.

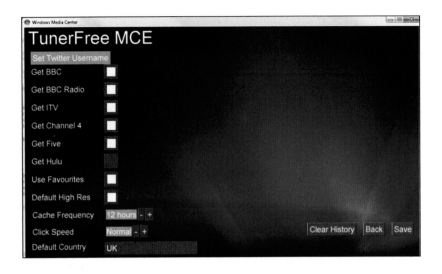

SOUND IMPROVEMENTS
The final adjustment is improving the sound when watching DVDs. Media Center's built-in audio decoder will let you listen to Dolby Digital soundtracks only if you're using analogue outputs, not DTS. This can be fixed easily, however. Download and install AC3Filter (*http:// ac3filter.net*). From the Start menu, run AC3Filter Config. Change the output to match your speaker configuration (surround-sound users should select 3/2+SW 5.1 channels).

The other settings, such as the Equalizer and Mixer for adjusting speaker volume, bass and treble, are best adjusted when you're listening to some audio. AC3Filter puts an icon in the Notification Area when compatible audio is playing, which you can double-click to adjust settings on the fly.

To get AC3Filter working in Media Center requires a bit of fiddling. First, you need to find out the CLSID of the software. You can do this by downloading the DirectShow Filter Manager (*www. softella.com/dsfm/index.en.htm*). Run the software and double-click the entry for AC3Filter. Copy the CLSID including the curly brackets.

Run RegEdit and navigate to HKey_Local_ Machine\Software\Microsoft\Windows\ CurrentVersion\Media Center\Decoder. Double-click PreferredMPEG2AudioDecoderCLSID and paste in the CLSID you copied earlier. Click OK and shut down RegEdit. Now when you watch a DVD, you'll be able to decode DTS soundtracks.

↑ TunerFree MCE lets you watch all of the UK's TV-on-demand services via Media Center

TIP
Check for TunerFree MCE updates regularly, as new TV services are added all the time.

Improve Media Center movies

A default Media Center installation can't play Blu-ray discs or multiregion DVDs. Here we'll show you how to turn your computer into the ultimate playback machine for your movies

BEFORE WE GET into the nitty gritty of improving video playback, we'll talk about sound. Depending on your PC, you'll have a choice of three sound outputs: analogue (the PC decodes surround sound), S/PDIF and HDMI (the sound is sent digitally and not decoded). We recommend using analogue outputs for two reasons: S/PDIF doesn't support HD audio, such as Dolby TrueHD, on Blu-ray discs, and the HDMI outputs on graphics cards downsample HD audio to standard-definition audio, as they lack a technology called PAP.

With analogue you can ensure that you get the best-quality sound, and it will also work better with some of the applications that we're going to talk about here. If you're not happy with the sound from your onboard sound card, upgrade to a PCI Express model, such as Auzentech's X-Fi Forte 7.1 (around £126 including VAT).

MORE FORMATS
Media Center's built-in DVD player is very basic and doesn't support HD formats such as Blu-ray.

↑ To get the best-quality sound, use your PC's analogue outputs

↑ Use TotalMedia Theatre 3 to get the best video playback and support for HD formats

To get better-quality video and HD support, you need a third-party player. We recommend using ArcSoft's TotalMedia Theatre 3 (TMT3) Platinum, which costs $100 (around £63) from *www.arcsoft. com/public/software_title.asp?ProductID=362*.

This software integrates into Media Center. Blu-ray and HD DVD discs will automatically play when you put them in, but DVDs will give you the option of Media Center or TMT3. Always select TMT3 when given the option.

THE MULTIREGION QUESTION
One of the most annoying aspects about using your computer to play discs is that it's hard to make it region-free so it will play movies from any anywhere. With DVD drives, you're allowed to change the region-coding on the drive up to five times. After you've done this, the drive will be locked to a specific region. Getting round this protection, which is known as RPC2, is difficult.

There are programs available that will bypass the region-coding on the disc and drive, but they also bypass the CSS encryption used to protect the discs, which is illegal under UK law.

The only way to get around the problem is to install new firmware on your drive that removes the region lock, turning the drive into an RPC1 model. Before we explain how to do this, you should be

↑ Drive Info tells you the exact model of drive you have and if it currently has a region lock on it

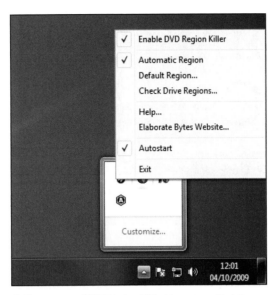

↑ You can use DVD Region Killer to ensure that you can play any DVD on your PC

aware that changing your drive's firmware will invalidate your warranty and, if you get the wrong firmware, can even break the drive. Currently, it's easy to find the right firmware for DVD drives, but firmware for Blu-ray drives is difficult to find.

First, you need to find out your exact drive model by downloading the latest version of DISCInfo (*http://discinfo.rpc1.org*). Run the file – it doesn't need to be installed – and it will tell you the make and model of your drive. You can use this information to find the right firmware. A good place to start is *http://tdb.rpc1.org*, which has tons of firmware for all the most popular drives. If your drive is listed, follow the provided instructions to update its firmware. If you can't find your drive here, you can try searching Google for the name and model of your drive plus "RPC1 firmware".

SOFTWARE UNLOCKING

Once you've unlocked your drive, you'll still have the problem that your DVD playback software also has region-coding built in, which you need to bypass. This can be done easily with DVD Region Killer (*http://tinyurl.com/regionkiller*).

Simply download the software and install it. After rebooting your computer, right-click on its icon in the Notification Area and select 'Enable DVD Region Killer'. You'll now be able to watch a DVD from any region.

BLU-RAY REGION

With Blu-Ray, the region-coding is set in software, but each playback software limits you to five changes. However, this is easy to bypass with the Blu-ray Region Tray Tool (*http://tinyurl.com/*

blurayregion), which lets you make an infinite number of region changes in PowerDVD and TotalMedia Theatre.

Download and run the software (it has to be run each time you start Windows, so save the file to your Startup folder in the Start menu). In the Notification Area you'll see an icon showing you which region (A, B or C) you're currently using. You can either click on the Notification Area icon to change the region or use the keyboard shortcut of Ctrl-Shift-1, -2 or -3 for, respectively, regions A, B or C. You can't have TotalMedia Theatre or PowerDVD running while you change regions.

PLAYING SMOOTH VIDEO

One of the biggest problems with a Windows Media Center PC is getting video to play back smoothly. If you watch carefully you'll notice that the screen will judder and jerk at times. The reason for this is down to the different frame rates of video that exist.

For example, films are all shot at 24fps and shown progressively (one frame at a time). PAL (UK) video is interlaced (each frame is split into two fields, one containing the odd lines and one containing the even lines) and shown at 25fps or 50 fields per second (50Hz refresh rate). NTSC (American) video is interlaced and shown at the bizarre rate of 29.97fps (59.94Hz).

So, the problem is that there are a number of different frame rates and refresh rates that don't match; for example, if you've got a UK PAL TV and a 24fps film, then the two don't match. The solution is to speed up the film to 25fps and interlace it to make the required 50 fields per

TIP
Current graphics cards can't output HD audio over HDMI, so consider using analogue outputs instead.

second. This is the reason that films on DVD in the UK are four per cent quicker than at the cinema.

However, for NTSC displays this technique doesn't make any sense, as doing the same thing and increasing a film from 24fps to 29.97fps would make it far too quick. Instead, a technique called 3:2 pulldown is used. First the film is slowed down by one per cent to 23.976fps, then for every fourth field of video, one extra field is added to bring the total frame rate up to the required 29.97fps. A good explanation of the technique, and why it's called 3:2 pulldown, can be found at *www.zerocut. com/tech/pulldown.html*.

LCD displays are progressive, not interlaced, so a PAL LCD TV runs at 50fps (a refresh rate of 50Hz). For PAL footage, then, it's a simple case of deinterlacing two fields and sending them as a single frame twice, thereby turning 25fps footage into 50fps footage.

However, put an NTSC disc into your PC's drive when you're running at a refresh rate of 50Hz and you've got a problem: using 3:2 pull down and deinterlacing the footage will get you too many frames (59.94fps), while doubling the disc's native frame rate as you would do for PAL would generate two few frames (47.952fps). In the first case, some frames would have to be dropped; in the second case some frames would have to be repeated more often that others; both create jerky video.

↑ You need to configure ReClock carefully to get it to work with your hardware

CLOCKING IN

Setting your PC to output the correct refresh rate can help matters, but NTSC discs can still cause problems. PCs can often only output refresh rates of whole numbers, so for NTSC that's 60Hz, even though the format is technically 59.94Hz. The slight difference leaves jerky video.

The wider problem is that PCs don't use the video card's onboard clock to detect the playback rate and make sure that video is being played at the right speed. Fortunately, that's where ReClock comes in.

This application examines the frame rate of a video that's being played and ties its playback into the graphics card's clock. It also checks the refresh rate at which your PC is running and adjusts the frame rate accordingly to make smooth video, so, for example, 23.976fps NTSC video is increased in speed to 25fps for computers running at a refresh rate of 50Hz.

The sound is dynamically adjusted, too, so that speeding up or slowing down video doesn't alter pitch and make it sound strange. It can also run a VBScript to adjust your graphics card's refresh rate, although this is quite complex to set up, and our instructions will leave you with smooth video. Search Google for RunEvent.vbs for more information on how to change your refresh rate to match the source material.

CONFIGURING RECLOCK

First, you need to stop Media Center from changing the refresh rate when it feels like it. Get up a Run command (Windows+R), type Regedit and hit Enter. Navigate to HKey_Local_Machine\Software\Microsoft\Windows\CurrentVersion\Media Center\Settings\DisplayService and change EnableRefreshRateChange to 0.

Next, you need to download ReClock (*http://forum.slysoft.com/showthread.php?t=19931*) and install it on your PC. Once installed, run ReClock Configuration from the Start menu. You can leave most of the default settings alone, but we had to change 'Audio interface to use for PCM sound' to WaveOut. Also make sure that 'Enable audio timestretching' is selected for both 'When slowing down media' and 'When speeding up media'. This will let ReClock adjust the pitch of audio to make it match the new frame rate.

If you're using an S/PDIF connection – which we don't recommend – then you may have trouble

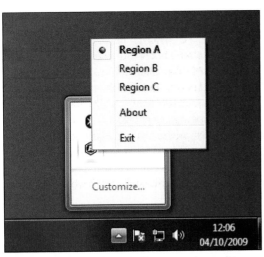

↑ You can change your PC's Blu-ray region easily

making ReClock work, and you may have to select the 'Use AC3 encoder for PCM sound' option.

Next, click on the Video settings tab and change the Hardware access method to DirectDraw. Under 'When frame rate is not found by previous methods, assume' select 24 (fps) for DVDs and 25 (fps) for other files. Click OK to apply the settings.

RUNNING RECLOCK

Now, start Media Center and put in a disc. Choose to play it in Media Center (TMT3 doesn't currently work with it). When the message pops up asking if you want to use ReClock, select 'Yes, always' and click OK. You'll need to do the same thing with any other video-playing applications that you use and for watching DivX video.

Play a DVD and put Media Center into a Windowed mode. You'll see a clock icon in the Notification Area; double-click this to select some more options. One you may be interested in is 'Enable sound compressor:'. This will make loud sounds such as explosions quieter, which is useful if you're watching a film at night.

The screen will give you details of the sound and frame rate of the video, and will also show you the speed at which it's currently playing your video. Your video will now play correctly, no matter what its frame rate is.

CHANGING THE REFRESH RATE

ReClock doesn't work with all applications, so the next best thing is to change the refresh rate manually. Download SetRR from *www.*

gianlucabove.it/v2/en/setRR and save the file to your hard disk. When you run this file and give it a number as an option it will change your computer's refresh rate to that number.

For LCD TVs, you should make three batch files (text files with .bat file extensions) that will change the resolution to match the three types of movie content (24p.bat for Blu-ray, PAL.bat and NTSC. bat). The files should contain, respectively, the lines setrr.exe 24, setrr.exe 50 and setrr.exe 60 (you can also try 59, if your PC and TV will accept 59.94Hz for NTSC). If your TV doesn't support 24p, don't make the 24p.bat file.

We can use our batch files to change refresh rates manually. First, you need to download the Media Center Launcher Configurator from *http:// tinyurl.com/mclauncherconfig*.

Install the software on your PC then run it as an Administrator by right-clicking on the short cut and selecting Run as Administrator. This software enables you to add your batch files to the Media Center menu. For each one, select the Path to Application (select the batch file), the image to display (search Google for an appropriate picture), the title, description and in which menu you want it to appear. Click Register to apply the settings. For each new program, remember to click the icon next to GUID to generate a new ID for each batch file, or you'll run into problems.

When you start Media Center, your batch files will be available through the main menu. For example, to watch Blu-rays at 24Hz, insert a disc, then select your 24p batch file. Start TMT3 and watch the film. When you're done, run the 50Hz batch file from Media Center's menu.

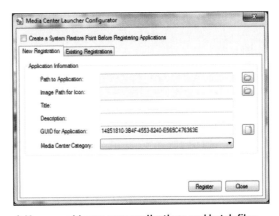

↑ You can add your own applications and batch files to Media Center

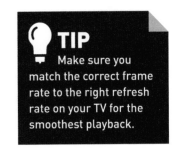

TIP Make sure you match the correct frame rate to the right refresh rate on your TV for the smoothest playback.

HOW TO...
Install Windows XP

1 START YOUR COMPUTER
Turn your PC on and put the Windows XP CD into your optical drive. If you're using a new hard disk, the XP installation routine will load automatically. If you're using an old hard disk that already has an operating system on it, you need to press any key when prompted onscreen. If you don't, your old operating system will start and you'll have to reset your PC to load the installer.

Your computer will take a few minutes to start the installation routine properly, so don't worry if you've got a blank page to look at for a bit.

2 ADD ADDITIONAL DRIVERS
If you've got a RAID controller or hard disk that's not detected (you'll discover this later on and may need to restart the installation routine), you need to add additional drivers. When prompted, press F6. Windows will continue copying files, but after a couple of minutes, a screen will ask what drivers you want to add. Press S to specify additional devices. You'll need to have the files on a floppy disk and a floppy disk drive, as XP can't read additional drivers from CD or USB drives. When you're done, press Enter.

3 SELECT HARD DISKS
On the next screen, press Enter to install a fresh copy of Windows XP. Press F8 to accept the licence agreement. You'll now be able to partition your hard disks. From the list of disks, select the one on which you want Windows to be installed. This is usually MB Disk 0.

Press C to Create a new partition. You have to select the size of the partition in megabytes (1,024MB = 1GB). Generally, we'd recommend leaving at least 40GB (40,960MB) for the second partition, which you can use for backups and storing files that you don't want to overwrite during a fresh operating system installation. Subtract the size of the second partition you want from the figure in the box and enter it. Press Enter to Apply. Select Unpartitioned Space and press C. Press Enter to create the partition. Don't worry if you have a tiny amount of unpartitioned space left, as the way XP deals with disks means that this space can't be used. Select C: and press Enter to install.

4 FORMAT THE HARD DISK
The installation routine has to format the hard disk before it can copy the Windows XP files

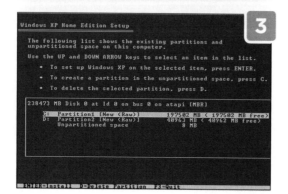

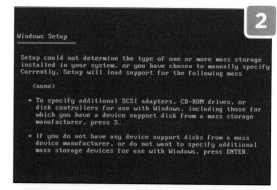

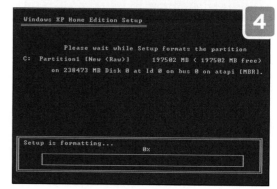

to it. Select Format NTFS and press Enter. While Vista has a speedy format option, XP's takes quite a while, and you may have to wait 30 minutes or more for it to complete.

Once the disk has been formatted, Windows files are copied to the disk. Your computer will reboot automatically once this is done and continue the installation using a graphical tool.

5 CHANGE REGIONAL SETTINGS

The first choice you get is to choose which language you want. Click Customize and change Standards and formats to United Kingdom. Change Location to United Kingdom, too. Click on the Languages tab and click on the Details button. Click Add, select United Kingdom as the input language and click OK.

Select US in the Installed services window and click Remove and then OK. You'll get a warning telling you it can't remove the US language because it's in use, but that it will be removed the next time you reboot your PC. Click OK on this message. Click on the Advanced tab and choose English (United Kingdom) from the drop-down menu. Click OK to apply these settings, then Next.

6 ENTER YOUR PRODUCT KEY

Enter your name in the next box, though you can leave the Organization field blank. Click Next. Enter your product key, which will be printed inside the box in which your copy of Windows XP came. On the next screen, give your PC a more meaningful name than the one that Windows gives it and click Next.

7 SET DATE AND TIME

Even though you told Windows in every setting that you're in the UK, it still sets itself to US time. Change the Time Zone option to GMT. Select the current date and time, and click Next.

Windows will next install the network drivers for your onboard network card. When prompted, leave the network setting as Typical settings and click Next. Windows will finish copying files and finalise the installation.

8 RUN WINDOWS FOR THE FIRST TIME

When Windows starts for the first time, click OK when the dialog box appears to tell you the screen resolution will be automatically changed. Click OK again to confirm that the new resolution

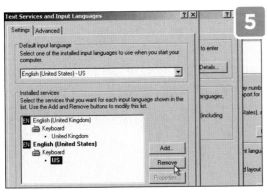

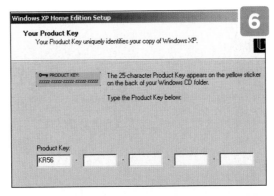

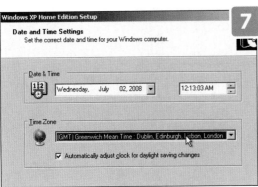

TIP
Make your choices carefully in the blue setup screens, as you can't go back once you've made a choice.

has worked. On the next screen, select Help protect my PC by turning on Automatic Updates now and click Next. Enter your name on the next screen, and anyone else that will be using your computer. Click Next and then Finish. You can now remove the Windows XP installation CD.

9 INSTALL MOTHERBOARD DRIVERS

Although Windows is now working, you still need to install all the relevant drivers to make sure that everything will work smoothly. The first place to start is with the motherboard drivers. If you downloaded the drivers earlier, insert the USB key or disc to which you saved them; if you can't do this, insert the driver disc and follow the onscreen instructions. You'll need to download the updated drivers later, and then follow these instructions.

For every driver you downloaded, run the associated file. It's best to start with the chipset driver, but the order afterwards doesn't matter. If Windows displays any warning messages, just click OK. Some files you download are just archive files that extract the real driver files on to your hard disk. If this is the case, navigate to the folder the files were extracted to and run the Setup program you'll find there. You'll probably need to restart your PC after each driver installation.

10 INSTALL GRAPHICS CARD DRIVERS

Windows will install its own graphics drivers for any onboard or dedicated cards that you have.

These are good enough to run Windows, but you won't be able to play games properly. Instead, you need to install the graphics drivers.

Both ATI and Nvidia provide a single driver package, so all you have to do is run the file you downloaded. If you couldn't download the drivers earlier, you need to insert the bundled CD, but remember to download newer drivers later on.

Restart your computer after the graphics drivers have been installed. Right-click on the desktop, select Properties, then the Settings tab and change your display resolution to match your monitor's native resolution.

11 INSTALL OTHER PERIPHERALS

You can now install the other peripherals that you've added to your PC. Install the relevant driver files for each device that's plugged into your motherboard. For USB devices, you need to install the driver file first and, when prompted, connect the device to a USB port. If you're in any doubt, you should read the manual that came with your peripheral. If you've installed a wireless adaptor, make sure that you connect to your wireless network, following the provided instructions.

12 INSTALL SERVICE PACK 3

When everything is installed, you should install Windows XP Service Pack 3, unless the installation disc you used included it, in which case you can skip to the final step.

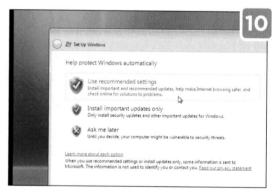

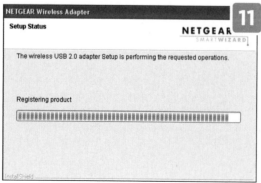

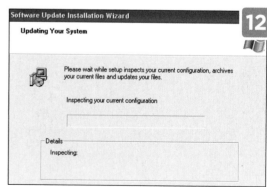

To install Service Pack 3, you should first connect to the internet. The easiest way to force it to install is to go to *http://tinyurl.com/XPservicepack*. Click Download and save the file to your hard disk. When it's finished, run the file you downloaded. Follow the wizard through. Service Pack 3 will take up to an hour to install, restarting your computer when necessary.

13 RUN WINDOWS UPDATE

Visit *www.windowsupdate.com* and click on the Custom button. Windows Update will then prompt you to download the Windows Genuine Advantage Tool in order to use the service. Click the Download and Install Now button and follow the wizard through. Click Continue until you get back to the first screen and then click the Custom button again. Windows Update will then search for the latest updates for your computer. When the list appears, select the updates that you want, click Review and install updates, and then Install Updates to install them.

14 ACTIVATE WINDOWS

If your computer wasn't connected to the internet while you were installing Windows XP, it won't yet be activated. Unlike Vista, which doesn't bother you about activation until you need to do it, XP puts a permanent icon in the Notification Area that displays regular messages warning you about activation. It's worth getting rid of this annoyance now. Double-click the icon that looks like two keys. In the next dialog box, select Yes, activate Windows over the internet now and click Next. Choose whether you want to register with Microsoft and click Next. Within a few seconds, you should get a message saying that you've activated Windows. Click OK. If this didn't work, you may need to activate your copy over the phone following the onscreen instructions.

15 CHANGE USER SETTINGS

Your PC and its users are not password-protected by default. If you'd like to add some security to your PC, you can change this. Click on the Start menu and select the Control Panel. Click on User Accounts, select your user and click on Create a password. Enter your new password and click Create Password. On the next screen, click Yes, Make Private to ensure your files and folders remain private. Repeat these steps for every user you want to be password-protected.

16 FORMAT THE PARTITION

The Windows setup wizard only formats the disk partition on which Windows is installed. If you created a separate partition, you won't be able to use it yet, as it's not formatted. Click on the Start menu, My Computer, right-click the D: drive and select Format. Click OK, make sure that NTFS is selected and then click Format. You can now install our recommended free software (see page 128).

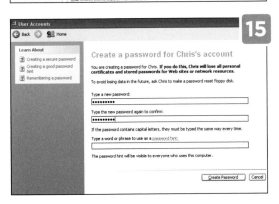

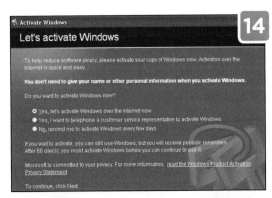

TIP
It's essential that you run Windows Update after an installation to get the latest updates and security patches.

HOW TO...
Install Ubuntu Linux

1 DOWNLOAD UBUNTU

First, download Ubuntu Desktop Edition from *www.ubuntu.com/getubuntu*. The download of Ubuntu 9.04 is 694MB and is an ISO file that needs to be burned to CD before you can use it. Nero Burning Rom and Roxio Creator have built-in tools for letting you do this, but you can also use the free ISO Recorder (available from *http://isorecorder.alexfeinman.com/isorecorder.htm*). Version 2 is for Windows XP and Version 3.1 is for Vista and Windows 7, so make sure that you get the right version for your operating system. Once you've downloaded it, use Explorer to find the ISO file, right-click it and select copy to CD.

Put a blank CD into your optical drive and click Next to copy the file to disc. If you don't have a CD writer, you can ask for a free copy of Ubuntu on CD, but the delivery time may mean that you're better off asking a friend to burn a disc for you.

2 BOOT FROM THE CD

Put the Ubuntu CD that you just created into your new computer's optical drive. Keep an eye out for the 'Press any key to boot from CD' message. If you miss this, you'll have to restart your computer to load the Ubuntu installation routine. The first Ubuntu installation screen should appear very quickly, and here you just need to select the installation language.

3 START INSTALLATION

You're then presented with an installation menu and a handful of options. The default installation option is to try Ubuntu without making any changes to your computer. This simply loads Ubuntu from the CD and doesn't write any files to your hard disk, and is a good way to try out Linux before making any commitments and filling up your hard disk. If you're still not sure about Linux, this is the safest option. To install Ubuntu properly, select the Install Ubuntu option.

The first thing you'll see is the Ubuntu loading screen, which looks a little like that for Windows. It can take a while for Ubuntu to chug through this part of its installation, so don't panic if the orange bar appears to freeze for a spell.

4 SELECT LANGUAGE

Eventually, you'll see the Ubuntu wallpaper and a welcome screen. Hopefully, this is in a

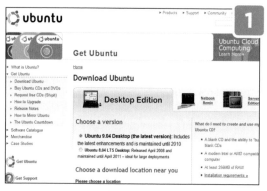

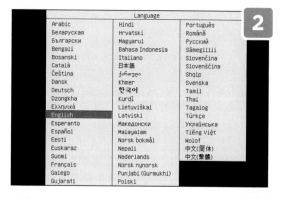

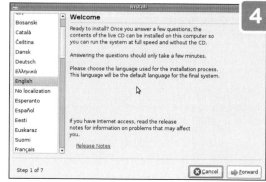

language you can understand; if not, select English from the list on the left.

If your computer is plugged into the internet via a wired connection, you can click the Release Notes link to find out more information on problems that may affect you. When you've finished, click the Forward button to continue.

5 SELECT LOCATION

Now select your location using the drop-down menu. UK cities are grouped under Europe towards the end of the list. Selecting a location in the UK should automatically select the correct time zone. If it doesn't, select the right one using the drop-down menu.

When you've chosen the correct settings, click Forward to continue. Your keyboard layout should be set to United Kingdom; if it's not, select this from the menu and click Forward.

6 SET UP HARD DISKS

By default, Ubuntu uses a simple partitioning system on your PC's hard disk. While perfectly adequate, this is worth tweaking to alter where files are stored. This will let you choose where

your user files (My Documents in Windows) are kept, as well as create separate partitions for program files and virtual memory.

Linux stores user files in the /home folder, and moving this to its own partition is easy. Unfortunately, if you opt to set up one partition manually, you have to set them all up this way, so we'll need to take a slight detour to complete this process. If you just want to stick with Ubuntu's default partition scheme, just leave the Guided option selected, click Forward and move on to step 12.

7 DELETE EXISTING PARTITIONS

Select the Manual option on the Prepare disk space screen and click Forward. The installer will then scan your hard disk and display the disk partitioning tool. The first step is to delete all existing partitions on the hard disk, so select each one in the list and click the Delete partition button.

8 SET BOOT PARTITION

You should now just have free space listed under /dev/sda (Linux's name for the hard disk on the primary IDE channel). Since we're creating

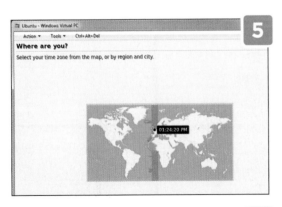

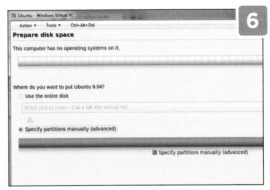

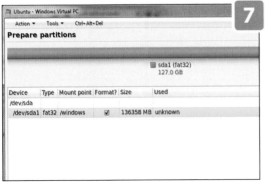

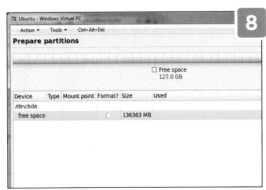

TIP You can try Ubuntu without installing it. Simply boot off the CD and explore the desktop. When you're ready to proceed you just need to run the installer.

partitions by hand, we need to create all the partitions Linux requires, starting with the /boot partition. Select free space in the list of partitions and click New partition. Enter a size of 50 (we're working in megabytes here) and select /boot as the Mount point. Click OK.

9 SET SWAP PARTITION

Linux also needs a /swap partition, which is the equivalent of Windows' swap file used for virtual memory. When your PC's real memory fills up, Ubuntu will swap bits of the memory that aren't currently being used (inactive applications, for example) to the hard disk. This gives the impression that your computer has more memory than it does, so you can run more applications.

Create another new partition in the free space and enter a size equal to the amount of RAM in the computer in megabytes (1GB = 1,024MB). Select Swap area from the Use as drop-down list, leave the other settings at their defaults and then click OK.

10 SET HOME PARTITION

Next is the /home partition, where user files are kept. This is the equivalent of Windows' My Documents folder, but kept on a separate partition.

The advantage of this method is that you can reinstall Linux and your documents won't be overwritten. Make this partition as large as you like, remembering to leave a few gigabytes free for the final /root partition. Select /home as the Mount point before clicking OK.

11 SET ROOT PARTITION

Last is the root or / partition. This is where Ubuntu is installed and it will use all of the remaining space. Set the Mount point as / and click OK.

You can see the final partition structure from the screenshot below, so click Forward when you're ready to continue. That's the end of the custom partitioning.

12 SET A USERNAME AND A PASSWORD

You now need to tell Ubuntu who you are. Type your name into the What is your name? box. This will automatically generate a username for you in the What name do you want to use to log in? box, but you can change this if you like. Type in a password to protect your account and prevent unauthorised users from logging on to your PC.

Finally, your computer will automatically have been given a name based on your name in the

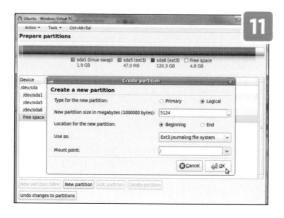

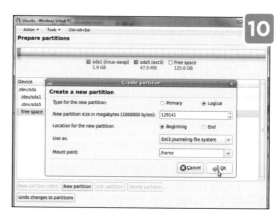

What is the name of this computer? box. You can change this to anything you like, if you prefer. Click Forward when you've finished.

13 INSTALL LINUX
So far, no files have been written to your hard disk, so this is the last chance you've got to back out of the installation. When you're ready to continue, click Install.

Ubuntu will now copy the necessary files to the hard disk partitions you created. This process will take a few minutes, so sit back and let it do its job.

14 START UBUNTU FOR THE FIRST TIME
Once the installation is complete, the Gnome desktop will load. This is very similar to the Windows desktop, and it's where the bulk of your interaction with Linux will take place. You'll find that a whole range of applications have already been installed and you can access them through the Applications menu at the top-left of the screen.

The applications that come bundled with Linux vary, but at the very least you can expect to find an office suite of some description, a web browser and an email client – Ubuntu comes with OpenOffice.org, Firefox and Thunderbird.

Applications can be found in the Applications menu at the top-left of the screen.

15 INSTALL NEW APPLICATIONS
Ubuntu also simplifies the process of finding and installing new programs. Its Add/Remove Applications utility (available in the Applications menu) works in a similar way to its Windows namesake, with the added advantage of offering new applications to install, as well as old ones to remove. New programs are downloaded from the internet and any additional components that are required (known as dependencies) are automatically downloaded, too, which goes a long way to making Linux more user-friendly.

16 INSTALL UPDATES
Just as you would do with Windows, Ubuntu needs to have the latest security patches installed. Its rising popularity means that it's attracting increased interest from malicious hackers.

Fortunately, Ubuntu has its own update manager and will periodically check for updates. When new updates are ready to be installed, you'll see a warning on the application bar. Click the warning to bring up a list of available updates, and click the Install Updates button to install them.

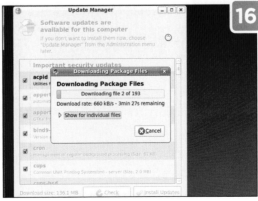

TIP
Finding drivers for all your hardware can be difficult, but a Google search should bring up some forums that may be able to help you get your hardware working.

Make your own NAS

If you have an old PC sitting around doing nothing, you could turn it into network storage for your new PC using FreeNAS. Here we show you how to get to grips with this powerful system

FREENAS IS A free operating system that turns any computer into a network-attached storage (NAS) device. Here we'll take you through installing the software on an old PC. You'll need a PC with at least one hard disk in it and an optical drive. The best installation of FreeNAS uses a USB flash drive. You'll need one with at least 64MB of disk space; you can buy 1GB models for around £3 if you don't have one.

To start, download the ISO CD image of the operating system from *www.freenas.org*. You need to download the LiveCD version. There are two versions for download: one for Intel processors and one for AMD 64-bit processors. Select the right version and download the ISO file to your PC. This file is an image of a CD that needs to be written to a blank disc. If you don't have any CD-writing software, the free CDBurnerXP (*http://cdburnerxp.se*) will do the job.

Once you've written the files to the CD, you can boot from the disc on the computer that you'll be using for FreeNAS. Before you do, however,

there are some configuration options you need to think about. First, for the maximum flexibility you should install FreeNAS on a USB flash disk, leaving your hard disks completely for data storage. For this to work, you need to set your BIOS to boot from USB devices.

To do this, turn on your FreeNAS PC, plug in your USB flash drive and enter the BIOS (normally you have to press Delete, F10 or F12, but look out for a message telling you which key to press). Typically the USB boot options will be under Advanced BIOS Features. There may be an option to boot from USB drives, you may have to select a USB flash drive from the Boot Device menu or the option may be called Boot Other Devices. In our BIOS, the USB drive was detected as a hard disk and we had to select it as the first device in the Hard Disk Boot Priority menu. If your PC can't boot from USB flash drives, you can install FreeNAS to one of your hard disks, but this makes configuration harder later on and prevents you from using this hard disk in a RAID array.

TIP

Booting from a USB flash drive makes FreeNAS easier to configure and gives you more disk space to play with.

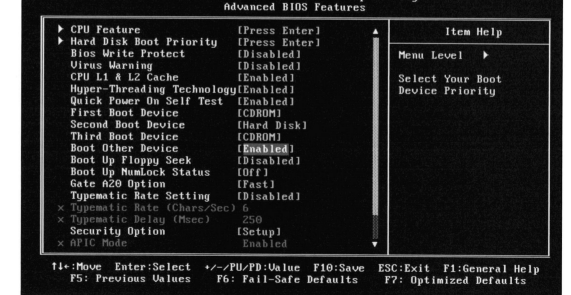

↑ You need to enter the BIOS and set your computer to boot from a USB disk for the optimal FreeNAS installation

Alternatively, you can connect the flash disk to a USB port and boot the PC from the FreeNAS Live CD. Your settings will be saved automatically to the flash drive, so there's no installation at all. However, this makes it trickier to upgrade FreeNAS to a later version.

While you're in the BIOS, make sure that you disable the option to halt on keyboard errors, as your FreeNAS PC won't need a monitor or keyboard connected to it when it's ready.

The other configuration option to consider is whether you want to use RAID. FreeNAS lets you use all common types of RAID (see *http://tinyurl.com/raidlevels* for an explanation). You'll need at least two hard disks to use RAID. The benefits are increased speed and reliability, and you can add extra hard disks to your PC later to increase the storage space. The alternative is to use each disk separately; this is your only choice if you have one hard disk. We'll show you both methods here.

CONNECTING YOUR PC

You're now ready to install the operating system via an Ethernet cable to your router or hub. Before you start, remove any USB flash drives (unless you're planning to start FreeNAS from CD each time, in which case start your computer and go to Step 3), or you'll get an error.

1 Boot from the disc you created. When the Console setup menu appears, insert your USB drive into a spare port, type 9 and then Enter to install FreeNAS to your PC's hard disk. Select option 1 and press Enter. FreeNAS will confirm the partitions that it will create and warn you that your entire USB flash disk will be wiped. Press Enter to continue. Select your optical drive from the list and press Enter. Finally, select the flash drive to which you want to install the OS (it will have a name that starts 'da') and press Enter.

2 FreeNAS will install itself to the flash drive, which should take only a few seconds. When it's finished, you'll get a message telling you that you can remove the optical disc and restart your

computer. Follow these instructions and make sure your computer is set to boot from USB devices.

3 When your computer restarts, you'll see a similar Console setup menu to the one in Step 1. Type 1 and then Enter to pick the network interface you want to use. Pick the one with (up) in brackets and press Enter. Go to Finish and exit configuration and press Enter, then Enter again.

Next, set the IP address that you want your FreeNAS computer to use by typing 2 and then

Enter. You'll be asked if you want to use DHCP. If your router has an option to fix the IP address it gives to a specific PC (many do), select Yes. Otherwise, select No. In this case you'll have to select an IP address manually.

The easiest way to find a safe address is to follow your router's instructions to access the web management page from your main PC and view the DHCP server settings. The page will contain a start address, such as 192.168.1.1, and either an end address, such as 192.168.1.49, or a number that says how many addresses it hands out, such as 50. In this example, 50 IP addresses would give us a range between 192.168.1.1 and 192.168.1.50.

All you have to do is pick an IP address outside this range. To be on the safe side, we recommend picking an address that's 10 higher than the last DHCP address. So, keep the first three numbers the same and add 10 to the last number – in our example, that would be 192.168.1.60 – and write this address down, as you'll need it later.

Type the address into FreeNAS and press Enter. You'll be prompted for your network's subnet mask. You'll probably have a network that uses 255.255.255.0, so type 24 and press Enter. On the next two screens, enter a Gateway and a DNS address. These are your router's IP address. Type it in both boxes and press Enter. Finally, say No to IPv6 and press Enter. You'll then get a confirmation that the IP address has been configured.

4 FreeNAS is now running, so you can switch to its web-based interface for further configuration. In a web browser on another computer, type the IP address of your FreeNAS server into the address bar. The default username is admin, with the password freenas.

The first job is to change the password. Click on the System menu and select General. Click on the Password tab, type in the old password and then your new password twice. Click Save and you'll be prompted to log into the management page again with your new password.

5 Next, it's time to set up file sharing. To do this, add the hard disks on which you want to share files to FreeNAS. Click on Management in the Disks menu, and then the big plus sign. Select a hard disk from the Disk drop-down menu (hard disks start with 'ad') and type in a description. We

recommend leaving the other settings alone, except for S.M.A.R.T., which is used to monitor your disk's health. Put a tick in this box and click Add. Repeat this step for each hard disk in your system, and then click Apply Changes on the Disks, Management screen.

6 Your hard disks now need to be formatted. To do this, select Format from the Disks menu. Remember that if you're using old disks you'll need to have copied off any files that you want to keep. If you're going to use each disk individually, leave the File system option on its default value of UFS, type in a Volume label and click Format disk. Repeat this procedure for all your disks and go to Step 8.

If you want to use RAID, select Software RAID from the File system menu and click Format disk. Repeat for all your hard disks, and go to Step 7.

7 To create a RAID array, select Software RAID from the Disks menu. Select the type of RAID array you want to create from the tabs and click

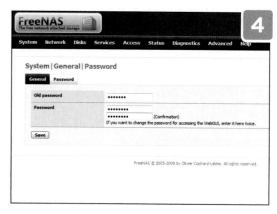

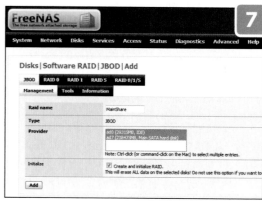

the Plus icon. Type in the RAID name (no spaces are allowed), select the hard disks you want to use in the Provider menu, select Initialize and click Add. Click Apply Changes on the next screen.

You have to format your new RAID array, so select Format from the Disks menu. Choose your RAID array from the drop-down Disk menu, type in a Volume label and click Format disk.

8 Now you need to share your disk. Click on Disks, then Mount Point. Select a hard disk or RAID array from the drop-down Disk menu. Type in a Share name and Description, then click Add. Click Apply Changes and your share is ready.

In order for Windows computers to be able to access the share, you need to enable the file-sharing service. Click on CIFS/SMB from the Services menu and put a tick in the Enable box. You shouldn't need to change many of the settings, but there are some you can: NetBIOS name is the name that will appear when Windows computers browse the network, Workgroup is the Windows workgroup in which your server will appear, and

Large read/write should be enabled if your computers run Windows 2000 or later. When you're ready, click Save and Restart.

Finally, you need to select which files you want to share. Click on the Shares tab. Type in the name you want the share to be known by and a comment, and then click the button next to Path. Select the mount point that you created at the start of this step (individual hard disks will have one mount point each and a RAID array has one mount point) and click OK. Click Apply Changes. You can repeat this for every mount point that you have.

9 On your Windows PC, get a Run command up (Windows+R) and type \\<*ip address of your FreeNAS server*>. You'll see an Explorer window with folders named the same as the Shares you've just set up. If you right-click a folder and select Map network drive, you can create a network drive that you can access in Windows just like a normal hard disk. Repeat this step for all the computers on your network that need access to the network share.

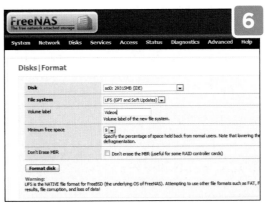

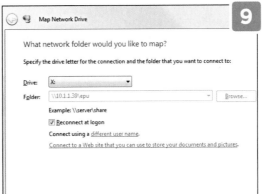

Configure FreeNAS

FreeNAS's advanced features let you add security, share files over the internet and share media with other computers. Here we show you how to set up, configure and use these features

THE FIRST PLACE to start is security. Our default installation of FreeNAS didn't have any usernames or passwords, so anyone could access the computer. While this is fine on a local network, if you're going to use more advanced features that are accessible over the internet, such as the FTP server, you'll need to know how to set up users and groups.

At the time of writing the current version of FreeNAS doesn't let you choose which users have access to each service: anyone with a username and password can access every feature and every share. For home use this shouldn't make any difference, unless you're really keen to restrict access for your family.

⬇ Adding users to your FreeNAS computer is very straightforward

BACKING UP YOUR CONFIGURATION

If your system develops a problem and you have to reinstall FreeNAS, you'll need to restore it quickly.

If you don't back up your configuration, you risk losing every file stored in a RAID array. Log on to FreeNAS's web-based management and click Backup/Restore from the System menu. Click Download configuration and save the file to your PC. If you need to restore your configuration, use the same menu, but click the Browse button, select the configuration file you backed up and then click Restore configuration.

It's also worth checking that you have the most up-to-date version of FreeNAS. To do this, go to *www.freenas.org*, click the Download link and select the latest version in the FreeNAS Images list (not the LiveCD list). This will download a .img file. In FreeNAS's web management page, select Firmware from the System menu. Select Enable firmware upload, click Browse, select the .img file you downloaded and then click Upgrade firmware. This will automatically upload the file and upgrade your FreeNAS computer, restarting it when it's completed.

ADDING A USER

To add a new user, go to FreeNAS's web-based management page and log on. Click on the Access tab and select Users and Groups. Click the blue Plus and you'll be prompted to add a user by typing in a username and password. It's best to type in the same usernames and passwords that are used to log into Windows, as this way you'll automatically be able to access network shares without having to authenticate.

You can also assign users to groups. At the moment, all users have access to every service; however, when this is updated in a later version of FreeNAS it will make security easier to deal with as you'll be able to allow or deny a whole group of users access to a service. For now, though, we've put all our users in the Admin group. When you've created one user, click Add, then Apply changes. Click the blue Plus to add another user.

TURNING ON SECURITY

Now you have users, it's time to use them. We'll start by showing you how to secure the network

Access | Users | Add

| Users | Groups |

Login	David
	Login name of user.
Full Name	David Ludlow
	User full name.
Password	••••••••
	•••••••• (Confirmation)
	User password.
User ID	1001
	User numeric id.
Primary group	admin ▾
	Set the account's primary group to the given group.
Additional group	admin / bin / daemon / ftp / guest / kmem / man / network / nobody / nogroup / operator / sshd
	Set additional group memberships for this account. Note: Ctrl-click (or command-click on the Mac) to select and deselect groups.
Home directory	Enter the path to the home directory of that user. Leave this field empty to use default path /mnt.
Shell access	☐ Give full shell access to user.

Add

share we helped you create on page 106. Select CIFS/SMB from the Services menu. To turn on security, select Local User from the Authentication menu and then click Save and Restart. When you get the message, "The changes have been applied successfully", all your network shares are secure and only authorised users can access them.

To check, type Windows+R to get a Run command and type \\<*ip address of your FreeNAS computer*>. If you created a username and password that matches your current Windows user, you'll be able to access the shares; if you didn't, you'll be prompted to type in a valid username and password.

SMARTER SHARES

You can share an entire Mount Point (hard disk or RAID array), but this isn't always the best use of disk space. It often makes more sense to share only a particular folder. For example, you could give each user their own share to use. A similar argument goes for other services here.

To share a folder, you first need to create one. FreeNAS has a built-in file browser that lets you do this. Click on Advanced and select File Manager, then log on with the same username and password that you use to log on to FreeNAS's

↑ You can password-protect your network shares for added security

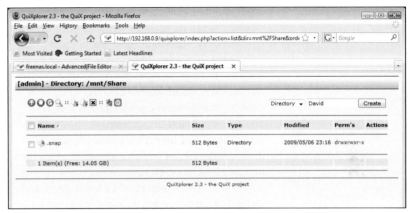

↑ The built-in file browser lets you manage files and folders from the web management console

web-management page. You'll see an Explorer-style file browser that you can use to view every file and folder. To create a new folder to share, you need to know where to put it.

Unlike Windows, which has different drive letters for each hard disk, FreeNAS is based on Linux. We've already explained that for each hard disk or RAID array you have to create a Mount Point, and it's the Mount Point that you need to access. These are stored in the 'mnt' folder, so click on this. Here you'll see a list of folders with the same names as the Mount Points that you created, each one referring to a hard disk or RAID array. Click on one to access it. Select Directory from the drop-down menu, type in a name and click Create to make a Folder.

The new folder will have the wrong permissions and won't let users write files to it. To change this, click on the link under the Perm's column next to the folder you've created (it will look something like drwxrwxr-x). Put a tick in the 'w' box under Public and click Change.

To use your new folder to create a share, click on CIFS/SMB from the Services menu of the main web interface window, and click on the Shares tab. Click the blue plus icon, type a name for your new share (we've chosen the name of one of our users) and a description. Click the button next to Path and navigate to the mnt folder. Click the Mount

TIP
Update FreeNAS regularly in order to add new features and improve those that are already there.

Point name where you created your new folder, then click your new folder. Click OK, then click Add followed by Apply changes. Your new share will then show up when you get a Run command and type \\<*ip address of your FreeNAS computer*>. It may be prudent to stop sharing the main share, which gives users access to an entire drive, by clicking the red minus icon next to a share's name.

SETTING UP FTP

The problem with network shares is that they're not easy to share over the internet. Fortunately, FTP provides a way for all users to access their files from anywhere. Be warned, though, that the FTP settings are quite basic and give users access to the mnt folder and, therefore, access to every hard disk and RAID array you have installed.

To turn on FTP, select FTP from the Service menu (don't select TFTP, as this is a very basic form of FTP). Put a tick in the Enable box and a tick in the box marked 'Only allow authenticated

↓ You can access your FreeNAS server over the internet using FTP

users. Anonymous logins are prohibited.' This will let only authenticated users access FreeNAS.

You can leave the other settings as they are, although you may want to turn on Resume, which lets users continue downloading a file if it's interrupted, and SSI/TLS, which allows users to make secure connections to your server. However, this latter option will put a bit of overhead on your server, so turn it off if performance becomes an issue. When you're done, click Save and Restart.

To test that it's working properly, open your web browser and type ftp://<*ip address of your FreeNAS computer*>. When prompted, type in a valid username and password, and you'll be able to browse all the files on your PC. This access is very basic, so for more control you're better off with a dedicated FTP client such as FileZilla (*http://filezilla-project.org*).

The next step is to give access to the computer over the internet. The first problem to overcome is that your home has an external IP address that's shared by all the computers on your network. This IP address can change, making it impossible to access your home. Fortunately, with Dynamic DNS you can create a simple URL that's updated regularly so that it always points at your home.

The only point to make is that if your router doesn't support DynDNS.org (the best free Dynamic DNS service), FreeNAS does, so you don't need to download any other software. Select Dynamic DNS from the Services menu, click Enable and type in your DynDNS.org account details.

With Dynamic DNS up and running, you need to configure your router so that it knows to send

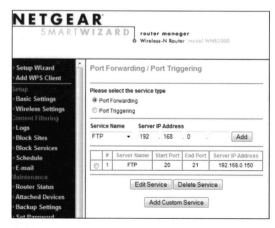

↑ You may need to reconfigure your router to get FTP working properly

incoming FTP requests to your FreeNAS computer. This is fairly straightforward and involves configuring port forwarding (called virtual servers on some routers). You need to configure a new rule that forwards all incoming traffic on Port 21 to the IP address of your FreeNAS computer. Your router's manual will tell you how to do this, and *www.portforward.com* has lots of information about it as well.

Once that's done, you can access your FreeNAS computer from over the internet. In a web browser, you type ftp://*<name of the DynDNS.org URL you created>*, such as ftp://computershopper. homeftp.net. You'd also use your DynDNS.org URL in a dedicated FTP client, such as FileZilla.

SHARING MEDIA FILES

If you want to share your media files, FreeNAS makes this easy. It has support for iTunes sharing, which lets you share your music files with computers running iTunes and some media streamers, and UPnP, which lets you share music with a wide range of media streamers. Both services work in the same way, so we'll just explain how to use UPnP.

First, you need a folder in which to store all your media. This can be an existing folder in a share or you can create one specifically using the instructions above. In either case, make sure that you have network access to this folder so that you can copy new files to it, by creating a new share if necessary.

To turn on the UPnP server, select UPnP from the Services menu and select Enable. Click the button next to Database directory and choose a folder in which to create the media directory. This can be stored anywhere, but for convenience we put ours in a directory called Media, which we also use to house our media files. Click Add, which is next to Content, and add the directory that houses your media. You can add multiple directories by repeating this step.

If you have a media streamer with limited format support, you can use transcoding to turn one file format into another. Put a tick in the Transcoding box, and FreeNAS will convert files into a compatible format. However, this operation is processor-intensive, so turn it off if your PC's performance suffers. If you do turn this feature on, select a Temporary Directory in which to store the transcoded files.

↑ Your FreeNAS computer can share media files using its built-in UPnP server

Finally, select Enable web user interface, click Save and then Restart. Your server will now be working. You can click on the URL link to view a web page with the status of your server.

To turn on iTunes sharing, select iTunes/DAAP from the Services menu and follow these instructions. The only difference is that you need to set a password for the administrator's web page, and click the Zeroconf/Bonjour link at the bottom of the page to make sure these two network services are selected and turned on, otherwise iTunes won't detect your NAS.

↑ The built-in iTunes server lets you stream music to other computers running Apple's software

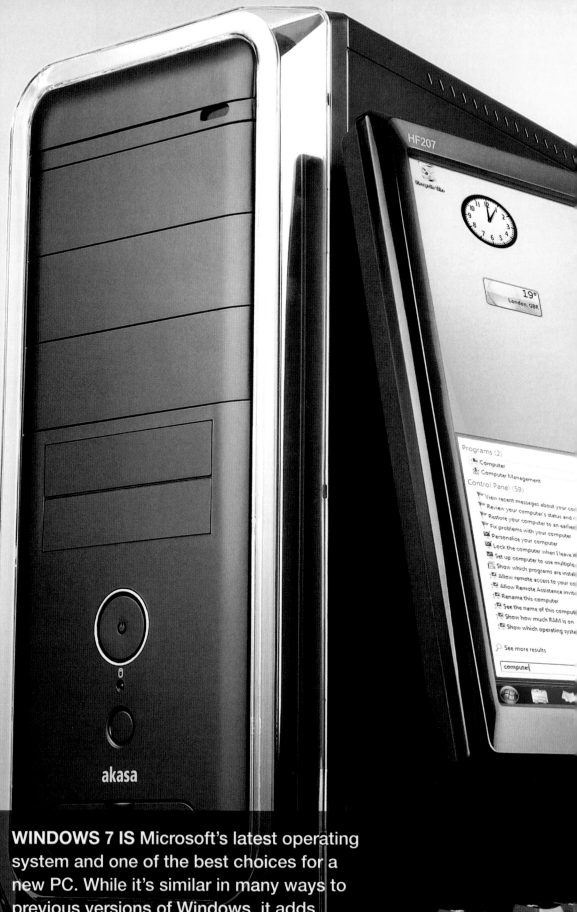

WINDOWS 7 IS Microsoft's latest operating system and one of the best choices for a new PC. While it's similar in many ways to previous versions of Windows, it adds many new features. Here we'll show you what some of these new features are and how you can use them.

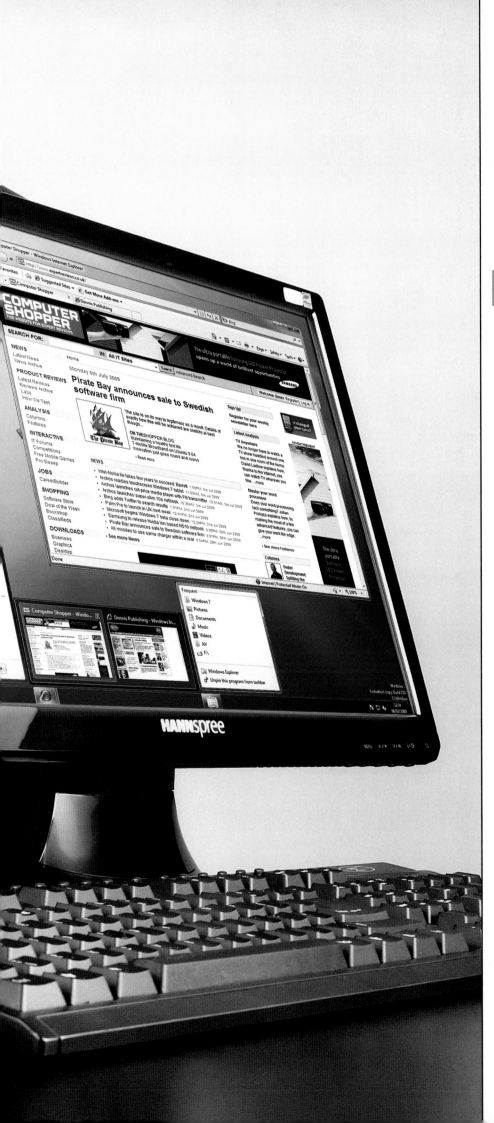

IN THIS CHAPTER

The new desktop

Gadgets
Gadgets display simple bits of information, such as the current weather and the time. You can add more by right-clicking the desktop and selecting Gadgets.

Preview windows
Hovering the mouse cursor over a highlighted icon displays a preview of the application's current windows. Hovering the cursor over one of these previews brings that window to the foreground for a better view.

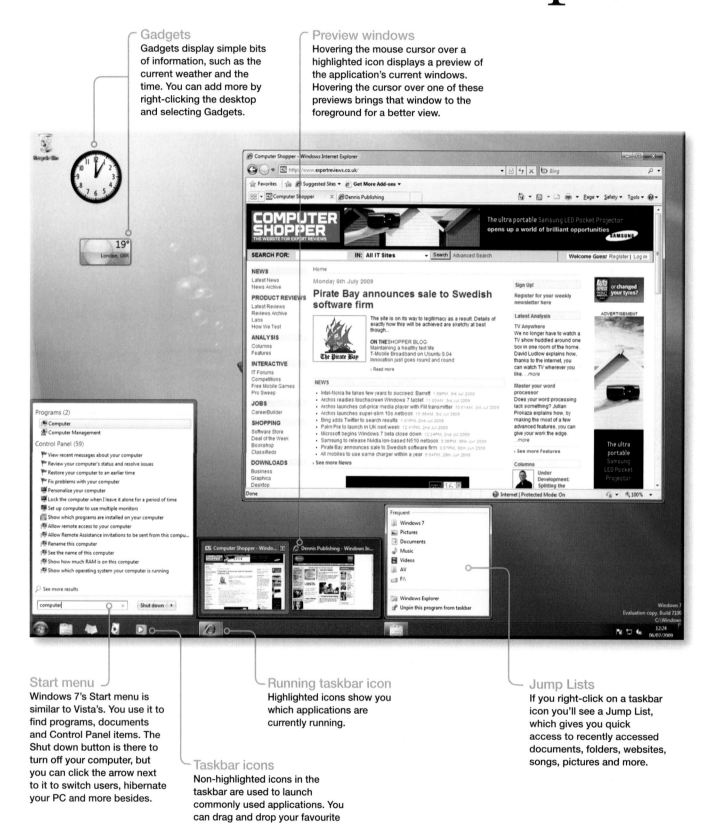

Start menu
Windows 7's Start menu is similar to Vista's. You use it to find programs, documents and Control Panel items. The Shut down button is there to turn off your computer, but you can click the arrow next to it to switch users, hibernate your PC and more besides.

Running taskbar icon
Highlighted icons show you which applications are currently running.

Jump Lists
If you right-click on a taskbar icon you'll see a Jump List, which gives you quick access to recently accessed documents, folders, websites, songs, pictures and more.

Taskbar icons
Non-highlighted icons in the taskbar are used to launch commonly used applications. You can drag and drop your favourite programs here from the Start menu.

Manage your windows

Grab an application and shake the mouse to minimise all other open windows. This is a great way to clear clutter onscreen, so you can focus on a single application. Do the same thing again to restore the other windows.

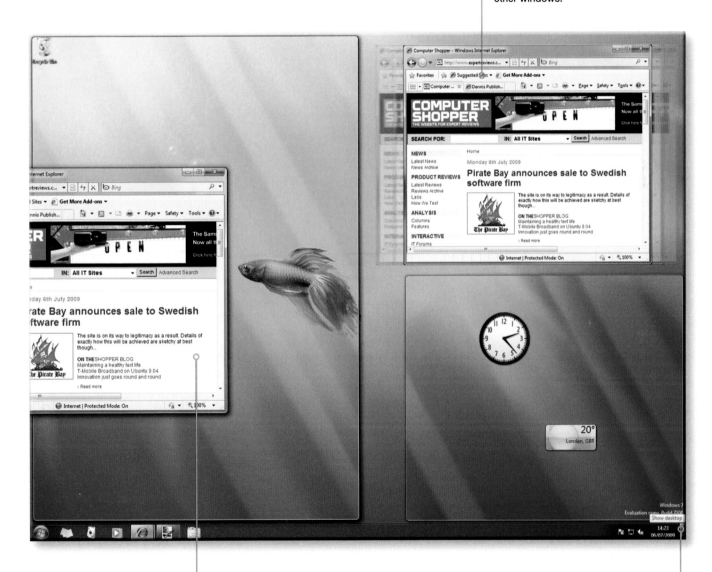

Grab an application and move it to either side so it takes up half your monitor. This is a quick way to compare two applications side by side. Move a window to the top of the screen and it's maximised to take up the whole screen. You can select a window and press Windows and → ← or ↑ for the same effect.

Move your mouse cursor to the bottom right of the screen and all the windows dissolve to an outline. Use this mode to view gadgets quickly and see how many windows you have open. Click the left mouse button to minimise all windows and click it again to bring them back.

HOW TO...
Perform an Anytime Upgrade

There's no reason to be stuck with the same version of Windows 7. With the help of Anytime Upgrade, you can take advantage of the benefits of other versions as your needs change

WHEN YOU INSTALL Windows 7, you install all the features of every version – it's just that some features are locked. However, with Anytime Upgrade you can upgrade your PC's version of Windows 7 instantly just by buying a new licence key. The Home Premium edition can be upgraded to Professional or Ultimate, while Professional can be upgraded to Ultimate.

The beauty of this type of upgrade is that you don't need to reinstall any software, and your files are left intact on your computer along with your Windows settings. For a full breakdown of the prices, go to *http://emea.microsoftstore.com/uk*.

1 RUN UPGRADE APPLICATION

Click on the Start menu and type Upgrade. Then select Windows Anytime Upgrade from the search results. Selecting 'Go online to choose the edition of Windows 7 that's best for you' lets you buy a new product upgrade key online and upgrades your computer. Meanwhile, selecting 'Enter an upgrade key' lets you type in an upgrade product key, such as the one provided in a retail Windows Anytime Upgrade box; we'll assume this is the choice you've made.

2 ENTER UPGRADE KEY

On the next screen, type in the Upgrade key you were given and click Next. Once the key has been verified, you'll be prompted to accept the licence terms. Click 'I accept'. You'll be presented with a warning telling you that the process takes about 15 minutes and that you should close all open applications and save your work. Click Upgrade and the process will start.

3 INSTALL NEW FEATURES

Your PC checks online to see if any updates are available before upgrading your version of Windows 7. It then begins the main upgrade procedure, which will take a few minutes. Once it's complete, your PC will restart and Windows will reload with the features of the new version unlocked. You'll see a welcome screen with a link to help you find out about the new features.

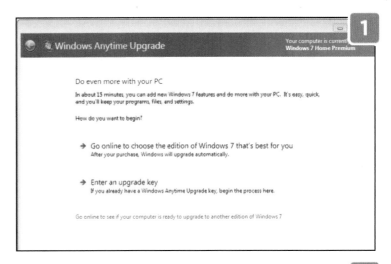

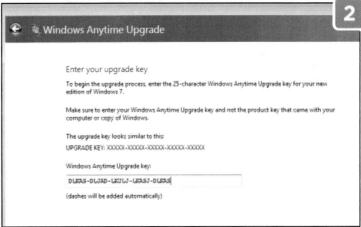

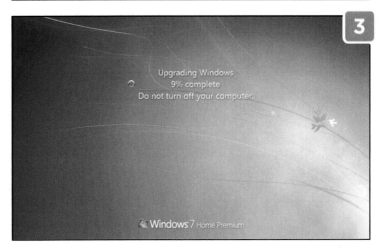

HOW TO...
Get HD TV on your Windows 7 PC

Do you have an old Sky minidish? If you do, we can show you how to watch and record free HD broadcasts with the help of Windows 7

THE NEW MEDIA Center is compatible with Freesat HD broadcasts, so you can watch high-definition television for free. To get HD TV on your Windows PC you'll need a satellite dish, such as a Sky minidish, and a Freesat HD tuner.

INSTALL TUNER

Install the PCI or USB tuner according to the instructions supplied. You should be able to download Windows 7-compatible drivers from the manufacturer's website. If these aren't available, try running the Vista driver installer, or install the drivers via the Device Manager – you can find this by typing its name into the Start Search box. The tuner is clearly marked as unrecognised hardware. Download the Vista BDA drivers from the manufacturer's website, and install them by right-clicking on the device and choosing Update Driver Software.

SCAN FOR CHANNELS

Launch Media Center and select Tasks, Settings, TV, Set up TV signal. Media Center will examine your TV signals. We had trouble getting it to recognise DVB-T and DVB-S tuners simultaneously. If this happens, select 'No, show me more options' and then 'Let me configure my TV signal manually'. Choose Antenna to set up DVB-T channels first, then add DVB-S after.

During DVB-S setup, you'll be asked if you want to use multiple satellites. Answer No, and you'll be asked to choose a satellite; you need Astra 2A-B-D (28.2E). Select your LNB type as Universal. The next screen shows the signal strength of your reception. If this is poor, your dish may be misaligned or the cabling damaged.

LOCATE HD CHANNELS

Media Center downloads the programme guide and scans for channels. Click on the Categories button to the left of the guide and select HD to find BBC HD. At present, getting ITV HD is trickier; the channel is named 10510 and appears as an audio-only channel. This will be fixed, but you can get it working by following the instructions at *http://tinyurl.com/lqu4ok*.

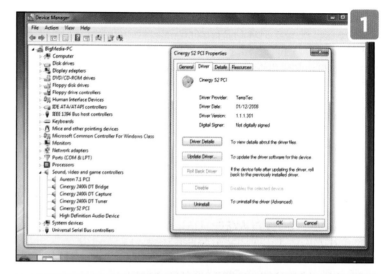

HOW TO...
Use a UPnP server

Windows 7 supports UPnP servers, which means you can stream media directly from a compatible device, such as a NAS. Here we show you how to set things up

ONE BENEFIT OF having a network is the ability to share media using the UPnP protocol – this is often provided by NAS devices. Previous versions of Windows shared media with UPnP using Windows Media Player, but were unable to view UPnP servers. With Windows 7, you can view all UPnP media servers, so it's easier to stream music, video and pictures from your NAS device or other PC. This is better than setting up file shares and works across multiple devices. It also means that you don't have to configure your computer, as it will find media automatically.

1 START MEDIA PLAYER
If you want to use Windows Media Player to view other files, simply start it and it will display all UPnP media servers under Other Libraries. Expand a library to view pictures, music and video. You can browse through these options as if you were using files stored locally on your PC.

2 SELECT WHICH FILES TO SHARE
You can use your UPnP server's controls to configure which files are shared. You'll find instructions on how to do this with your UPnP device, such as your NAS. Here we'll show you how to configure Windows Media Player. To add new folders to share, right-click one of your own libraries (such as music), select Manage and click Add. Navigate to the folder you want to share and click Include folder. The files in that folder will become part of your library and will be shared over the network. You can also add files manually by dragging them into Windows Media Player's main window. The files will be copied to the Default save location as specified in the Manage dialog box.

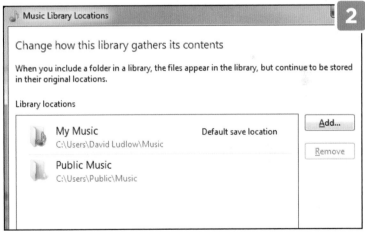

3 CONFIGURE MEDIA CENTER
Media Center's ability to access files on UPnP servers is also useful. Launch Media Center from the Start menu and browse to one of the libraries. Scroll to the left of the menu and select Shared. You can then choose a Library stored on another PC and view its content. This lets you navigate through your media in the same way as if it were stored on your own computer.

Touchscreen interface

Windows 7 has been designed to be used with touch gestures in a similar way to Apple's iPod Touch, with a multitouch display. We show you how to ditch your mouse

PAN

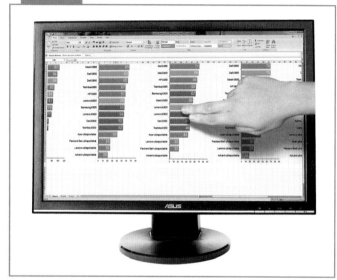

↑ Using one or two fingers, you can drag your fingers across an open application to scroll round it. Move your fingers up or down to move the vertical scrollbar, and left and right for the horizontal scrollbar.

ZOOM

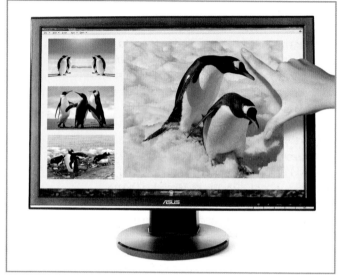

↑ To zoom in on a picture or document, pinch your finger and thumb together on the screen and then slide them apart. To zoom out, place your finger and thumb far apart, then bring them together.

ROTATE

↑ To rotate an object, such as an image, in an application that supports the gesture, place your thumb and finger on it. Rotate your finger around your thumb in the direction you want to rotate.

PRESS AND TAP

↑ To access the right-click mouse menu, simply place one finger on the object you want to interact with and then tap the screen with another finger. You can then tap the menu option you want.

HOW TO...
Use the new disc-burning features

Windows 7 supports Blu-ray discs and ISO image files as well as direct disc-burning that enables you to turn an optical disc into a flash drive. Here's how to make the most of these new features

WINDOWS 7 HAS massively improved the built-in disc-burning features and added support for Blu-ray discs. There's also support for burning ISO CD images, such as those you download to create a Linux installation disc. All you need is a suitable optical drive and some blank discs. These steps will work for any type of media: CDs, DVDs and Blu-ray discs.

1 INSERT A BLANK DISC

Insert a blank disc into your PC's optical drive and the AutoPlay menu will appear. To write new files, select 'Burn files to disc'. On the next menu, choose the disc you want to create. The 'Like a USB flash drive' option lets you add extra files at a later date and delete existing files, but this format can be used only with other Windows PCs (XP or later). However, you can finalise a disc so it works with other PCs.

The 'With a CD/DVD player' option is a standard way to write discs. Once you've written files, the disc is finalised and you can't add or delete files. These discs will work in any computer, so are best for compatibility.

2 ADD FILES TO DISC

If you select the first option, the disc will be formatted and then a new Explorer window will appear. Drag and drop files into this window and they'll instantly be written to your disc. If you want the disc to be read by all PCs, click the Close Session button and the disc will be finalised. If you select the second option, you'll just get the Explorer window. Drag and drop the files you want to record to disc into this window. Click 'Burn to disc' when you're done and the files will be copied.

3 BURN AN ISO IMAGE

To create a disc from an ISO image file, right-click the image file in Explorer and select Open With, Windows Disc Image Burner. On the next screen, click Burn and the image will be written to a blank disc. To make sure the disc has been created correctly, click 'Verify disc after burning' before clicking the Burn button.

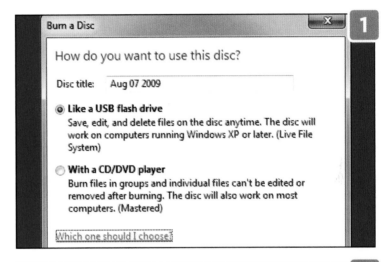

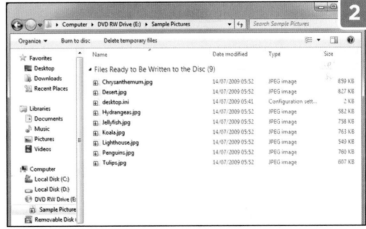

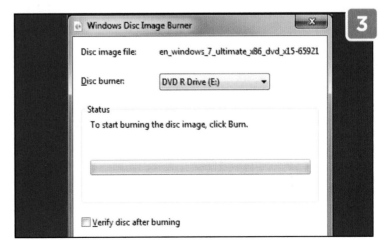

HOW TO...
Set up HomeGroups

Home networking is much easier in Windows 7 thanks to the introduction of HomeGroups. Here we show you how to set them up so you can simplify the process of file-sharing

SHARING FILES AND printers has always been a pain with Windows, as it often fails to work or causes intermittent problems. Fortunately, the arrival of HomeGroups promises to alleviate a lot of the hassle. You can have one HomeGroup per network, and every computer connected to the password-protected service can share files and printers with the every other HomeGroup computers. This makes it incredibly easy to share files and printers on a home network, and beats Vista's file-sharing wizards as it requires very little configuration to get working. This feature works with Windows 7 PCs only, although standard file-sharing means that older computers can still share files with the new operating system.

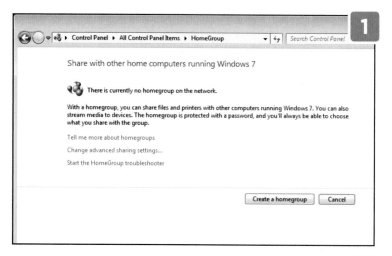

1 CREATE A HOMEGROUP
Windows 7 should prompt you to create a HomeGroup the first time your PC connects to a network; if it doesn't, open the Control Panel and select Network and Internet, HomeGroup and click Create HomeGroup.

On the next page, select Libraries to share and click Next. Save the default password or type your own. Make it something that's easy to remember, but hard to guess.

2 ADD OTHER PCs TO HOMEGROUP
On another Windows 7 PC, bring up the HomeGroup application from the Control Panel. Click the Join HomeGroup button. Select Libraries you want to share from this PC and click Next. Type in the same password generated in Step 1 and click Next. Once the PC has joined the HomeGroup, you can share files and printers using the HomeGroup icon in Windows Explorer.

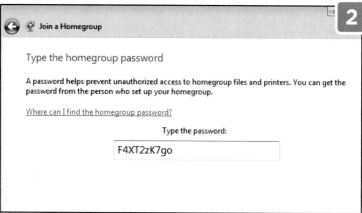

3 SELECT WHAT TO SHARE
To adjust the files your PC is sharing, open HomeGroup from the Control Panel. You can select which Libraries you want to share, and choose to make your media available to network-streaming devices. To stop sharing a file or folder, use the old file-sharing interface. Click on the 'How do I exclude files and folders?' link for more details.

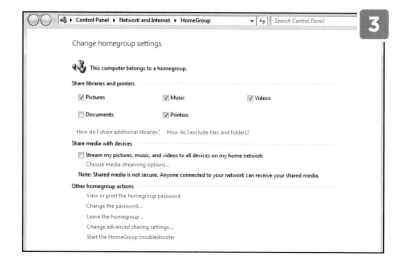

HOW TO...
Share media over the internet

Your media doesn't have to stay locked up on your home computer. With the new Media Player, you can stream all your files over the internet to another computer

ONE OF THE best features of Windows 7 is the ability to share media in Windows Media Player over the internet to other Windows 7 computers. Be warned, though, that your PC won't go into sleep mode with this feature turned on.

1 CREATE ONLINE ID
Start Windows Media Player and click on 'Allow internet access to home media' from the Stream menu. To share music over the internet, click 'Link an Online ID'. On the next screen, select 'Add an online ID provider', then select Windows Live. You'll be prompted to download an application to your hard disk. Do so and then run the file to install the Live ID Sign-in Assistant, following the installation wizard all the way through.

2 LINK ONLINE ID
Once the software has installed, you can go back to the Link Online IDs page. This time, click Link Online ID next to WindowsLiveID. On the next screen, enter your Windows Live email address and password. If you don't have one, click 'Don't have a Windows Live ID?' Fill out the form to associate your email address with a Windows Live ID. Once you've verified your account, go back to the Windows Live login screen, enter your email address and password and click Sign in. Then click OK on the Link Online IDs screen.

3 ALLOW INTERNET ACCESS
Go back to Media Player and click 'Allow internet access to home media'. Click OK on the next box, and your computer is ready to share files over the internet. To play files from your computer on another Windows 7 PC, you need to configure the other computer in the same away, linking it to the same Windows Live account. When done, your home PC will appear in the Other Libraries section of Media Player.

If you have any problems, you may need to configure port forwarding on your router to allow the necessary network traffic. Windows Media Player has a help page that it will show if this is the case, while details on how to configure your router can be found at *www.portforward.com*.

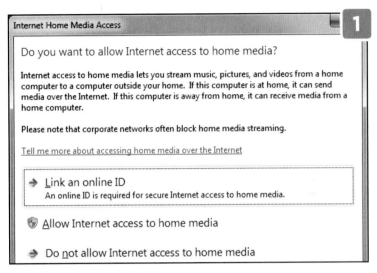

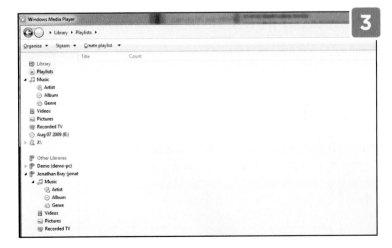

HOW TO...
Create a repair disc

If you've got a problem with Windows 7, a repair disc can help. Here we explain how to create your own and use it to fix a variety of PC problems

WITH WINDOWS 7, Microsoft has created an application that builds you a bootable repair disc. Starting your computer with this tool lets you run several automatic and manual repair utilities so you can fix common problems. The features here are replicated on the original installation disc, but they're easier to access when you create a repair disc. Remember, this disc doesn't replace any other protection methods, and you should still back up your PC.

1 CREATE REPAIR DISC

Click on the Start menu and type Repair, and click on Create a system repair disc. Put a blank CD or DVD into your optical drive and click Create disc. The process will take a few minutes. When it's done, take out the disc and label it clearly.

2 BOOT FROM REPAIR DISC

To use the disc, put it into your computer's optical drive and restart your computer. Make sure that your PC's BIOS is set to boot from the optical drive (see page 68 for details of how to do this). Press a key when prompted and the repair utility should load automatically. Choose United Kingdom as your keyboard type and click Next.

System Recovery will now look for your Windows 7 installation. When it's found it, click Next. If your copy of Windows failed to boot, an automatic Startup Repair job will run and look for faults; otherwise, you'll be taken to the main menu (see Step 3). For automatic fault finding, System Recovery will ask if you want to use System Restore to flash your PC back to a working state. Click Restore to do this, or Cancel to continue.

3 USE ADVANCED TOOLS

The Repair Disc will look for other faults. If it can't find any, it will ask if you want to submit an online error report.

You can also click Advanced Tools to bring up the System Recovery Options. These will let you run System Restore, restore a System Image, run a memory diagnosis or run a Command Prompt, which can be used to run some diagnostic tools; these are for advanced users only.

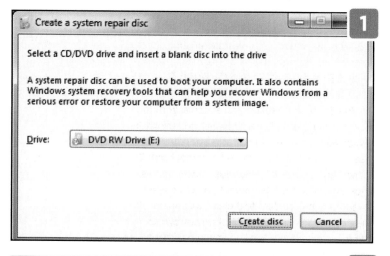

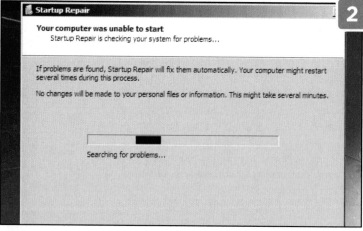

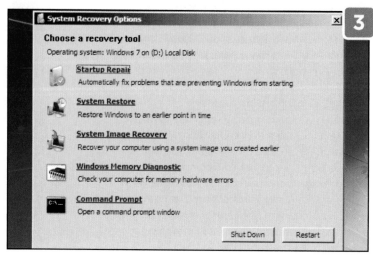

HOW TO...
Back up your PC

Windows 7 has complete image-based backup built in, so you can save a full working copy of your computer, including all your applications, files and settings

TAKING A BACKUP of your PC is simple with Windows 7's built-in image-based and file backup. You'll never lose an important file again.

1 CREATE BACKUP SCHEDULE

It makes sense to set up a backup schedule. To do this, select Backup and Restore from the Control Panel and click on the Setup Backup link. Windows will search for suitable backup devices. Assuming that you're using an external hard disk, select that device from the drop-down menu and click Next and then 'Start backup'. Click Next, select 'Let me choose' and click Next again. Untick the 'Include a system image of drives' option, or Windows will schedule a full image backup once a week, which eats up disk space. Choose the folders you want to back up and click Next. If you're happy with the schedule (every Sunday) click Next; otherwise, select Change schedule. Click on Save settings to run the first backup.

2 CREATE SYSTEM IMAGE

To make a system image, click on Create a system image. Windows will search for suitable backup devices. If you're using an external hard disk, select that device from the drop-down menu and click Next and then Start backup. Windows will back up your entire PC.

You can have only one schedule, so you must manually make a system image regularly to keep your full backup up to date. Old backups are deleted when your backup hard disk becomes full. If you want to keep a backup of a clean Windows 7 installation, we recommend backing up to DVDs for the first backup.

3 RESTORE FILES

Files can be restored through the Backup and Restore Control Panel application. To restore a system image boot from your repair disc (see opposite), select 'Restore your computer using a system image you created earlier' and click Next. By default, Windows will choose the latest system image, but you can select your own. Click Next when ready, then Next again and Finish. Your PC will now be restored to a previous state.

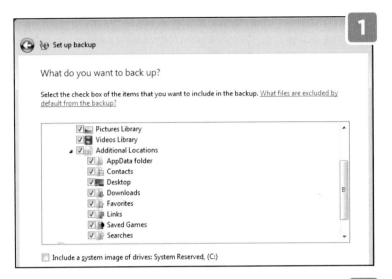

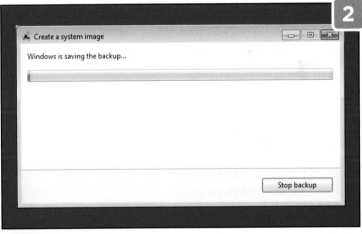

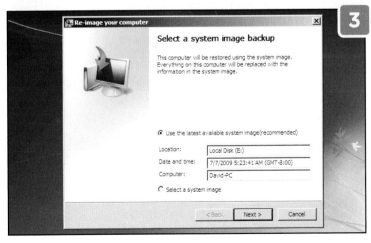

Windows 7 security features

WITH HACKERS AFTER our identities and information, it's never been so important to have a secure system. We wanted to find out if Windows 7 was more secure in its default state when compared with Vista.

We exposed our test system to a random sampling of known malicious URLs using our virus lab (the only one of its kind in the UK to download live virus samples). All were defended against by Internet Explorer 8, which – in combination with the most up-to-date versions of plug-ins such as Flash – blocked them from running. We also tried some common file compression (Zip) malware, but found that Windows Defender prevented us from opening the malicious files; the same was true on Vista.

The fact that malware is blocked is no surprise, as these kinds of attacks are targeted at specific flaws in the world's most popular operating system and browser: Windows XP with Service Pack 2 running Internet Explorer 6.

Where Windows 7 wins out is with User Account Control (UAC), which requires you to manually allow major system changes, such as an application trying to modify system files. UAC is much more sophisticated than the Vista version and designed to present messages only at crucial moments. The basic rule with the new version is that if you've just done something, such as installed an application, any UAC warnings are probably safe to apply. If you're browsing the internet or using your computer normally and you get a warning, it's probably something malicious and you should deny the operation.

UAC now has a range of options giving you control over how it works (in Vista, it was either on or off). To access the settings, go to Control Panel

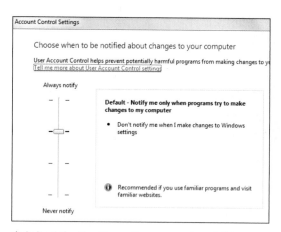

↑ At its default settings, the new version of User Account Control helps you stay secure without all those frequent interruptions

and select Action Center, then Change User Account Control settings. You'll see a slider bar that lets you choose when you want UAC to warn you. Its default option notifies you before a program is allowed to make changes to your computer, but doesn't do anything if you change Windows settings. The most secure UAC setting is similar to the old Vista version. It'll ask for your permission when any program is installed and almost any setting is changed.

There are also two lower UAC alert settings. The first is the same as the default option, but displays alerts in a normal window rather than dimming the desktop. We don't see any point in choosing this over the unobtrusive default setting.

Finally, if you're bold or easily annoyed by your operating system's attempts at interaction, there's the 'Never notify' option, which disables UAC completely, along with all its security benefits. We definitely don't recommend this.

The default UAC setting is the security sweet spot for most users and didn't annoy us with any of the constant interference of Vista's version. However, UAC can't defend you against files that you allow to run. While Windows 7 seems secure now, there's always the possibility that a flaw will be found that will open it up to hackers. For this reason, we recommend applying the latest updates regularly, for both your operating system and applications, and installing dedicated security software.

TIP
UAC is no longer annoying, as it was in Vista, so leave it enabled for extra protection from internet threats.

↑ Web-based 'drive-by' infections have to get past your browser's defences before UAC comes into play

THE WEAPON OF CHOICE.

Agile. Strong. Deadly. Get Ballistix™ and Ballistix Tracer™
high-performance memory from Crucial.

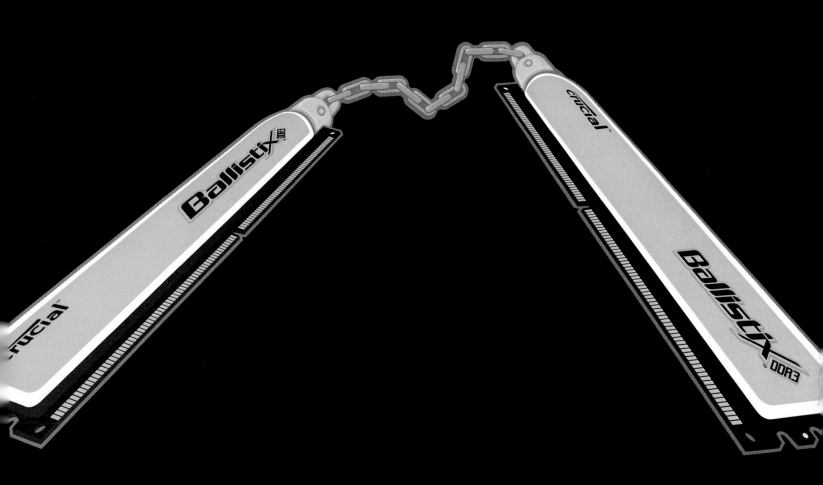

Find out why Ballistix memory is the weapon of choice.
www.crucial.com/uk/custompc

CHAPTER 8
NEW PC ESSENTIALS

EVEN THOUGH YOUR new PC is up and running and you've installed your operating system, you're not quite finished if you want your computer to be the best it can be. We'll show you which free utilities no computer owner should be without, and our guide to taking a complete image of your fresh PC will show you how to make a complete backup of your PC, including the operating system, applications and data.

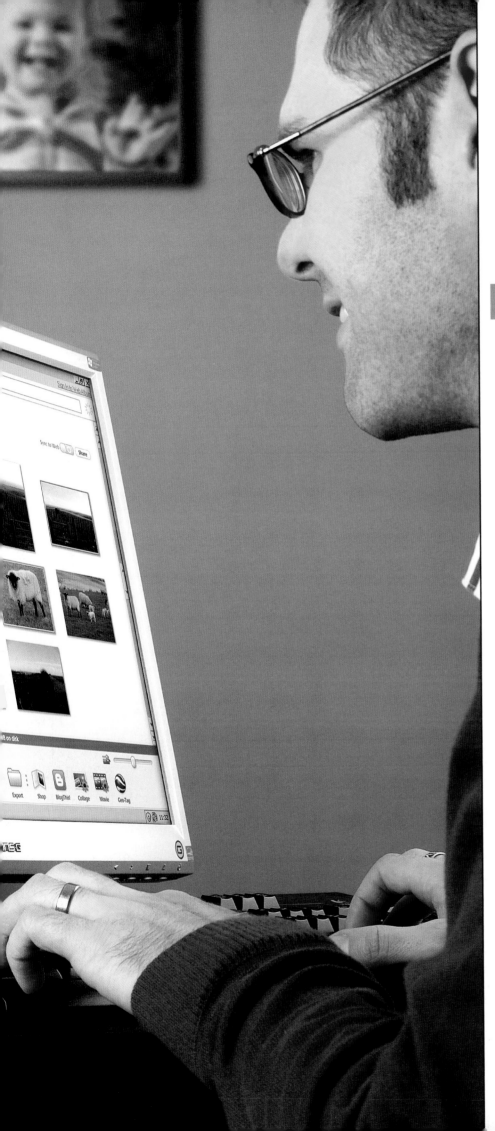

IN THIS CHAPTER

Essential tools

ONCE YOU'VE BUILT your PC and everything is working perfectly, you may feel that your computing experience isn't quite complete. This is because, unlike a Mac OS installation, very little extra software is installed with Windows. You get a primitive word processor called WordPad, an image program called Microsoft Paint, which has barely changed since 1992, and very little else. There's no way to create complicated word-processing documents, do your accounts in a spreadsheet or edit photos.

More importantly, as Windows doesn't come with a virus scanner, you're left wide open to all kinds of internet threats. Windows XP can't even burn files to DVD, and Vista's disc-authoring capabilities leave much to be desired. Both versions also lack a credible alternative to Apple's iPhoto image organiser, although Windows 7 is an improvement .

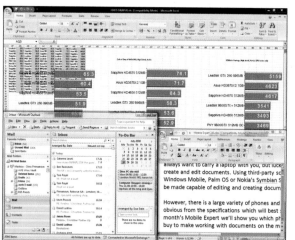

↑ Microsoft Office 2007 looks great and is very powerful, but it's expensive and most people won't touch half its features. OpenOffice is compatible with Office file formats, and is a credible and free alternative

In the not too distant past, you had to splash out on products such as Microsoft Office, Adobe Photoshop Elements, Norton Internet Security and Roxio Easy Media Creator to make your PC usable. Recently, though, a few software packages have emerged that offer the same features for free. As you'll see, OpenOffice is an impressive office suite, Paint.NET is a powerful image editor, AVG Anti-Virus will keep you safe online and CDBurnerXP lets you burn discs to your heart's content. Furthermore, Google's Picasa will let you organise your photos and share them online.

We've also covered some smaller free utilities that will make your new system easier and more fun to use, as well as keeping your data secure. Read on to find out about the essential free software to install on any new PC.

OFFICE SOFTWARE

OpenOffice.org
OpenOffice.org 3

DOWNLOAD DETAILS **www.openoffice.org**
FILE SIZE **130MB**

As far as office software is concerned, a clean installation of Windows will come with an unimpressive word processor and nothing else. Fortunately, you don't have to splash out on the full version of Microsoft Office to give yourself powerful word processor and spreadsheet applications.

OpenOffice.org includes both of these essentials, as well as a presentation program, the Draw vector drawing package and the Base database application. The Writer word processing, Calc spreadsheet and Impress presentation applications are all compatible with Office file formats up to Office 2003, and can open and save documents either in Microsoft's formats or in the suite's OpenDocument format.

There's very little missing from the applications, and most are easy to use. Writer has a spellcheck, and a selection of styles and fonts, as well as word count and table of contents generation features. We can't really see anything missing from what Calc can do, as it supports all the functions and formulas we've ever needed. It even handles charts better than Excel 2007. Impress looks like an older version of PowerPoint, and comes with a couple of different templates

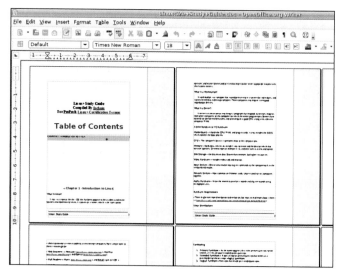

↑ Packed with features, OpenOffice.org is an essential download

to get you started. The last two applications are more niche, but could still be useful. Draw is a reasonable program, but we found it the most fiddly part of the suite to use and it took us a while to master it. Base is a powerful SQL-compatible database, which lets you create searchable linked data tables.

OpenOffice.org may not look as flashy as Microsoft Office 2007, but there's little missing in the way of features and it's free, rather than £167. It's an essential download for every new PC.

SECURITY SOFTWARE

AVG Technologies
AVG Anti-Virus
Free Edition

DOWNLOAD DETAILS **http://free.avg.com**

FILE SIZE **47MB**

Even though Microsoft claims that Windows 7 is more secure than any previous version of the operating system, you'd be mad to go online without security software on your PC. A good security suite will protect you against viruses, but will also spot other malware, such as spyware and adware, which can lead to anything from a few annoying pop-ups to your banking logon details being passed on to unscrupulous criminals.

As new viruses and spyware programs are discovered all the time, your security suite needs to be continually updated to maintain the appropriate level of protection. Most security software companies make you pay a subscription to receive the updates, but AVG offers both its software and the subscription for free for non-commercial use. There's no catch, either.

The AVG software includes a virus scanner, which can be set to scan your hard disk at regular intervals, a resident shield that lives in your computer's memory and detects viruses as they appear, an email scanner and a program, which scans links

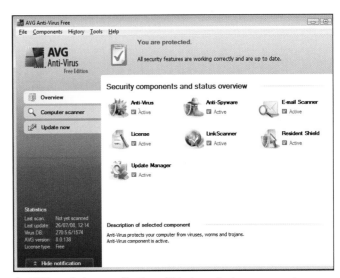

↑ AVG's anti-virus application will help protect your computer

in search engine results to check whether or not they lead to malicious websites. Recently, AVG also added a spyware resident shield, so you're protected against all the threats the internet has to offer.

If you're seriously worried about security threats, consider a paid-for program, such as Kaspersky Internet Security 2009, but AVG Free is certainly a credible home alternative.

IMAGE EDITING SOFTWARE

Rick Brewster/Ed Harvey
Paint.NET

DOWNLOAD DETAILS **www.getpaint.net**

FILE SIZE **1.5MB**

While Windows has a reasonable image viewer as standard, Microsoft Paint is laughable as an image editor. Adobe Photoshop Elements is our favourite image-editing program, and, at around £50, is fair value. However, a good free alternative is Paint.NET. It's not the only free image-editing application for Windows, as you can also download GIMP from *www.gimp.org*. GIMP's user interface may make your head hurt, though, which is why we prefer Paint.NET.

The program is a tiny download of just 1.5MB, though if you have Windows XP, you'll also need to install Microsoft's .NET framework, which is a free download from *www.microsoft.com*. It has a clean interface that's reminiscent of Photoshop, with floating palettes and information windows. The package supports all the usual image-editing functions, such as layers, cropping and levels and curves adjustments. It also has several image effects as standard. You can save images in most standard formats, including JPEG, BMP, GIF and TIFF, and compressed image settings are handled with a clear preview to show you what your saved image will look like.

It does have a couple of omissions, most notably an Unsharp Mask feature, which is a popular method to sharpen an image.

↑ Paint.NET's clean user interface is reminiscent of Photoshop's

However, the application has an active user community producing plug-ins to use with the software, including an Unsharp Mask plug-in. You will have to search through the forums to find what you need, though.

Paint.NET is astonishing for a free program, and has the advantage of being a small download. It may take you a bit of work and research to add all the features you will need, but it's well worth the effort.

Google
Picasa 3

DOWNLOAD DETAILS **http://picasa.google.com**

FILE SIZE **6MB**

Picasa 3 is a fantastic photo organisation and editing program from Google. It's a relatively small download, and is easy to install and set up. You should be careful when installing the program that you select the options you want, as by default it'll add shortcuts to your desktop, Quick Launch and System Tray, and set Google as your default search engine.

Picasa will scan your PC for any images when you first run it, read the time data encoded in each photo and arrange your pictures by date. The Library view displays all your photos as thumbnails, and double-clicking on a picture takes you into the editing view. This gives you most of the editing options you'll need to make your photos presentable, such as cropping, red-eye reduction, straightening and contrast and colour adjustment. There are also several effects, including Sharpen, Sepia, Black and White and Soft Focus.

Once you're happy with your pictures, you can view them as a slideshow, with a lovely fade effect between each photo. The best thing about Picasa, though, is its online storage. To use this you'll need a Google Mail account, which you can get at *http://mail.google.com*. Once you have an account, you simply

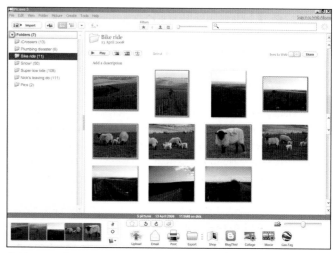

↑ You can share your pictures online with Picasa 3

select the pictures you want to upload and click the Web Album button. You can upload photos in a quality suitable for viewing in a web browser, or upload bigger files that are good enough to print. Once your photos are online, you can make the album publicly available, or restrict it to only the people you invite to view your pictures. Google gives you 1GB of storage for free, which is enough for around 5,000 photos at web-quality settings. Vista users should try the built-in Windows Photo Gallery first before downloading Picasa, though.

Canneverbe Limited
CDBurnerXP

DOWNLOAD DETAILS **http://cdburnerxp.se**

FILE SIZE **2.9MB**

Windows 7, Vista and XP all have built-in CD-burning capabilities, and the later versions of the operating system can also burn DVDs, but these applications are fairly primitive and not particularly easy to use. CDBurnerXP is a powerful free program that makes it easy to burn data files to disc, turn audio files into a music CD and create CD and DVD images.

As with Paint.NET (page 129), if you're running Windows XP, you'll need to download and install the .NET Framework to use CDBurnerXP. The program itself is only a small download, and is simple to install.

The main interface will be familiar to anyone who's used a CD-burning program such as Nero. To create a CD, you just need to drag and drop files from the folder view at the top of the screen into your disc compilation at the bottom. You don't have to choose which type of disc you want to burn before you start your compilation, as CDBurnerXP automatically chooses the right file system depending on which type of disc is in the drive.

Once you've created your compilation, you just click the Burn icon to create your disc. You can also select Save

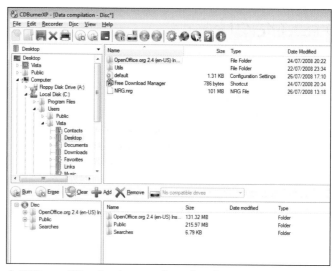

↑ CDBurnerXP makes it easy to burn data files to CD

compilation as ISO file from the File menu to create a disc image to burn later. Usefully, the program also has the option to convert NRG and BIN image files, as used by Nero and some other CD-burning programs, to the more compatible ISO format.

Commercial applications such as Nero and Easy Media Creator have some impressive video disc-authoring features, but for most people CDBurnerXP will be the only disc-burning program they'll need.

Free Download Manager
Free Download Manager

DOWNLOAD DETAILS **www.freedownloadmanager.org**
FILE SIZE **5.6MB**

Essentially, Free Download Manager makes downloading files faster. When you start to download a file, the program splits the file into blocks and downloads all of them simultaneously. We found downloads were often four times faster using this program. You can also pause and resume downloading most files.

The application also has some other powerful features. You can use it to download movies from various video-sharing sites, such as YouTube and Google Video, and you can automatically convert these from the FLV format to more compatible formats such as MPEG4. Free Download Manager can also be used as a BitTorrent client, so is the only program you need to install to take care of all your downloads.

↑ You can download video from sites such as YouTube

Freebyte.com
Freebyte Backup

DOWNLOAD DETAILS **www.freebyte.com/fbbackup**
FILE SIZE **785KB**

Freebyte Backup is a simple program that lets you back up the contents of your PC's hard disk to an external hard disk. To make a backup, you simply add the drives and directories to be included, then specify any files you want to exclude from the backup, either by the date they were created or by file type. You then just click the Start button and the files you specified will be backed up.

Once you've made your first backup, you can set the software to copy only files that are new or have been changed since the last time you backed up your PC, which drastically cuts down the amount of time the process takes. Automatic backups can be scheduled using the Windows Task Scheduler, although this can be tricky to configure.

↑ Back up your data with Freebyte

Nathan Moinvaziri
ExtractNow

DOWNLOAD DETAILS **www.extractnow.com**
FILE SIZE **940KB**

Even though Windows-supported ZIP files are the most common form of archive, there are many other kinds. ExtractNow can extract the majority of archives, including the popular RAR format, and CD and DVD image ISO files.

The program is particularly useful for extracting batches of archives. You just have to drag files into its window, click Extract and the program will extract each archive's contents into the folder where the archive is situated. You can also associate archive file types with the program, so it will open automatically when you double-click on an archive in Windows.

ExtractNow is an easy way to deal with different types of archive without having to install multiple programs, and it's a tiny download. The only thing that it doesn't let you do is create files, but Windows has this functionality built in.

↑ ExtractNow can deal with different types of archive

VideoLAN
VLC media player

DOWNLOAD DETAILS **www.videolan.org**
FILE SIZE **9.3MB**

Playing back audio and video files on a PC can be tricky. Even though all PCs come with Windows Media Player, there are many types of file that it doesn't support, so you'll need to install specific audio and video codecs to play them. Windows XP doesn't even have support for DVD movies as standard.

Finding out which codec is missing from your system can be a tricky business, but VLC takes much of the pain out of this process. It will play most types of audio and video files, including DVDs. It's simple to install, and will launch automatically when you double-click on a compatible file type. It can even play files that are incomplete. With built-in support for DVDs, it's one of the most comprehensive media players and it's completely free. VLC is the simplest way to play back media files.

↑ VLC lets you play DVDs as well as most other media files

Saving power with your new PC

THE RISING COSTS of electricity and increasing concerns over the environment are two very good reasons to consider ways of cutting down on power consumption. PCs are one of the worst offenders in the home, but other devices connected to them, such as printers, monitors and external hard disks, all have their part to play.

Fortunately, there are several things you can do to save power and make your computer more efficient. We'll show you how much power your devices really use, how much it costs you to run them and how to save money by putting your devices into standby mode.

COST OF LIVING

First, it's worth explaining how costs are calculated. Every electrical device draws power, measured in watts (volts x amps). This is the figure used to describe light bulbs – a 100W bulb draws 100W of power. Over an hour this would be a watt hour. Electricity companies then charge your consumption based on the number of kilowatt hours (kWh) you're using. As a kilowatt is 1,000W, you first have to convert the wattage of any measured product into kilowatts by dividing by 1,000. So, a 100W light bulb uses 0.1kW. Over an hour, this would be 0.1kWh. If your electricity company charges you 11p per kWh, your 100W light bulb would cost you 1.1p per hour to run. In reality, most electricity companies use a two-tier system of charging. A fairly common tariff is 14p per kWh for the first 728 kWh per year and then 12p for each kWh thereafter.

For our calculations we've assumed the higher figure of 14kWh. While this means that we've ended up with higher costs overall, it gives us a fair comparison between each device. You can try our Google Docs spreadsheet for calculating running costs by visiting *http://tinyurl.com/powersaver*. You'll need a Google account to access it, but can

↑ Devices left on can use a huge amount of power, which will cost you a small fortune

↗ Devices such as the Intelliplug can help you save power

DEVICE	POWER WHEN ON	STANDBY POWER	TYPICAL COST PER YEAR*
PC	129W	3W	£40
Laptop	32W	3W	£17
LCD monitor	29W	2W	£8
Inkjet printer	Varies**	3W	£2
Network storage	41W	1W	£34
LCD TV	158W	3W	£33

*We've assumed a typical day's use for each product (eight hours a day for PCs, four hours a day for TVs), using standby modes where appropriate and being turned off at the plug when not in use

**Inkjet printers typically use between 10W and 30W to print a page of paper, but this is for a short amount of time, so the standby power is the biggest factor

sign up for a free one on that web page. Once you've accessed the spreadsheet, select Copy spreadsheet from the File menu to edit it in your own account. All you need to do is set your kWh cost and, for each device, type in its power usage figures, the number of hours a day it's on, off (at the socket) and in standby mode and the sheet will work out the rest.

MEASURING YOUR DEVICES

Measuring electrical devices is easy. All you need is a plug-in power monitor, such as the Plug-In Mains Power and Energy Monitor (£28, *www.maplin.co.uk*). This plugs into your wall socket, and then you just plug the electrical device you want to test into it. The reading on the screen tells you how many watts your device is drawing. Using the calculations above, you can work out how much a device will cost you each year.

You'll be quite surprised at the results. For example, a typical PC uses around 120W when on, while an LCD monitor will use around 29W (149W in total). If you were to leave both on all day every day for a year, you'd be using 1,305kWh per annum, which would cost a staggering £183 a year. However, putting a PC into standby mode means that it uses only around 3W, which is similar to an LCD monitor's 2W in standby mode. Turning them off at the plug when you're not using them would save more money, as you're not drawing any power.

Typically, a computer that's on eight hours a day with no standby modes turned on would cost around £61 a year to run. If you were to set the PC to go into standby mode when not in use for, say, three hours a day, it would cost £47 per annum to run – a saving of around £14 every year. The same can be said of every device that you use. The table

(above) shows typical usage figures for electrical devices you have in your home.

COMBATTING THE PROBLEM

To save money, devices need to use less electricity. For PCs this means following our advice over the next two pages to adjust Windows' power-saving settings. For other devices, you need to power them down when they're not in use. Ideally, you should switch devices off at the plug, because many still draw power when they're in standby mode. For example, the average LCD TV draws 3W when in standby mode. If this was to be left on all year, it would cost you £3.67 every year. That's not a huge amount of money, but multiply this sum for every device you own and it adds up to a small fortune. For computer devices, such as printers, switch them off when you're not using them.

If the thought of having to switch off a plug under a desk sounds like too much hassle, then consider buying a product such as OneClick's Intelliplug (£17, *www.oneclickpower.co.uk*). This has a master socket for your PC and two slave sockets that get power only when your PC is turned on. It's ideal for your monitor and printer, as they'll be on only when your computer is.

You can try other power-saving techniques, too. For example, if you've got network storage, check to see if there's a sleep mode. Setting your storage to shut down overnight when you won't be using it can save you money every year. Follow this advice for all your electrical kit and you could knock more than £100 every year off your electricity bills.

↑ Measuring how much power your devices use could be a real shock

HOW TO...
Save power with Vista

1 CREATE YOUR OWN CUSTOM PLAN
Open the Control Panel from the Start menu and select System and Maintenance and then Power Options. Vista has three built-in power plans, but it's best to make your own. Click Create power plan, type in a name for your plan and click Next. On the next screen choose how long Windows should wait before turning off your monitor (10 minutes is reasonable). You can also set how long your PC should wait before it goes into Sleep mode (30 to 45 minutes is recommended). It takes only a few seconds to exit Sleep mode and Vista will save your data to hard disk, protecting unsaved work. Click Create when you're done.

2 PUT THE HARD DISK TO SLEEP
To change other settings, you need to click Change plan settings under the plan you created. Click Change advanced power settings.

First, expand the Hard disk setting and set Turn off hard disk after to 20 minutes. If you've got a wireless adaptor, you can set the Wireless Adapter Settings to power off when it's not in use. There are three options: Lower Power Saving; Medium Power Saving and Maximum Power Saving. The difference is how long your PC waits before shutting down the adaptor. This can cause problems with some wireless routers. If you're having trouble, adjust this setting to Maximum Performance.

3 SLEEP
We've already set the system Sleep time in Step 1, but Vista can also automatically go into Hibernation mode, where it saves your current state to hard disk and powers down the computer completely. To do this, expand the Sleep section and the Hibernate after section and set the time in minutes that you want to wait before your PC hibernates. We recommend two hours.

4 OTHER SETTINGS
There are some other settings that you can consider changing. First, under Search and Indexing, change the Power Savings Mode to Power Saver. This will stop Vista from thrashing your hard disk while it indexes your files. Next, your computer might not go into Sleep mode if you're sharing media files. To change this, expand the Multimedia Settings section and set When sharing media to Allow the computer to sleep. Click OK to apply.

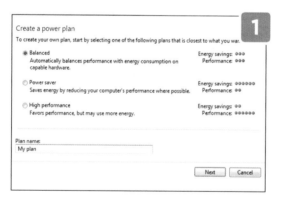

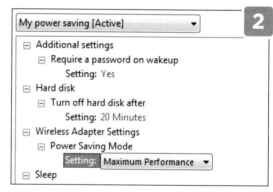

TIP
Turn your devices off at the plug to save money by not using power for standby.

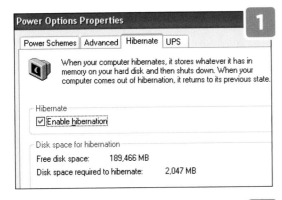

HOW TO...
Save power with XP

1 ENABLE HIBERNATION
Click on the Start menu and click on Control Panel. Click on Performance and Maintenance, and then Power Options to bring up the controls for power management. Click on the Hibernate tab and tick the box called Enable hibernation. This will let Windows save the current state of your computer to hard disk, including the current status of all your applications and all your open windows. Not only is it handy for power saving, as we'll show, but it's great if you've got lots of documents open but want to power down your computer for the night.

2 SET INITIAL POWER SCHEMES
Click on the Power Schemes tab. Windows has several default schemes, but it's best to edit the default Home/Office Desk instead. The default scheme turns the monitor off after 20 minutes, but this is probably too generous. Set the monitor to turn off after 10 minutes.

The default scheme doesn't turn the hard disks off at all, but you should do so to reduce power. Setting the hard disks to power down after 20 minutes should do the job.

3 STANDBY AND HIBERNATION
Now standby has been enabled, you can set Windows to hibernate automatically if the PC hasn't been used in a while. First, it's best to set the System standby time. This puts your PC into a low-power state, where it uses just a few watts of power (the S3 setting that you used in the BIOS). Generally, we'd say that if you haven't used your PC for 30 to 45 minutes, then it's good to put it into Standby. Finally, set your PC to hibernate after two hours.

4 ADVANCED SETTINGS
Click on the Advanced tab for more control. By default, your PC will ask you for a password when it resumes from standby or hibernation, but you can remove this tab if you'd prefer. You can also control what the power button and sleep button (if you have one) do. By default, the power button is set to Shut down, but you can change this to Hibernate if you'd rather save your current system state. You can also ask Windows to prompt you every time you push the power button, in a similar way to when you click Turn Off Computer in the Start menu.

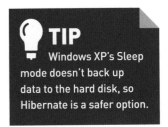

TIP
Windows XP's Sleep mode doesn't back up data to the hard disk, so Hibernate is a safer option.

Making an image of your hard disk

NOW YOU'VE FINISHED building your PC, installed Windows and downloaded all the drivers and extra software you need, you'll understand just how much work is needed to get a computer up and running from scratch. Beyond simply getting it working, there's all the additional hassle associated with ensuring that Windows looks and feels right, setting up all your applications the way you like them, and organising all your favourites and home page in your web browser.

It's hours of work, so imagine how you'd feel if your PC suddenly shut down, taking your hard disk with it. Thankfully, this is very unlikely, but a more probable scenario is that as time goes on Windows will become increasingly bloated. Over the years, you will install and uninstall any number of extra applications and additional hardware, which will leave a large number of extra files and services on your hard disk. These will slow your PC down to a crawl, and reinstalling everything from scratch isn't a huge amount of fun.

This is where using a disk-imaging program can save you a world of trouble. It will take a complete copy of your hard disk, including the operating system, your applications, all your settings and every file on your hard disk.

NO MORE REINSTALLING

When restored, the image will take your computer back to the day that the image was made. Instead of having to reinstall Windows when it's no longer working the way you want it, you can just flash the image back and return to when you first installed Windows, complete with all your original settings and applications. So instead of hours of work, with a disk-imaging application it takes only a fraction of the time.

The best thing is that you're not just limited to taking one image. With the right software, you can also schedule images to occur regularly, so that you're constantly making a backup. If you should suffer a problem, you simply restore your computer back to the last good image – a little bit like a super System Restore.

Disk-imaging applications also include standard file backup options, so you can take less regular images, which use a lot of disk space, but still protect all your data.

HARD DISK

Ideally, you should store images on an external hard drive so you won't lose them if your main hard disk fails. This also means that you can restore the image to your old hard disk (or to a new one in the case of a major problem), getting up and running again in a short period of time. You could also back up to a secondary partition on your primary hard disk.

NORTON GHOST

We can't stress the importance of using disk-imaging software enough, particularly when you build a new PC, as you can create an amazing recovery disc just like the one you'd get with a new computer from a manufacturer. Over the next few pages, we'll show you how to image your PC using the best application on the market: Norton Ghost 14. We used the download version of Ghost, which costs £40 and is available from *www.symantec.co.uk* (click on the online store). This is identical to the boxed version, although the installation steps may differ very slightly. You'll also have to download the recovery CD image file, which we'll show you how to use later.

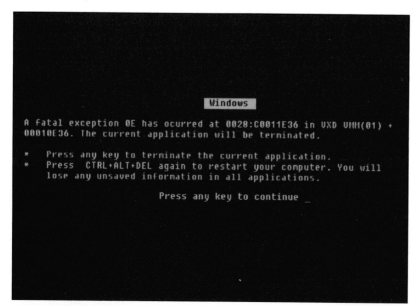

↑ To recover from a system error quickly, you need a disk image of your hard disk

HOW TO...
Make a hard disk image

1 INSTALL GHOST
Run the Ghost installation program and follow the wizard. The software should install quickly and automatically, without asking you any questions. When it's finished, you'll be prompted to restart your computer. Do this and wait for your PC to load Windows again. When prompted, enter the product key that you were provided with when you bought the application, click Next, and then click Next again to run LiveUpdate and to download the latest version of the software. Restart your computer again if prompted.

2 CHANGE SCHEDULE
After LiveUpdate has finished, the Easy Setup application starts. This automatically sets up a scheduled imaging job and a scheduled file backup job. These tend to be a bit extreme, though, so you should change some settings.

First, under My Computer Backup, click the box next to Schedule to specify when you want a backup taken. The default is set for every Sunday and Thursday, but once a week should be sufficient. These backups record only the changes to files since the last image to save on disk space.

Ghost is also set to create a full new image set, which takes up a lot of disk space, once every three months. This should be fine for most people.

3 ADD TRIGGERS
You can also set Ghost to run a backup when certain triggers are detected. Click on the General link under Event Triggers, and select the options you want – Any application is installed, for example. Be warned that using any of these options will increase the amount of disk space you'll need for backups, so use them carefully. When you're happy with your settings, click OK.

4 MANAGE FILES
Ghost will also take regular file backups. It's set by default to back up the Documents, My Video, My Pictures and My Music folders, Internet Explorer favourites and desktop settings. Click on the blue text to the right of Select at the top of the screen to add more options. Click OK when you're done. You can now change the schedule for this backup in the same way as in Step 3.

Finally, Norton Ghost tries to pick a suitable backup destination, such as an external hard disk.

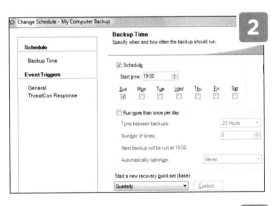

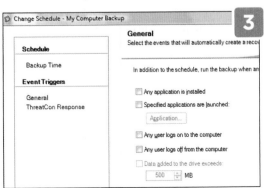

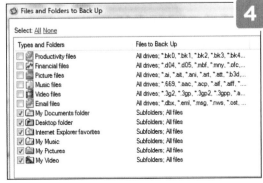

TIP
A second physical hard disk or external disk are the best places for backups, as they won't be affected if your main hard disk fails.

You can also back up to a separate partition, like the one we created when we installed Windows in Chapter 6. This will be safe from Windows crashes, but not hard disk faults, so an external hard disk is the safest option. Use the secondary partition if you don't have an external disk. Click OK, select Run first backup now and click OK again.

5 MANAGE BACKUPS

While your backups will run to the schedule you set, you can modify this or choose to start a backup manually if, for example, you've just saved a lot of new files or made a major system change. Start Norton Ghost and select Run or Manage Backups. The next window will display your current jobs. Select one and click Run Now to run it. You can Change schedules and edit what's being backed up by clicking Edit Settings. With the default My Documents Backup, you can now add your own custom files and folders.

6 RECOVER FILES

If you want to recover individual files, click Recover My Files from Ghost's main screen. You can search for a specific file or click Search to find all your backed-up files. Right-clicking a file or folder lets you view the different backup versions and recover the one you want. You can also restore files from an image. Click Recovery Point, select

the backup you want and choose Explore from Tasks. You can browse the image in the same way as a regular folder and drag files to your computer.

7 RECOVER A HARD DISK

You can restore an image to a hard disk by selecting the Recover My Computer link from Ghost's Welcome page. Select the Recovery point you want and click Recover now. Provided the Recovery point isn't for your boot partition (the one with Windows on it), Ghost will restore the image. If it is for your boot hard disk, Ghost can't recover it while Windows is running. Instead, you need to follow Steps 8 to 12 to create a recovery CD.

8 CREATE A RECOVERY CD

If you bought the download version of Ghost, you should have also downloaded the recovery CD image file. This needs to be recorded to a CD. You can do this with CD-writing software such as CDBurnerXP (see page 130). If you don't have CDBurnerXP, you can download ISO Recorder from *http://isorecorder.alexfeinman.com*. Version 2 is for Windows XP and version 3.1 is for Windows 7 and Vista, so make sure that you get the right one. Install the software.

Browse to the directory to which you downloaded Norton Ghost and look for the ZIP file (NGH140_AllWin_EnlishEMEA_SrdOnly.zip). Open

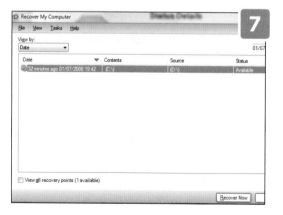

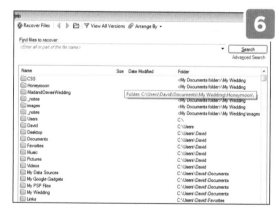

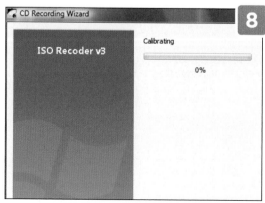

this by right-clicking on it and selecting Extract. Right-click on the resulting ISO file and select Copy image to CD. Click Next and then Finish when the operation is done. You now have a bootable restore CD.

9 BOOT FROM YOUR RESTORE DISC

Make sure that your BIOS is set to boot from your optical drive (see page 72) and then restart your PC. You'll be prompted to hit a key to boot off the CD, so make sure you're ready. When the Windows loading screen starts, click Accept to accept the Norton Ghost licence agreement.

There are several options on the next screen. Click on Analyze to perform system tests, and Check Hard Disk for Errors to run a system scan on your hard disk. The Virus scanner is useful only if you've also got Symantec Anti-Virus, otherwise the definitions will be too old. You can also click on Explore your hard disk.

10 ADD DRIVERS

While this recovery disk will recognise most hard disks, it can't identify them all, particularly if you're running RAID. If the image you want to restore is saved on a networked hard disk, then you may have to install a driver for the network adaptor, too. To do this, click on Utilities and then Load drivers. You need to use the Explorer-like window to navigate to a folder with the relevant driver in it. You can plug in USB drives or use a CD, so adding extra drivers shouldn't be hard. You should also have them available if you had to add extra drivers when installing Windows.

11 RECOVER YOUR COMPUTER

Click on Home and Recover my Computer. Select the recovery point you want to restore (if the list is blank, select View by filename and click Browse to find it) and click Next. Click Finish and then Yes to start recovering your PC. The files will then be restored to your computer.

Once it's completed, you can reboot your computer and it will be back to the exact state at which you made the recovery point.

12 RECOVER FILES

Alternatively, you can use this interface to recover individual files from a restore point. Select Recover from the main screen and then Recover My Files. Navigate to a recovery point, select it and click OK. You'll then be presented with the Symantec Recovery Point Browser.

You can navigate through this like an ordinary disk. When you find the file or files you want to recover, you just have to select them and click Recover Files. You can then choose where to restore the files to, such as another drive.

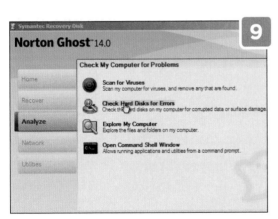

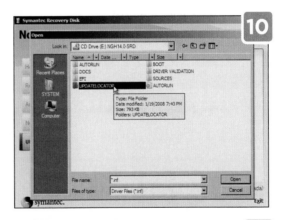

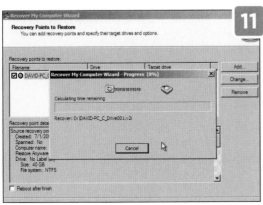

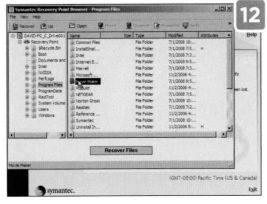

TIP You should run a hard disk scan before recovering your files to make sure there's nothing wrong with your disk.

CHAPTER 9
TROUBLESHOOTING

HOPEFULLY THIS BOOK has given you everything you need to build the perfect PC. However, you may have run into problems along the way or simply haven't understood some of the terms we've used. Don't worry – we haven't abandoned you. In the next few pages, we'll give you some essential troubleshooting and problem-solving tips. There's also a glossary, so you can look up any terms you don't know.

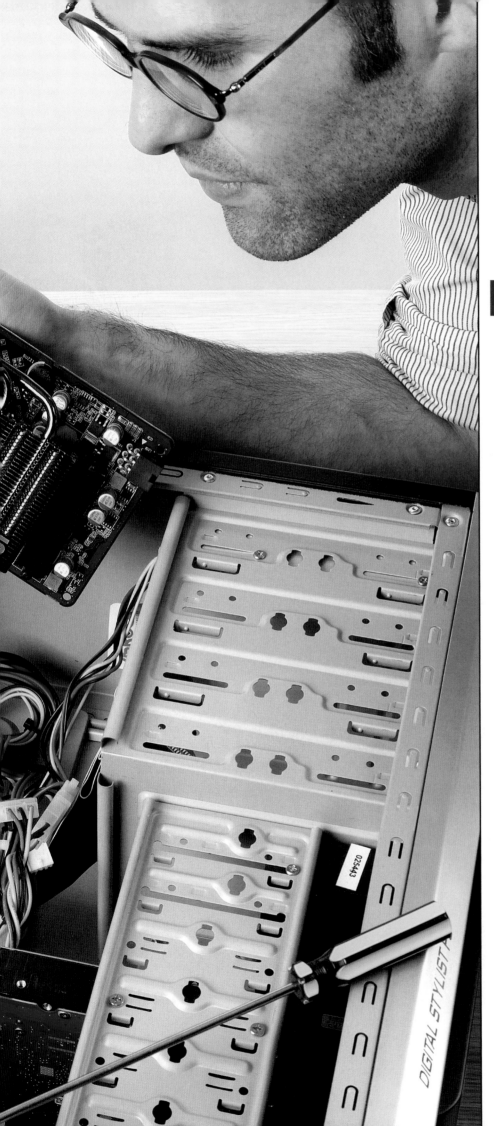

IN THIS CHAPTER

Troubleshooting hardware problems

PCs ARE FINICKY beasts that seem to thrive on causing their owners trouble by not working properly. If you've followed our instructions all the way through but are still not happy with the way your computer works, don't panic.

The vast majority of problems are best solved by trying one fix at a time. After each attempted fix, try and run your PC again to see if the problem has been solved. This is better than trying several things at once, as you'll be able to track down what the problem is, which could be useful if your computer has similar difficulties later on. The other thing to remember is that a lot of problems are caused by something simple, such as cables being plugged in the wrong way round, so check the easy stuff first before you start taking your computer apart.

We'll go through all the common problems that might affect your PC and suggest fixes that should get your system running. Before we start, though,

you should never rule out problems such as a blown fuse or faulty cables. Changing power or internal cables can often solve a problem quickly and with much less hassle.

While our suggestions are general, if you get a specific error message, you should make a note of it. From another computer, either yours or a friend's, type this message into a search engine. This should help you narrow down the problem. *Computer Shopper* magazine also offers a regular computer clinic, which you can read every month and contact by emailing helpfile@computershopper.co.uk.

Finally, if your PC stops working just after you install a new bit of hardware, remove it and turn your computer back on. If this fixes the problem, you can try and reinstall the device again. If you still don't have any luck, then your new hardware probably doesn't work and you should ask for a refund or replacement.

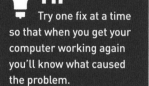

TIP
Try one fix at a time so that when you get your computer working again you'll know what caused the problem.

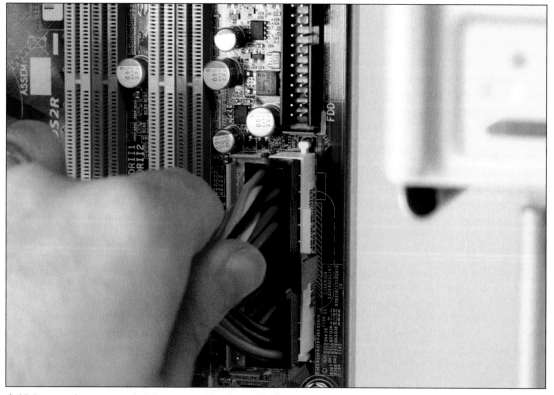

↑ Make sure the power switch is connected to the motherboard

↑ Resetting the CMOS can fix loads of hardware errors. The jumper pins are highlighted

PC WON'T TURN ON

One of the most frustrating problems you can have after building your PC is that it won't turn on. At this point, it can feel as though all your hard work was for nothing, but this problem is usually easily fixed. First, check that the power cable is plugged in all the way and that the wall socket and power switch on the power supply are turned on. If that doesn't fix the problem, you'll need to open up your PC and have a look inside.

First, check that the case's power button is connected to the motherboard's power switch jumper. You'll need to check your board's manual to find the exact pins to which it's supposed to be connected. The other main reason that a computer won't start is because the power cables haven't been connected to the motherboard correctly. Make sure that the ATX power connector (the large 24-pin connector) is plugged into its socket and the secondary power connector is also connected (see page 48).

If you're still not having any luck, reseat the processor (page 52), check that the memory is in the right slots and connected properly (page 54), and, if fitted, the graphics card (page 62). Finally, remove any expansion cards you've fitted. If your computer still won't turn on, try removing the graphics card and the memory. If your PC turns on it will now beep at you (see below for more information) to warn you that there's a problem. Refit the memory and graphics card and try again.

If you still haven't found the source of the trouble, try using one stick of memory at a time to find out if one of them is causing the problem. You could also try removing the graphics card and all your other expansion cards one at time.

TURNS ON BUT BEEPS

A more usual scenario is that your computer will turn on, but you'll either get a blank screen or some beeps. The number of beeps is designed to tell you what the problem is. Unfortunately, your motherboard's manual won't decipher these codes. Instead, go to *www.pchell.com/hardware/ beepcodes.shtml* for a list of the common codes, and the problems they relate to. This site also contains some helpful troubleshooting information,

so we recommend printing out the page and keeping a copy in a handy location. The site covers BIOSes manufactured by AMI, Phoenix and IBM. Phoenix is the most popular BIOS, followed by AMI; you're unlikely to have an IBM BIOS. The manual for your motherboard should tell you which company manufactures the BIOS you're using.

The beeps can give you an idea of what's causing the problem, and you may think that the solution will probably entail replacing a faulty part in your computer. In our experience, however, this is rarely the case, and the fault is normally caused by devices not being connected properly. You should always check that your memory, processor, hard disk, optical drive and power connectors are all in place before you start worrying about getting a replacement. Try installing one stick of memory at time, in case there's a faulty module causing problems.

Sometimes faults are caused by the motherboard not detecting your hardware correctly, particularly the processor. The easiest way to get it to do this is to reset the CMOS, which wipes the BIOS back to its default state. This should force it to detect your hardware correctly and can solve a lot of problems. Your board's manual will tell you how to do this.

In general, most motherboards have a jumper that has to be placed over two pins to reset the CMOS. First, you need to change the jumper and turn the PC on. Then turn the computer off and put the jumper back to its original setting. Some motherboards designed for overclocking have a dedicated button on the back. Hold this in and press the power button. Turn your PC off, take your finger off the button and turn your computer back on.

When you reset your CMOS, you'll be prompted to hit F1 when your PC starts, as a warning message tells you the CMOS has been reset. This will reset the BIOS back to its default settings. You'll now be able to follow our instructions on page 68 to configure your BIOS properly.

ERROR MESSAGE BEFORE PC STARTS

When computers are first turned on they run a Power On Self Test (POST) to check that hardware is working correctly. This will identify if your processor isn't working, the keyboard isn't connected or memory isn't working.

Read any message carefully and then check the component that's at fault to make sure it's plugged in correctly. In the case of memory, you can try installing one stick of RAM at a time to make sure that there's not a fault with one of the modules.

DRIVE TROUBLE

If your optical drive isn't being detected, make sure that it's connected properly. This is easy for SATA drives, as you just need to check the cable. For IDE drives, check the cable and the jumpers on the back. If you have only one optical drive, it should be set to master; if you have two, one should be set to master and one to slave.

You should also check that the IDE cable is inserted the right way round on both the drive and the motherboard. If your cable doesn't have a notch in it, then the red cable needs to be next to the power connector on the drive; on the motherboard, the red cable needs to be plugged into pin 1 (this will be marked on the board or, at least, in the motherboard's manual).

For hard disks, make sure that the cable is connected properly. The easiest first step is to go into your computer's BIOS and restore it back to its default settings. To do this, you need to access your BIOS by pressing a certain key (usually Delete or F2) when your computer boots. Your motherboard's manual will explain how to do this, but look out for an onscreen message that will tell you which key to press when you first turn your computer on. Check the manual to find out how to access the hard disk screen. Our guide to the BIOS on page 68 tells you how to configure your disks correctly.

If your hard disk still isn't being detected, make sure it's plugged into the right SATA port and not one for RAID. After that, you may have a broken hard disk. Put your ear to the disk when it turns on – if you repeatedly hear a clunking noise, then it's probably broken.

If your hard disk is detected in the BIOS but can't be seen by Windows, you'll need to install a driver for your computer's hard disk controller. For

TIP
Check that expansion cards and cables are connected properly, as loose connections can cause intermittent problems..

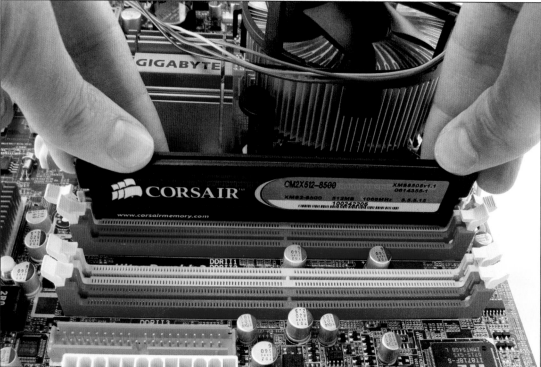

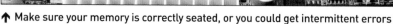
↑ Make sure your memory is correctly seated, or you could get intermittent errors

XP this involves getting a floppy disk with the driver on it, while Vista and Windows 7 let you use optical drives, floppy disks and USB drives to store the driver.

CRASHES WHEN INSTALLING

Perhaps the most frustrating problem is when your PC turns on correctly and recognises all your hardware, but crashes without warning when you try to install an operating system. We've seen this happen on lots of computers before, and the fix is to check your hardware methodically. The first step is to go into your BIOS and reset it back to its default values. When you get into your BIOS, you need to find the section that lets you load default values. Quite often this is under the Exit menu, but this differs between manufacturers, so check your manual. Given the choice, try and load the Optimal default first, and the Fail-Safe default second. If you don't have these options, the basic default setting is best. Select Exit Saving Changes and your computer will restart. You may need to set your BIOS up the way you want it again by following our advice on page 68.

Typically, these kinds of problems are usually caused by just a few components. Overheating is one of the big causes, especially in the case of the processor. It's worth checking that your processor cooler is fitted properly (page 52). This is particularly true for Intel processors, as the four push-in feet don't always go in smoothly. It's easy to miss one and end up with the cooler not making proper contact with the processor. Also check that the processor has an adequate covering of thermal paste, applying more where necessary.

If that doesn't do the job, the memory could be the culprit. Running an application such as Memtest86+ (see page 151) can help you test your memory and find any errors. If this application won't run, then it's worth manually checking your memory. First, make sure that all the modules are seated properly in the correct sockets (page 54). If you're still having trouble, then it may be that one stick of memory is causing the problem. Remove all but one stick and try it again. Swap the stick of memory for another one and try your computer again. By a process of elimination, you should be able to work out which stick of memory, if any, is damaged.

Other bits of hardware can also cause problems, so it's worth checking that your optical drive (page 60) and hard disk (page 58) are connected properly. For the hard disk, make sure that it's connected to the right SATA port on your computer by checking your motherboard's manual. Some boards have ports that are reserved

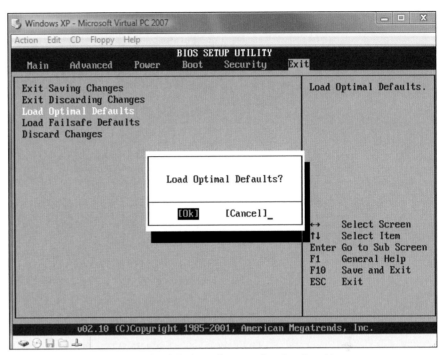

↑ Resetting the BIOS back to its default settings can fix a lot of problems

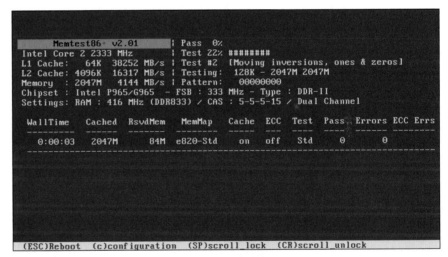

↑ Bad memory can cause lots of problems in PCs, including random Windows crashes. Memtest can help you track down the problem by running diagnostic tests on your RAM

for RAID. It may be worth disconnecting your hard disk entirely and trying the install process again. We've seen damaged hard disks before that have caused the Windows installation to crash.

If removing the hard disk lets the installer work, it's worth running Hitachi's free Drive Fitness Test (page 153) to see if you can identify a fault with the hard disk. You can also try connecting the hard disk to a different SATA port. Finally, remove all non-essential hardware such as wireless adaptors and TV tuners one at a time to see if this fixes your problems. If you get Windows to install, you should reinstall the removed hardware.

Troubleshooting Windows

WHILE WINDOWS HAS improved a lot since its early days, there are still times when it will give you a headache and simply refuse to work properly. This this can be frustrating, particularly if you've just spent hours building a new PC. Luckily, the problems aren't usually fatal and can be solved with a bit of perseverance.

Here, we'll talk you through some common problem-solving techniques to help you get your PC back on track. The main thing to do is to be methodical and rule out one problem at a time. If you do too much in one go, you might solve the problem, but you'll never know its source, which could cause trouble further down the line.

In most cases, problems with getting peripherals or other hardware to work are usually caused by the drivers you've installed. Most of the time, simply using Add/remove programs to delete the offending driver and installing a new one will fix your woes. In other cases, downloading the latest drivers from the device manufacturer's website will fix the problem.

UNSTABLE WINDOWS CRASHES
If you find that your computer's not very stable and keeps crashing, and you've made sure that your

hardware isn't getting too hot (see page 154), then the problem is probably down to one of two things: hardware compatibility or software compatibility.

In both cases, note down the error message that appears. If you type the exact phrase into a search engine, there's a good chance you'll find a website that will tell you what caused the error and how to fix it. Look for tell-tale signs in the error message, as Windows will usually say which bit of software or hardware has caused the problem. You can then look for support from the relevant manufacturer.

If your machine just crashes or the error message isn't particularly helpful, remember what you were doing when your computer crashed. If it always occurs when you open a particular application, then it's probably that piece of software causing the problem. This is especially likely to be the case if you're installing an old application that you used in an earlier version of Windows.

Fortunately, most manufacturers carry updates for software on their website, so visit the site and look for a new update. If there isn't one, you may need to upgrade to a newer version of the application that is compatible with your version of Windows. Look for upgrade offers, as these usually provide you with the latest version of the software at a reduced price.

HARDWARE
If your PC crashes randomly and not always when you're using a particular bit of software, then it's probably a piece of hardware that's misbehaving or hasn't been properly detected. However, this is easy to check.

First, right-click Computer in the Start menu (My Computer in Windows XP) and select Properties. This will display System Information windows, which will tell you which processor is installed and how much memory your PC has. If this information doesn't match up with what you put in your PC, then you've probably got a problem. You should try to reseat the memory and processor, and reread the section on setting up your BIOS (see page 68) to find out how to get your computer to detect your hardware properly.

↑ Device Manager shows you if any of your hardware isn't installed properly

If everything is detected properly here, then it could be another bit of hardware that's causing the problem. To see if this is the case, you need to check Device Manager. In Windows 7 and Vista, right-click on Computer and select Properties. Click on the Device Manager link on the right-hand side of the screen. In XP, right-click on My Computer, select Properties, click on the hardware tab and select Device Manager.

If any devices aren't installed properly, a yellow warning triangle containing an exclamation mark will be displayed. This is Windows' way of highlighting that there's a problem. If the warning icon is next to an Unknown Device, then the problem is probably that you haven't installed all the necessary drivers. Go back through your list of downloaded drivers and make sure that you installed everything. If you did, then you should check your device manufacturers' websites to make sure that you downloaded everything you were supposed to. The motherboard manufacturer's site is worth checking, as it's easy to miss a driver download.

If the warning triangle is next to a known device, then its driver is not working properly. First, try to reinstall the driver. If that doesn't work, you may have an incompatible driver and should check the manufacturer's website for an updated version. You should also look for compatibility information online to make

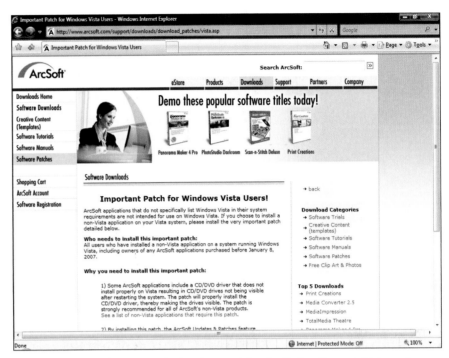

↑ Software manufacturers routinely release patches for their software, which can fix bugs and introduce compatibility for newer operating systems

sure that the device is compatible with your operating system.

SPECIFIC HARDWARE DOESN'T WORK
The steps above give you information on specific hardware problems, but just because a device is listed correctly in Device Manager doesn't mean that it's working properly. Here we'll examine some of the most common bits of hardware and take you through some troubleshooting techniques for them.

KEYBOARDS AND MICE
Windows has built-in drivers, so any keyboard or mouse that you plug in will work automatically. However, while you'll get all the basic functions if you've got a keyboard with extra controls, such as buttons to control volume and media playback, or a mouse with programmable buttons, you'll still need to install the manufacturer's software.

This will be easy to find by visiting the manufacturer's website and searching the support section for your product. Once you've downloaded and installed the recommended software, you should find that all your buttons will start working correctly.

AUDIO
If you're using a dedicated sound card, you should read its manual for full instructions on how to install it, as well as troubleshooting advice.

↑ Windows' System Information screen tells you what hardware has been detected

TIP
Check the manufacturer's support forums for help on a specific problem. The chances are that if you're having a problem, someone else will have already encountered it and has a solution.

Windows will automatically install sound drivers for your onboard sound, but they're not as good as the real drivers. If you're having problems, make sure that you've installed the proper ones from your manufacturer.

If you can't get the sound working at all, there are several things you can check. With most onboard sound, you should notice an icon in the Notification Area (to the left of the time), which looks like a speaker. Double-click this to bring up the audio-management software. Your speaker configuration should be set to match the number of speakers that you have. It's worth checking at this point that your speakers or headphones are connected to the right ports on your motherboard. Check your board's manual for full details.

You can also test the sound from the Control Panel. In Vista, open the Control Panel from the Start menu and select Hardware and Sound (Sound in Windows 7), Manage Audio Devices. Right-click the audio device you want to use and select Test. This will play a sound through each of your speakers. If you only hear it through some of the speakers, you either have a faulty connection somewhere – in which case you should plug all the cables in again – or you haven't told Windows the correct speaker setup you're using.

Finally, the sound output you're using should have a tick next to it. If it doesn't, it's not the default device. Right-click it and select Set as default device. Click on OK to apply the settings.

In XP, select Sounds, Speech and Audio Devices, Sounds and Audio Devices from the Control Panel. Click Advanced under Speaker settings to choose your speaker setup. Click on Audio to choose your default playback device. There's no way to test your speakers, so play an MP3 file to test your audio output.

GRAPHICS CARDS

In order for you to be able to see the desktop before you've had a chance to install the proper graphics card drivers, Windows can use a generic display driver that works with all cards. So, just because you can see something onscreen, it doesn't mean your graphics card is set up properly.

In Device Manager, expand the Display adaptors section and see what's listed. If the full name of your graphics card isn't there and it says something like Generic VGA adaptor, your drivers aren't installed properly. For onboard graphics cards, download the drivers from the motherboard manufacturer's website.

For graphics cards, make sure you have the latest driver from Nvidia's or ATI's website. With both of these, it's important to fill out the request forms properly, as doing so will take you to the latest driver for your card. Not all downloads contain information for all cards, though. The latest Nvidia driver, for example, may not have drivers for a GeForce 8800 GTS graphics card, so trying to install from that will display an error message.

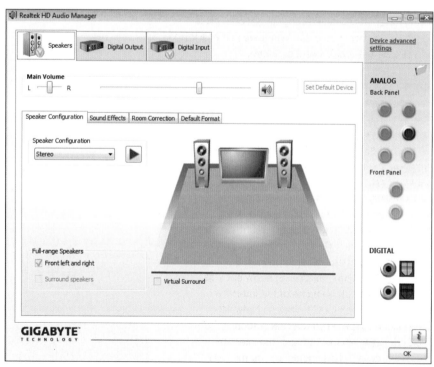

↑ Your sound card should have a control panel where you can test the audio

↑ Windows can help you choose which audio device you want to use for sound

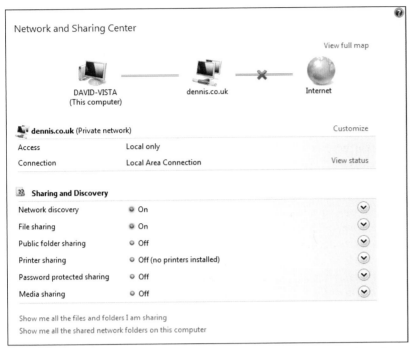

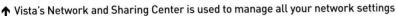

↑ Vista's Network and Sharing Center is used to manage all your network settings

↑ To use the graphical features in Windows 7 and Vista, you need to enable the Aero interface

Once your graphics card is correctly installed, you can check that it's working by pressing Windows-R, typing dxdiag and pressing Enter. This will show you details of your hardware and let you know which version of DirectX (required for playing games) you're running. Windows 7 and Vista users will have DirectX 10 or 11, while XP owners should be running DirectX 9.0c. If dxdiag doesn't work in XP or you're running an older version of it, update to version 9.0c on Microsoft's website (*http://tinyurl.com/directxinstall*).

If you're running Windows 7 or Vista and find that you can't use some of the new features, such as Flip3D (this turns all open windows into a 3D slideshow, and is accessed by pressing the Windows key), then it's because Aero has been turned off. Aero is the new Windows manager, and is turned on only when a graphics card that supports its features is detected. All too often, though, Windows can't properly detect a dedicated graphics card at installation, and so turns this feature off. To turn it back on, right-click on the desktop and select Personalize. Select Windows Color and Appearance, choose Windows Aero from the list and click OK.

WIRELESS NETWORK ADAPTORS

If you're using wireless networking and have installed your network adaptor, you may find that Windows' wireless network configuration tool can't see any networks. In all likelihood, this is because your wireless adaptor has installed its

own management software. You can use this application to control access to wireless networks, but often this software isn't very good. You'll also have to turn to the wireless adaptor's manual to find out how to use it.

A better way is to force Windows to take control over a network adaptor. This can be done in several ways. First, a lot of client software can be turned off by right-clicking the icon in the Notification Area and selecting an option. This is usually along the lines of Let Windows manage this connection or Disable client software.

You may still have problems with Windows displaying a message that it can't manage a wireless connection, though. This can be easily fixed. In XP, right-click on the wireless icon in the Notification Area and select Open Network Connections. Double-click the wireless network connection, click Properties, click the wireless networks tab and select Use Windows to configure my wireless network settings.

In Windows 7 and Vista, it's a little harder. Click on the Start menu and type cmd. Right-click on cmd.exe and select Run as administrator, selecting OK in the dialog boxes that appear. At the command line, type 'netsh wlan show settings'.

Make a note of the name of the interface on the final line (probably Wireless Network Connection). Type netsh wlan set autoconfig enabled=yes interface="name of the interface you noted down". This should let you manage your wireless card through Windows.

Testing memory

MEMORY IS ONE of the most important components in your PC. It stores every aspect of the programs and data that you're currently running, from the window showing your holiday snaps to the spreadsheet with your accounts. Memory also holds important Windows data, such as device driver information and the core components of how Windows works.

A problem with memory can, therefore, be incredibly serious. For example, if your memory should corrupt a critical part of Windows, when the processor tries to use this data, it can end up causing a serious system crash. This can result in damage to Windows and the loss of any important data that you were working on.

To prevent this happening, it's worth running some diagnostic tests on your computer using the free Memtest86+ (*www.memtest.org*). This utility runs directly from a bootable CD before Windows has started and runs a series of tests on your system memory. Any problems reported here could lead to major problems in Windows. The step-by-step guide opposite shows you how to run the test, but here we'll explain what to do with the results.

ERRORS

An error doesn't automatically mean that you have a major problem with your memory. First, try checking the BIOS to find out what speed your memory is running at (see page 68 for instructions on how to do this). If it's running faster than it's supposed to, then you could be pushing it too much. Our guide on testing for system heat

(page 154) is also worth reading. If your system temperature is too high, then you could be suffering from its effects.

It's always worth checking the obvious things, too. If you didn't plug your memory all the way in, it may be detected but cause intermittent faults. Try unplugging your memory and reseating it. Once you've done this, run the Memtest86+ program again to see if the problem has disappeared. If it hasn't, it's time to try a new tack.

SWITCH SLOTS

It could be that one of the memory slots is causing the problem. Try switching memory slots on your motherboard and rerunning the test. If you're getting the same error, there's probably something wrong with your memory. You can attempt to find out which stick of RAM is causing the problems by taking out all the memory apart from one stick and running the tests again. By rotating the stick of installed memory, you'll be able to track down the offending stick.

As processors access memory through their own onboard caches, your processor could be causing the error. If you change your memory and the problem persists, you should change the processor or motherboard.

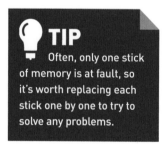

TIP
Often, only one stick of memory is at fault, so it's worth replacing each stick one by one to try to solve any problems.

↑ A problem with your system memory can make your new computer frustrating to use

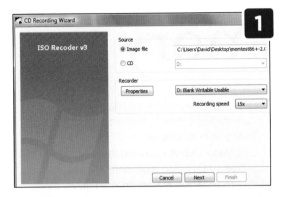

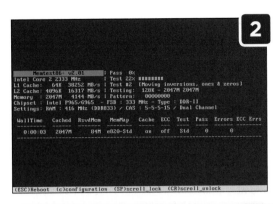

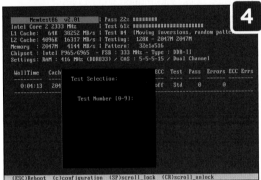

HOW TO...
Test your memory

1 CREATE A BOOT DISC

Memtest86+ runs from a CD. Download the ISO file from *www.memtest.org* and save it to your hard disk. If you've already got a CD-burning utility such as CDBurnerXP, you can follow the instructions for writing the ISO file to CD. If you haven't, download the free ISO Recorder from *http://isorecorder.alexfeinman.com*. Version 2 is for XP and Version 3.1 is for Vista and Windows 7, so make sure you get the right one.

Once the software's installed, find the ISO file you downloaded, right-click it and select Copy image to CD. Put a blank disc in your optical drive and click Next.

2 BOOT FROM THE CD

Put the CD that you just created into your drive and restart the computer. Make sure that your BIOS is set to boot from the optical drive. The CD will automatically load the test environment and start running the tests.

On the screen, you'll see system information and the current test status. The test can take 20 minutes or more to run, so you should leave it running. When it finishes, you'll either get details of

the errors discovered or a message saying that your memory has passed the test.

3 COMPARE DATA

The details on the screen show you the speed at which your memory is running. This is displayed after the settings heading, in brackets after DDR. You should compare this to the speed at which it's supposed to be running. If the detected speed is faster than the memory's rated speed, you could have a problem. However, don't worry about small fluctuations in speed, such as a difference of around five per cent. It's common for the timings to be slightly wrong, and components can run a bit quicker than their rated speeds.

4 CONFIGURE TEST

If you want to configure which test to run, you need to press C while the initial test is running. You may need to reset your computer and boot from the CD you created to get this option. In the menu, press 1 to access the test selection. Press 3 to select the test you want to run, and then type a number from 0 to 9 to run that test. You can find a list of the tests on the Memtest website.

Testing your hard disk

WE'VE ALL BECOME used to having masses of storage space, which most of us stuff full of gigabytes of photos, videos, music and important documents without a second thought. As wonderful as this all is, hard disks are mechanical and are, therefore, quite sensitive. They can fail rapidly and, even if they don't lock up completely, they can cause problems to some files.

Although you should make regular backups, it's also worth checking your hard disk after you've built your PC to make sure that it's reliable and won't cause you problems. Don't worry if you find a problem, as you can use the guide on taking an image of your PC (page 136) to save your installed operating system and restore this to a new hard disk. We'll show you how to test for free using Hitachi GST's Drive Fitness Test application (*www.hitachigst.com/hdd/support/download.htm*). Although it's made by Hitachi, it works on all brands of hard disks. It's run from a bootable CD, which we'll show you how to make.

↑ Hard disks are mechanical devices that can malfunction in a number of different ways

HOW HARD DISKS WORK

The problem with hard disks is that they're mechanical, and are therefore prone to faults. Inside the sealed enclosure are a series of platters, which are disks stacked above each other. These platters, like floppy disks, store data magnetically, and are written to and read by heads that sit just above the surface. Hard disks are therefore very sensitive to movements, as sudden jerks can make the heads touch the platter and destroy any data that's stored on the disk.

If you get problems when you run Drive Fitness Test, make sure your hard disk is firmly attached inside the case and that your computer is standing on a level surface. We've known of a computer that was kept on an old wobbly desk constantly having problems with corrupted Windows files.

PROBLEM DETECTION

Other problems can affect a disk, including lots of bad areas on the disk (known as sectors). These might be detected in normal use only when you fill your disk up and your computer starts trying to access these areas. By running a system scan beforehand, you can detect these bad sectors

now. These will be marked as bad by the hard disk, which prevents data being written to them, but you should replace the hard disk if you find that you get a large number of bad sectors.

Mechanical problems are also a big worry. A damaged disk can make a horrible, metallic clunking sound. While there's little that can be done to prevent this in the long term, running diagnostic tests that access the whole disk can warn you of potential mechanical failure in the future by giving the hard disk a good workout.

Heat, as for other components, can cause massive problems inside a hard disk, so make sure that the inside of your PC is kept cool, and add more cooling if necessary (see page 154 for more information).

Modern hard disks have built-in S.M.A.R.T. technology. This lets your BIOS and other applications talk to the disk and see if there are any problems. S.M.A.R.T. can also notify you of an impending disk failure before it happens.

Finally, the interface between the hard disk and your PC can cause problems if it's damaged. In this case, there's nothing you can do but replace the hard disk.

HOW TO...
Test your hard disk

1 CREATE A BOOT DISC

Drive Fitness Test runs from a CD that you can create yourself. Download the ISO file from *www.hitachigst.com/hdd/support/download.htm* and save it to your hard disk. If you've already got a CD-burning utility, you can follow use that to write the ISO file to CD.

If you haven't, download the free ISO Recorder from *http://isorecorder.alexfeinman.com*. Version 2 is for Windows XP and Version 3.1 is for Vista and Windows 7, so make sure you get the right one. Once the software's installed, find the ISO file you downloaded, right-click it and then select Copy image to CD. Put a blank CD into your optical drive and click Next.

2 BOOT FROM THE CD

Put the CD in your optical drive and restart your PC. Set the BIOS so that your optical drive is the first boot device. You'll be given a menu with a choice of two options. Select the second option and press Enter. Accept the licence agreement by selecting I Agree. The Drive Fitness Test program will then detect your hard disks, and ask for confirmation that this list is correct. Select Yes.

3 RUN A QUICK TEST

Select the hard disk you want to test and then choose Quick Test. On the next screen, click Start. Drive Fitness Test will now run a series of diagnostic tests on your hard disk to make sure it's working properly. If the software detects any errors, you'll be told at the end of the test; otherwise you'll get a green completion message. Click OK to accept it.

With a brand new disk this should be good enough to show that it's working correctly. If you're using a hard disk from an old computer, follow Step 4 for a more in-depth test.

4 ADVANCED TEST

The Quick Test doesn't give the drive a full workout. For this you need to run the Advanced Test, which will run more thorough tests and check the surface of the disk for errors.

As this involves checking every part of the disk, this test will take a lot longer to run than the Quick Test, but it's worth doing, particularly if you're using an old disk from an existing PC. It's also essential if you think that your hard disk could be causing problems.

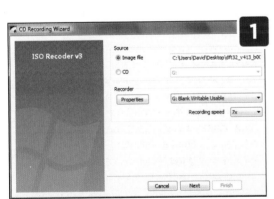

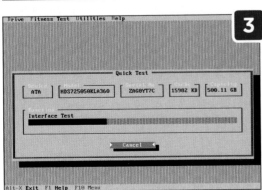

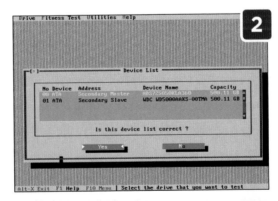

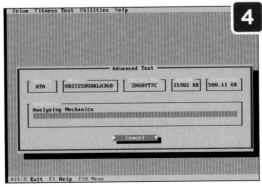

TIP
You should run Windows Check Disk on your hard disks regularly to find and fix faults before they become too serious.

Testing your new PC for heat

EVERYTHING INSIDE YOUR computer generates heat to some degree. It may seem obvious that your processor does – after all, it has a giant fan and heatsink on top of it – but all components produce a certain amount of heat. Memory, hard disks, graphics cards and even your optical drive all contribute to the overall internal temperature of your PC's case.

Heat is a big problem inside computers. If it's too hot, you'll find that your PC will crash more often, as the components shut themselves down to prevent damage. In the long term, the effects of heat inside your system can cause your components to have a shorter lifespan. In the case of your hard disk, this could see it failing before its time, taking some of your important data with it.

MONITOR AND MEASURE

It's really important, therefore, to make sure that your PC is running at the right temperature. Keeping it cool will save you trouble and hassle down the line. Our step-by-step guide on the opposite page shows you how to monitor your computer's temperature with the free utility SpeedFan. You can download this from *www. almico.com/speedfan.php*. Click the download tab and click the link in the download section of the page. Once installed, it can monitor and help control the temperature inside your PC. Before you can set it properly, though, you need to know what should be expected from your system.

IDEAL TEMPERATURES

To get SpeedFan working properly, you'll have to set some maximum temperatures. These can be tricky to work out, but we've got some tips that should help. Hard disks, for example, shouldn't run any higher than 55°C, or they can be damaged. Overall system temperature inside the case should be kept below 50°C, but the lower the better.

Processors are harder to measure, as it depends on the type you're using. Generally speaking, AMD processors should have an external temperature of less than 40°C. Intel processors should have an external temperature of less than 55°C.

↑ Keeping your PC cool will extend its lifespan

You may find that, depending on your system, your temperatures are either close to these figures or a lot lower. A lot of this depends on the temperature sensors in your PC. Motherboard manufacturers use different quality sensors placed in different locations, which can cause a lot of variance between boards. As long as you're running your computer at temperatures less than we've highlighted, it will be fine.

MORE FANS

If your PC is running really hot, there are some things you can try to lower the temperature. First, try reseating your processor cooler, making sure it has enough thermal paste on it to increase the efficiency of the heatsink. Make sure your case's fans aren't clogged up with dust. If you have manual control over your fans, try turning them up.

Finally, if you haven't got any case fans or have enough space for more, then install some. They're easy to fit, and pretty much every case has mountings for them. Inspect your case's manual for full instructions on the size of fans you can install. Ideally, you want to get airflow moving through the case to extract hot air. So, if the fan at the rear is blowing out the back of the case, fit one in the front that blows into the case. This will bring in cool air from outside and help push the hot air out of the case. If you've got one hot component, such as a hard disk, then you need to try to fit fans near it to help cool it down.

TIP
Fans have arrows printed on them showing the direction of the airflow.

HOW TO...
Monitor system temperature

1 READINGS

SpeedFan automatically detects temperature sensors on the motherboard and displays their current readings. Unfortunately, it doesn't always give them very good names, so it can be hard to tell which one is your processor's temperature and which one is the system temperature. The easiest way to tell is to leave your system idle for a few minutes until the temperatures settle. Note down the temperatures, restart your computer and go into the BIOS. Its monitoring section will give you real names for the sensors; all you have to do is match the relative values you recorded.

SpeedFan places an icon next to each temperature reading, which is designed to show you the current status of your computer. A green tick means that everything's all right, arrows show whether the temperature is increasing or decreasing, while a fire means that it's too hot. However, SpeedFan doesn't always get the warnings right, so ignore them for now.

2 HDD AND CORE

As well as accessing the motherboard, SpeedFan can read the temperature of your hard disks using S.M.A.R.T.. Each disk in your PC will be numbered (HD0, HD1 and so on) and have its own temperature. You can also get a report on your hard disk by clicking on the S.M.A.R.T. tab. The core temperatures are the readings directly from inside your processor.

3 CONFIGURE SETTINGS

Click on the Readings tab and then on Configure. You'll see the list of temperature sensors. Click to select one, wait a few seconds and then click again. You can now rename the sensor to match what you identified in Step 1. Press Enter to set the name. Single-click a sensor and you'll see two readings: desired and warning. The first is an ideal temperature, while the warning determines when a flame will be displayed. You only need to set the warning temperatures for hard disks and the external processor temperature, as defined by the limits we set out opposite.

4 CHARTS

Click on the Charts tab and put ticks in the sensors that you want to measure. SpeedFan will then track temperatures over time. This is a good way to see how your system responds when you do different jobs. For example, if you play a lot of games and see that your temperature is running very high during this activity, you'll know that you need to get some extra cooling. This can also be useful when running burn-in tests, such as Hot CPU Tester (see page 157).

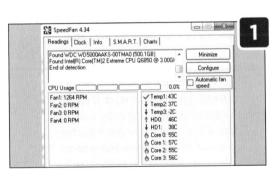

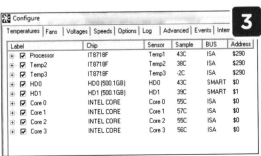

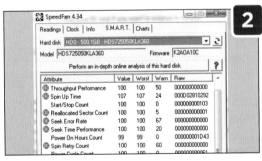

Testing your processor

THE PROCESSOR IS just about the most important part of your PC. Without it, you'd just have a collection of components that wouldn't be able to do anything. It controls every single aspect of your computer, from loading and running the operating system to running the clever artificial intelligence in the latest games.

Processors are constantly being updated, and are also becoming more complicated. These days, it's the norm for a single chip to house at least two processors (called cores in this context), but four cores are rapidly becoming more affordable. While this extra complexity means that computers today can storm through tough tasks such as video encoding quicker than ever, the result is that there's more that can go wrong. A processor crashing will immediately freeze your computer, losing any unsaved work in the process. If the hard disk was being accessed at the time with

an important Windows system file open, a processor crash can even mean that you need to reinstall Windows. Here we'll show you how to test your computer for stability with the free Hot CPU Tester (*www.7byte.com*).

PROBLEM SOLVING

The free version of Hot CPU Tester doesn't run the full suite of diagnostics, like the Professional version. However, there's enough there to make sure that your processor is running properly. Using its Burn-in test, you can find out how effective your processor's cooling is.

The most common reason for a processor to fail any of the diagnostic tests is heat. Processors are sensitive to heat, and can start causing errors when they get too hot. Intel's processors try to deal with the problem by slowing themselves down, which can make your computer very sluggish until the core temperature has dropped. Alternatively, processors can shut themselves down completely, meaning that you'll need to restart your computer.

COOL OFF

The essential thing with processors is to make sure that there's plenty of cooling. Follow our step-by-step advice opposite to work out how hot your processor is. If it exceeds the limits we set on page 154, you've got a problem. Take your PC apart and make sure that its fan is working and that there's decent contact between the processor and the cooler. You may need to reapply thermal paste.

If heat doesn't seem to be the problem, and your processor is still failing diagnostics checks, make sure you're running it at the intended speed in the BIOS (see page 68). Running the processor faster than it is meant to can cause errors.

Finally, try taking the processor out of its socket. In Intel LGA-775 sockets, look for any bent pins. If you see any, push them gently back into place with a jeweller's screwdriver. For AM2 and AM2+ processors, make sure that you haven't bent any pins on the processor. Inserting a credit card between the rows should let you bend them back into shape.

⬆ The most complicated part of your computer, the processor needs to be kept cool and stable if your new build is to be successful

HOW TO...
Test your processor

1 **SET TEST DURATION**
Install Hot CPU Tester (*www.7byte.com*) and run it when the installation has finished. Click OK to skip the message about upgrading to the new version. Before you start, click on the Options tab and select the Test Modules item. You'll see that the test duration is set to six hours. While this will give your PC a thorough workout, it's probably too much for most people. We'd recommend setting it to an hour or slightly under.

2 **RUN TEST**
Click on the Diagnostic button and click Run Test. Hot CPU Tester will then give your processor a thorough workout. It will run lots of mathematically complex tasks to stretch your processor to its limit. It will use every core in your PC, so you'll be unable to use your computer for anything else during this time.

Once the program has finished the test, you'll receive a report telling you if your processor failed any of the tests. If it didn't, you know it's working properly.

3 **BURN IN**
Click the Burn-in icon. This test will run your processor at 100 per cent load, and is useful for checking how temperature affects it. However, in the free version of Hot CPU Tester, which tests only a single core, you can run only a single thread. A workaround is to run Hot CPU Tester as many times as you have cores by double-clicking the program icon.

4 **MEASURE**
Before you start the Burn-in test, run SpeedFan (see page 155) in order to measure the temperature. Keep it somewhere onscreen where it will be visible. Start the Burn-in test on every open copy of Hot CPU Tester by clicking the Run CPU Burn-in button. SpeedFan may stop responding, as your processor is too busy to deal with it. Don't worry; just leave the test running for around 10 minutes and then stop all the Burn-in tests. When they've stopped, look at the temperature of the processor in SpeedFan. If it's exceeded the limits you set for it, you may have overheating problems.

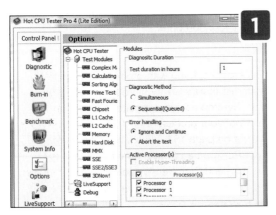

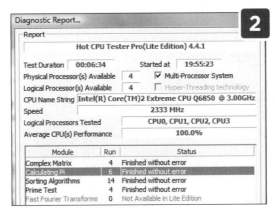

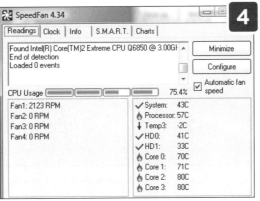

TIP
If you have fan speed switches inside your case, try using them to increase the fan speed to cool down a hot processor.

Glossary

From ADSL to ZIF, we explain 100 key PC terms

10/100Mbit/s See Ethernet.

10BASE-T See Ethernet.

64-BIT 64-bit processors have an extended instruction set, allowing them to process more data at once and access more memory. Only software that supports 64-bit extensions will benefit.

802.11b, 802.11g See WiFi.

ADSL Asymmetric digital subscriber line, the commonest form of broadband. It works over existing BT phone lines, provided that the local exchange is ADSL-enabled.

AGP Accelerated graphics port, a slot for graphics cards. Several versions of increasing speed and decreasing voltage were launched. Now superseded by PCI Express.

ATA AT attachment. See IDE.

ATAPI AT attachment packet interface. See IDE.

ATHLON 64 AMD's current mainstream processor. Has been made for Socket 754, Socket 939 and now Socket AM2.

ATX POWER CONNECTOR This PSU connector supplies the PC's motherboard. It was previously a 20-pin connector, but a 24-pin version started appearing on motherboards in 2005. A split connector is commonly provided to power either version.

ATX See Form Factor.

BIOS The basic input/output system configures your motherboard at startup and boots your PC. It's stored on a flash memory chip and keeps its settings in the CMOS.

BLANKING PLATE Used to cover unoccupied PC case cutouts. You must remove one to install a PCI, PCI Express or AGP expansion card.

BTX See Form Factor.

CARDBUS The 32-bit expansion slot most commonly found on laptop PCs, equivalent to the PCI slot on desktops. Is now being superseded by ExpressCard.

CAT5, CAT6 See Ethernet.

CELERON Intel's budget processor. Current models are cut-down Pentium 4s, available for Socket 478 and LGA775.

CLOCK SPEED All computer components work in time with a clock signal. Each has a maximum clock speed, shown in megahertz (MHz) or gigahertz (GHz), at which it's designed to run. Running the clock faster (overclocking) boosts performance, but can cause a PC to crash.

CMOS Battery-backed memory where the BIOS stores its settings. Cleared using a jumper.

COMPONENT VIDEO A high-quality analogue video connection using three cables.

COMPOSITE VIDEO A basic-quality video connection using a single cable.

CORE 2 Intel's newest processor, available for LGA775 in mainstream Duo and premium Extreme versions.

CPU Central processing unit, also known simply as the processor.

CROSSFIRE ATI's system for combining the power of two Radeon graphics cards in a single PC. Also see SLI.

CRT Cathode ray tube. Refers to a conventional glass-tube monitor.

DDR The type of memory used in most current PCs, called double data rate because it runs twice as fast as SDRAM of the same clock speed. Comes in several speeds, including PC1600, PC2100, PC2700 and PC3200. PC3200 DDR runs at 200MHz but is called 400MHz DDR because of its doubled effective speed.

DDR2 The type of memory used in the newest Pentium 4, Core 2 and Athlon 64 systems. Available in speeds from PC2-4200 (533MHz effective).

DHCP Dynamic host configuration protocol. This allows PCs on a network to obtain their network configuration automatically from a DHCP server, often running on a router.

DIMM Dual inline memory module, a common name for the similar physical packages in which

SDRAM, DDR and DDR2 come, with 168 pins, 184 pins and 240 pins respectively.

DIRECTX Windows extensions from Microsoft that give games and other performance-hungry software fast access to hardware. Check that your PC has the latest version – currently 10 – installed.

D-SUB Analogue monitor-to-graphics-card connection, also known as a VGA cable.

DUAL-CHANNEL Capability of a processor or motherboard to access two DIMMs at once, improving performance.

DVB-T Digital Video Broadcasting – Terrestrial, a standard used by Freeview digital TV in the UK.

DVI Digital visual interface. A monitor-to-graphics-card connection that can include digital and/or analogue signals. The commonest form, DVI-I, has both.

ETHERNET Non-specific networking term, today used to refer to any networking hardware using RJ45 plugs and one of a number of compatible standards including 10BaseT, 100BaseT and Gigabit Ethernet (GbE). Older 10/100Mbit/s hardware supports only the two slower speeds, and runs reliably with the Category 5 (Cat5) grade of cable. The highest grade, Cat6, is a safe choice for Gigabit networks.

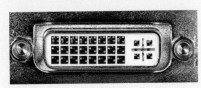

EXPRESSCARD Expansion slot found on new laptop PCs, equivalent to PCI Express on desktops. Incompatible with CardBus.

FAT32 See NTFS.

FIREWALL Software or hardware designed to protect networks from hackers or from software that they control.

FIREWIRE Also known as IEEE 1394 or i.Link. Fast data connection used by PCs, digital camcorders, external hard disks and more. The connector comes in four-pin and six-pin versions, the latter including pins to power one device from the other. A faster nine-pin version, known as FireWire 800, is backward-compatible.

FIRMWARE Software used by a hardware device and stored on a flash memory chip so that it can be upgraded, typically to improve compatibility.

FLASH A type of memory chip that stores data permanently unless it is deliberately overwritten, a process known as flashing.

FLOPPY POWER CONNECTOR A compact four-pin power connector for floppy drives.

FORM FACTOR Motherboards adhere to standards called form factors that dictate size and layout. The commonest are ATX and its compact relative microATX. BTX is Intel's newest standard. Cases will support one or more form factors, telling you which motherboards can be fitted.

FSB The frontside bus connects the processor and other parts of the system. On all but the latest motherboards, the memory runs at the same speed as the FSB – typically 133MHz, 200MHz or 266MHz.

GIGABIT ETHERNET (GbE) See Ethernet.

HEADER A group of pins on a motherboard where you can connect additional ports. USB and FireWire headers are the most common.

IDE A common name for the ATA disk connector, strictly called ATAPI in its modern form, which supports a variety of devices. All three are also known as PATA (Parallel ATA), to distinguish them from SATA (Serial ATA).

IEEE 1394 See FireWire.

JUMPER A plastic-enclosed metal contact used to connect two pins to configure a hardware device. Also see Master.

LGA775 Intel's current processor socket, with pins rather than holes. Used by Pentium 4, Celeron and Core 2 processors.

LINE-IN Audio input for signal of standard 'line-level' volume (louder than microphone input). Usually light blue and takes a 3.5mm jack.

LINE-OUT Audio output of standard 'line-level' volume. Usually lime green, and takes a 3.5mm jack.

MASTER Two IDE devices can share a single cable, provided that one is configured as a master and the other as a slave. This is done using jumpers on the devices.

MICROATX A compact mainstream motherboard form factor with a maximum size of 244x244mm.

MIMO Multiple-input, multiple-output: a way of improving the range and performance of wireless (WiFi) networks using multi-faceted antennas. A technology, not a standard. See Pre-N.

MOLEX Common name for the four-pin power connector used by hard disks and other drives. It has yellow (12V), red (5V) and two black (ground) wires.

NTFS Hard disk file system used by XP, Vista, Windows 7 and other advanced versions of the operating system. Replaces FAT32, as used by Windows 95, 98 and Me.

OEM Original equipment manufacturer. Used to describe products intended for PC manufacturers rather than end users. Typically these will have minimal packaging and manuals.

PATA See IDE.

PC100, PC133 See SDRAM.

PC1600, PC2100, PC2700, PC3200 See DDR.

PC2-4200 See DDR2.

PCI A motherboard expansion slot used for all kinds of upgrade cards except graphics cards. Internal modems, TV tuners and sound cards generally use PCI.

PCI EXPRESS (PCI-E) The relatively new expansion bus for all kinds of upgrades. Slots come in several lengths. Long, fast x16 slots are for graphics cards; short, slower x1 slots are for devices previously made for PCI. A slower card can be used in a faster slot.

PENTIUM 4 Intel's current mainstream processor.

PHENOM AMD's latest processor is designed for Socket AM2+ motherboards, but can work with some older Socket AM2 boards, too.

PHONO Hi-fi style interconnect, correctly known as an RCA jack and used for various audio and video connections. Red and white plugs are used for right and left audio channels, yellow for composite video.

POST Power-on self-test, performed by PCs when switched on, generating the text output that you see before Windows loads.

PRE-N A term used for wireless networking equipment based on the draft 802.11n standard, which has only recently been finalised. Uses MIMO technology.

PRIMARY CHANNEL Most motherboards provide at least two IDE connectors for hard disks and other drives. The PC will boot from the master disk on the connector marked as the primary channel. The secondary channel is typically used for CD and DVD drives.

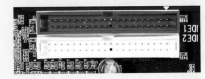

PS/2 CONNECTOR Used for keyboards and mice, although these now often connect via USB.

PSU Power supply unit. Refers to the device inside a PC that converts mains electricity and distributes it to the system's components, and also to the external mains adaptors supplied with some peripherals.

RAID Redundant array of inexpensive disks: a way of storing data on several hard disks to improve performance, or to provide a backup if one disk fails, or both. Modern motherboards support RAID on their PATA or SATA ports.

RAMBUS The company responsible for the expensive RDRAM type of memory used for a few years in Pentium III and Pentium 4 systems. Now obsolete, RDRAM came in modules called RIMMs. If your PC needs it, try eBay.

RCA See Phono.

RDRAM See Rambus.

RF Radio frequency, referring to the coaxial cable connection of TV antennas. An RF signal carries many video channels, while S-video and composite carry only one.

RIMM See Rambus.

RJ45 Plug used for Ethernet network cables, with eight wires. Larger than, but often mistaken for, RJ11.

SATA The Serial ATA interface is used for modern hard disks because it's faster and neater than PATA (Parallel ATA). The original SATA ran at 150MB/s, but the current standard has a 300MB/s mode, compared to PATA's maximum of 133MB/s.

SDRAM The memory type used by most Pentium II and Pentium III PCs. Common speeds are PC100 (100MHz) and PC133 (133MHz).

SECONDARY CHANNEL See Primary Channel.

SERIAL PORT Old, slow port rarely used today but still present on many motherboards as a nine-pin connector.

SLAVE See Master.

SLI Nvidia's system for combining the power of two GeForce graphics cards in one PC. Also see CrossFire.

SOCKET 478 Intel's previous-generation processor socket, still supported by a handful of new motherboards and Pentium 4 and Celeron processors.

SOCKET 479 Socket for Intel's Pentium M and Core Duo mobile processors, the predecessors of Core 2.

SOCKET 754 Socket used by AMD's early Athlon 64 and current Sempron processors. Only supports processors with a single memory controller.

SOCKET 939 Socket used by AMD's Athlon 64 processors, including dual-core X2 versions. Supports processors with a dual memory controller.

SOCKET A Also known as Socket 462, used by AMD's old Duron, Athlon, Athlon XP and Sempron processors. Now obsolete.

SOCKET AM2 AMD's processor socket, which supports DDR2. Used by Athlon 64, Athlon FX and Sempron processors. Very similar to Socket 939 with one extra pinhole.

SOCKET AM2+ AMD's latest processor socket, which supports PC-8500 DDR2 memory and Phenom processors. Backward-compatible with older CPUs.

S-VIDEO An average-quality analogue video connection with a four-pin cable.

TV-OUT Generic analogue output used for connection to a TV. Includes S-video and composite.

USB Universal serial bus. These ports are used to connect all manner of external devices.

USB2 The latest version of USB, which supports the Hi-Speed 480Mbit/s mode as well as older USB 1.1 devices.

VIVO Video in, video out. A compound connector on graphics cards that combines video inputs and outputs. Usually has a breakout cable that maps the pins to standard S-video or composite video connectors.

WEP Wired equivalent privacy. An encryption standard used to secure wireless networks. Comes in various strengths up to 256-bit, all weaker than WPA.

WIFI Name used collectively for the IEEE 802.11 wireless networking standards, including the 11Mbit/s 802.11b and 54Mbit/s 802.11g standards.

WPA WiFi protected access. An encryption standard used to secure wireless networks more reliably than WEP.

ZIF Zero insertion force: a processor socket where the chip is clamped using a lever.

BUILD A BETTER PC 2010

EDITORIAL

Editor
David Ludlow

Production
Steve Haines

Design and layout
Colin Mackleworth

COVER ILLUSTRATION
Ian Naylor

PHOTOGRAPHY
Danny Bird, Jan Cihak, Linda Duong, Pat Hall, Timo Hebditch, Andrew Ridge, Hugh Threlfall

Digital Production Manager
Nicky Baker

MANAGEMENT

Magbooks Manager
Dharmesh Mistry

Publishing Director
John Garewal

Production Director
Robin Ryan

Managing Director of Advertising
Julian Lloyd-Evans

Newstrade Director
Martin Belson

Chief Operating Officer
Brett Reynolds

Group Finance Director
Ian Leggett

Chief Executive
James Tye

Chairman
Felix Dennis

MAGBOOK

The 'Magbook' brand is a trademark of Dennis Publishing Ltd. 30 Cleveland St, London W1T 4JD. Company registered in England. All material © Dennis Publishing Ltd, licensed by Felden 2009, and may not be reproduced in whole or part without the consent of the publishers.

ISBN 1-907232-08-7

LICENSING

To license this product, please contact Winnie Liesenfeld on +44 (0) 20 7907 6134 or email winnie_liesenfeld@dennis.co.uk

LIABILITY

While every care was taken during the production of this Magbook, the publishers cannot be held responsible for the accuracy of the information or any consequence arising from it. Dennis Publishing takes no responsibility for the companies advertising in this Magbook.

The paper used within this Magbook is produced from sustainable fibre, manufactured by mills with a valid chain of custody.

Printed by BGP

BYGONE BRITAIN

AT WORK

1900–1970

LONDON: HMSO

Researched and prepared by Publishing Services, Central Office of Information

© Selection and introduction Crown copyright 1996

Applications for reproduction should be made to:

HMSO, The Copyright Unit, St Clements House, 2-16 Colegate, Norwich NR3 1BQ

ISBN 0 11 701896 1

Published by HMSO and available from:

HMSO Publications Centre
(Mail, fax and telephone orders only)
PO Box 276, London SW8 SDT
Telephone orders 0171 873 9090
General enquiries 0171 873 0011
(queuing system in operation for both numbers)
Fax orders 0171 873 8200

HMSO Bookshops
49 High Holborn, London, WC1V 6HB
(counter service only)
0171 873 0011 Fax 0171 831 1326
68-69 Bull Street, Birmingham, B4 6AD
0121 236 9696 Fax 0121 236 9699
33 Wine Street, Bristol, BS1 2BQ
0117 9264306 Fax 0117 9294515
9-21 Princess Street, Manchester, M60 8AS
0161 834 7201 Fax 0161 833 0634
16 Arthur Street, Belfast, BT1 4GD
01232 238451 Fax 01232 235401
71 Lothian Road, Edinburgh EH3 9AZ
0131 228 4181 Fax 0131 229 2734
The HMSO Oriel Bookshop
The Friary, Cardiff CF1 4AA
01222 395548 Fax 01222 384347

HMSO's Accredited Agents
(see Yellow Pages)

and through good booksellers

Acknowledgments

We would like to thank the staff of the British Library Newspaper Library at Colindale for their ready and cheerful assistance and co-operation, and for their expertise in problem solving. The staff at the British Library at Bloomsbury have also helped in turning up rare and distant journals. We are also indebted to the following, who so kindly allowed us access to their archives: the National Magazine Company (*Queen* and *She* magazines), the National Federation of Women's Institutes (*Home and Country*), Thomas Cook, Swan Hellenic Cruises, Trade and Travel Handbooks (*South American Handbook*), and the John Lewis Partnership.

We stress that copyright in the extracts quoted belongs to the newspapers and magazines concerned, and to their successors in business. Present owners have been most kind in granting permission to quote. These include Times Newspapers Limited, Express Group Newspapers Ltd, Associated Newspapers, Mirror Group Newspapers Ltd, The Telegraph plc and Ewan MacNaughton Associates, the *Observer*, IPC Magazines Ltd, Punch Publications Ltd and Condé Nast Publications Ltd.

In spite of all our efforts, it has not been possible to trace all present copyright owners in some of the extracts quoted. If we have in any way offended, we invite those concerned to get in touch with us.

We would like to thank our colleagues in COI Pictures Section for helping us to choose the photographs for this book, several of which are from Crown Film Unit productions. The photographs on page 102 are by courtesy of the Trustees of the Geffrye Museum (top) and the Royal National Lifeboat Institution.

The centre cover illustration is by courtesy of the Post Office. The photo on the right, showing a London housewife with her washing in 1948, is by courtesy of the Hulton Deutsch Picture Library.

PREFACE

By Sir Harry Secombe

There's nothing quite like coming across a 50-year-old newspaper or magazine – when you're moving house, perhaps, or having a particularly vigorous spring-clean. The shape and size of their yellowing pages may look familiar, but their contents seem to come from another world.

The Bygone Britain series explores our past through the pages of these old newspapers and magazines, which were only ever meant to be bought, read for a day or so and thrown away, but often end up lining people's drawers or wrapped round their crockery.

I find them endlessly fascinating. On the one hand here are events familiar through the reasoned analysis of history – battles, political upheavals – reported with vivid immediacy. Yet news items such as Chamberlain's successful appeasement mission to Berlin can only be viewed through the lens of hindsight. There are also the news stories that took a long time to happen: the earliest of many items about the Channel Tunnel in Bygone Britain is dated 1907!

Quite unselfconsciously, the articles, letters and advertisements reveal completely different priorities from our own. It is quite shocking that a small and ostensibly sentimental item about the discovery of an abandoned baby finishes with the casual disclosure that the infant was then consigned to the workhouse. Conversely, the behaviour of these aliens from another age has the power to amuse us in a way that would make them quite indignant: the excruciating niceties of visiting cards are surely no laughing matter, and what on earth is wrong with attempting to banish grey hair with radium? Likewise, in these knowledgeable days of niche marketing and core business, we find it absurd to see an advertisement urging hairdressers to sell the odd bicycle on the side.

But there are many hints that the people who populate these pages are not such strangers to us after all. Get-rich-quick schemes and dubious books already feature prominently in the small ads, and the slimming advertisements seem as widespread as in our own press. Some of the ideas voiced in the articles are ones that we thought our own generation had come up with: domestic science as a subject for boys, the dangers of too much exposure to the sun. And, needless to say, affairs of the heart loom large across the pages, whatever the decade.

The things that we can recall ourselves exert their own particular attraction. Coverage of events we remember, pictures of celebrities, advertisements for objects we coveted excite a warm glow of recognition and affection. Other pictures may arouse quite opposite emotions: horror and self-loathing to think that we ever went around with lapels like that! Our reactions to our memories are as much a gauge of how we as individuals have changed as of how society has changed.

So what conclusions can we draw from leafing through the pages of the Bygone Britain books? The increasing pace of technological change is evident, as is the growing informality – in manners, in language, and in address to the readers. The problem page letters confirm this. Early in the century, the letters themselves do not appear; all we see are the replies, addressed to a mysterious correspondent with a fanciful name: Heart's Ease or Sapphire. Fifty years later many writers think nothing of revealing their true identities along with their troubles. (In passing, let us be thankful for the demise of the enterprising service offered by the *Hairdressers and Toilet Requisites Gazette*, whereby people sent in samples of falling hair – and worse – for trichological analysis.)

Does the very different look of the articles in the 1900s and those of the 1960s – tiny, dense text with small headlines giving way to more spacious type with *Sun*-style screamers – mean that our powers of concentration are declining? That papers and magazines have to try harder to wrest our attention from television is obvious, but modern technology, availability of newsprint, and more widespread literacy have all played their part in shaping our contemporary press.

Whether you have a serious interest in British history and society, or you're an avid consumer of trivia; whether you can remember most of the first seventy years of this century, or you weren't even born, you will find plenty to wonder at, to mourn and to laugh about in the Bygone Britain series.

INTRODUCTION

One hundred and fifty years ago, England was the 'workshop of the world' and the Great Exhibition of 1851 'marked the peak of English confidence in the industrial economy'. Disraeli described the greatest Victorian boom as a 'convulsion of prosperity': during 1851–81 per capita income rose from £25 to £75. In 1913 Britain accounted for a quarter of the world's trade in manufactured goods, but the United States and Germany had already overtaken her as industrial powers: 'England shows traces of American enterprise and German order, but the enterprise is faded and the order muddled', as a contemporary observer put it. Wages were low, and expectations were low too. In some areas, there had not been much advance on conditions in 1806, condemned by William Cobbett in his *Political Register*:

> A labouring man in England, with a wife and only
> three children, though he never lose a day's work,
> though he and his family be economical, frugal
> and industrious in the most extensive sense of these
> words, is not now able to procure himself by his
> labour a single meal of meat from one end of the
> year unto the other. Is this a state in which the
> labouring man ought to be ?

This book uses contemporary newspaper cuttings – sometimes serious, sometimes odd, sometimes funny – to shed light on the changing pattern of work in the first seven decades of this century. It reveals how men and women felt about their work, whether it was paid, voluntary or for pleasure, and how others viewed them.

In the nineteenth century trade unions had become part of the economic and political system. By the 1890s they had 1.5 million members. In 1900 the National Union of Women Workers held its first conference. But the London General Omnibus Company could still dock the pay of crews who arrived two hours late because of thick fog (*Daily Express*, 1901). The majority of workers still had no union to back them. A cartoon from *Justice* (1903; see p. 8) stands out as a bitter protest against poor pay and high profits. Labour unrest, with the coal miners to the fore, was to grow from small beginnings to impressive demonstrations of trade union power; but even miners could suffer a drop in wages (*Illustrated Sunday Herald*, 1921). However, a series of developments in the first half of the century radically altered the nature of work and of society itself: old age pensions (albeit meagre ones) from 1908; Labour Exchanges in 1909; National Insurance (for certain workers only) in 1913; the Sex Disqualification Removal Bill in 1919; the shortage of labour caused by war (some 4.9 million industrial workers joined the armed forces in 1914-18); economic slumps; the increasing importance of women in the workforce; the Holidays with Pay Act in 1938 (which affected 11 million people); the second world war; and the coming of the welfare state. Organised labour in the prosperous years after 1950 became increasingly powerful, and in 1969 the Labour Government was forced to shelve its 'In Place of Strife' programme, with which it had hoped to curb that power.

Such is the very broad backdrop. Against it we have set out not only some of the historical milestones, but also random stories and details – entertaining or illuminating. From the *Daily Mail* in 1900 we find 'lady doctors' qualifying at their own School of Medicine, under the eye of that redoubtable pioneer Elizabeth Garrett Anderson. The *Rhyl Journal*, however, confirms that by 1932 women doctors had not always found things easy, and we can breathe a sigh of relief that the doctor in question didn't have to resign because she had married.

On another level, two popular entertainers catch the eye. In 1901 the 4th Marquess of Headfort announces his engagement to the lovely Rosie Boote, one of the famous Gaiety girls, who does not allow her coming elevation to interfere with her work. In 1907 *Reynolds* tells us about Alice Lloyd (Marie's sister), who will earn £75,000 in five years touring music halls in the United States.

A report of a visit by workhouse inmates to Broughton Castle (*Banbury Guardian*, 1905) offers more than a hint of patronising attitudes, and undue deference to authority, which can make us squirm today, and which lasted longer, perhaps, than we would care to own. After all, in 1908 one of the speakers in the House of Lords (*Catholic Herald*) thought that old age pensions would demoralise the working classes and do away with thrift.

Among women mould-breakers – apart from the suffragists Christabel Pankhurst ('We have blown up the house of the Chancellor of the Exchequer') and Millicent Fawcett – are Mrs Hughes, the first woman police inspector (*Police Review*, 1914), who would enquire into 'delicate cases'; trade union leader Mary Macarthur (*Illustrated Sunday Herald*, 1921), her career and promise cut short by early death; and Laura Bowen (*Evening News*), who in 1930, at 24, became general manager of the Peter Jones department store and did not anticipate any difficulty in dealing with the men under her control.

Spare a thought for Percy Callard, who worked hard, and in vain, on the parish council to prevent installation of electric lighting in Monken Hadley church (*New Age*, 1930). In 1933 the reclusive Sir John Ellerman, who 'pays more tax than any other individual in the United Kingdom', begins work in his father's shipping business at the age of 23, and the young Kenneth Clark starts as Director of the National Gallery (*The Times* and *Illustrated London News*). We can catch up on the growing number of millionaires in Britain (*The Times*, 1937). And the man who missed being one – Jack Pick, an inventor of genius, who could not master finance, turned down an advantageous offer from the future Lord Nuffield and ended his days growing vegetables (*Daily Mail*, 1954).

For the war effort, Queen Mary, wearing an apron and serving teas to troops in the west of England, is reported 'delighted' (*Oxford Mail*, 1941) to be addressed as 'Missus'. King George VI, tireless in his wartime visits to all parts of Britain, lends a hand at a cannon gun factory whenever he can find the time to look in (*Sunday Express*, 1943).

The period 1950–70, so close in time, has been completely overtaken by the ever more rapid pace and changing temper of life. The 1950s boom brings fortunes to the world of pop, so the *News Chronicle* tells us in 1954, with British singers earning £1,000 a week and satisfying the demand from America for their 78 rpm discs. The threat of automation to jobs is already reflected at the Standard Motor Car Company in 1956, with 12,000 on strike. Fourteen years later the *Islington Gazette* reports the closing of London's last manual telephone exchange.

Kenneth Horne (as popular a businessman as comedian) and Walter Lines are witnesses to the vigour and inventiveness of the British toy industry (*British Toys*, 1955, 1962). And inventiveness is still recognised as a very British quality in 1963, when the Germans praise the all-British patented 'Wizard' hose examining machine, which enabled Mrs Lettie Jones to turn a dozen pairs of stockings in 45 seconds (*Knitwear and Stockings*, 1963). But what some would see as enterprise can still invite discouragement. In 1966 Gladys Cooper and Denise Robins seem especially hard on a young woman who wants to go on working before starting a family.

One wonders what Cobbett would have said.

John Collis
COI
March 1996

1900 ▪ 1909

Evening Standard 1900

WOMEN DOCTORS.

NEW POSTS OFFERED THEM AT A LONDON HOSPITAL.

At the corner of Handel-street, Brunswick-square, hard by St. George's-gardens, where ragged schildren play all day among the crumbling tombstones, stands the London Royal Free Hospital School of Medicine for Women, and here yesterday it was announced, amid applause, that the institution had decided to open its resident posts to women.

From twenty to thirty qualified lady doctors are turned out by this School of Medicine every year. A large proportion go out to India as medical missionaries. Others obtain posts in women's and children's hospitals and infirmaries and other public institutions.

Diplomas can now be obtained from practically every medical examining board, with the exception of the Royal College of Surgeons.

The new buildings of the school will contain sets of rooms for such students as care to make use of them. "I am not, however," explained Mrs. Garrett Anderson, the dean of the college, yesterday to a "Daily Mail" reporter, "going to be a mother to the girls. If they are old enough to study medicine they are old enough to take care of themselves."

Daily Mail 1900

THE HOT WEATHER.

In London at noon to-day the thermometer registered 90 degrees in the shade and 128 degrees in the sun, compared with 80 and 122 degrees respectively at the same hour yesterday.

On the river wharves and in the large markets, notably in the Borough and Covent Garden Markets, some of the porters were incapacitated at an early hour. Seven inquests were held yesterday on victims of sunstroke, and over a dozen bodies of persons who have succumbed to the heat still lie in the various Metropolitan mortuaries. It is computed that since the present tropical weather set in nearly 400 cases of heat stroke had been treated at the hospitals and ambulance stations. A number of the omnibus drivers had to go off duty again to-day, and the horses suffered terribly, a number of them being led on to the Embankment and considerately treated to a douche from the water mains. Hundreds of workmen in exposed situations also ceased work during the hottest period of the day.

A Swansea telegram states that John Welsh, 7½ years, died from the effects of sunstroke to-day.

Mr. Drew yesterday held no fewer than four inquests on former residents at Chelsea and Fulham, who had died from the effects of the excessive heat. Inquests were also held by other Metropolitan coroners in cases in which death was attributed to the same cause.

Evening Standard 1900

WATER COMPANIES AND THE DROUGHT.

TO THE EDITOR.

SIR,—It can at least be pleaded for the Lambeth Water Company that they give some notification, however vague, of their intention to limit the supply. Other Companies see no necessity for even this. Among these delinquents is the Grand Junction Waterworks Company, who yesterday cut off the supply here at midday for an hour, and again in the afternoon for about two hours. My hose was playing on the lawn at the time when the water was first cut off, and the discontinuance of the supply was notified to us by dense clouds of steam rising from the grass, the cold water cistern having been exhausted and the hot water having taken its place. One result will be the spoiling of the lawn for the rest of the year—an experience suffered by a neighbour of mine a year or two ago from a precisely similar cause. The immediate result was that we were deprived of the use of our kitchen range, as, to prevent an explosion, the fire had to be raked out, and all cooking done on a gas stove.

I pay a heavy garden water rate, amounting to two-thirds of that charged for the house supply, and as water is only used in the garden for three months at the outside, I am practically charged about three times as much for the garden as for the house. I naturally want to know what this heavy charge is for, if, when water is most needed for the garden, I am to be deprived of it. If the cutting off the supply had been due to an accident to the mains, I should not complain, but this kind of thing is of constant occurrence in both Summer and Winter, and is simply done to husband the Company's supply of water, though it is practically unlimited, save for expense. During the great frost of 1895 the Grand Junction Company played the same trick, with the result that the consumers' pipes froze all over this parish, and in one case a kitchen boiler burst, with loss of life. In a previous Winter the Company did the same thing, and I only discovered it just in time to prevent a serious accident.

Complaints to the Company are useless, and rarely receive even the courtesy of a reply. Unfortunately, a safeguard like that once suggested against railway accidents—placing a Director on the locomotive—is not available in this case.

I am, Sir, your obedient servant,
E. C. E.

Teddington, July 25.

HIS HEAVIEST TOOL—A PEN.

William Power, who is a clerk by occupation, but who has been an inmate of the Camberwell Workhouse since August last, refused to perform his allotted task of work, and as a result appeared in the dock at Lambeth Police-court.

Power informed Mr. Hopkins that he was not used to breaking stones. He was only a clerk, and had never handled anything heavier than a pen.

Mr. Hopkins: Five days' hard labour.

Evening News and Evening Mail 1902

Mr. R. Edrich, a shoemaker, of Coltishall, Norfolk, has now six sons serving in the Army and Navy. Of these three are at the seat of war, viz., one in the 10th Hussars, another in the "A" Battery Royal Horse Artillery, and a third in the 84th Field Battery Royal Artillery. Mr. Edrich has just received from the Privy Purse Office an order for £4, "as a small present from the Queen."

Evening Standard 1900

* * * * * *

At a recently held meeting of that very enterprising body, the Bournemouth Town Council, the Horse Committee in their report recommended that the licences of the nine motor-car drivers be not renewed, but before the report was adopted this clause was withdrawn.

The Road 1900

Accommodation for Welsh gold miners, c. 1905.

Women in a Lancashire cotton mill, 1902.

THE COLONIAL WOMAN.

AN article appearing in your last week's issue (Oct. 13), writes a correspondent, entitled "The Colonial Woman," page 577, gives rise to much interesting thought. The problem which the above article propounds might apply in many cases to women of the mother country, and it is a problem which, though not of very wide proportions as yet, is growing daily in England, with the greater opportunities for women's education and the widening sco pe for thei work.

Many of the occupations which women have undertaken are too great a strain on their mental and physical strength, but, owing to their very precarious position in the working world, they are bound to conform to the same hours and regulations as their fellow-workers, men. Besides being very seriously handicapped in this way, there are countless other drawbacks, which, although they appear trivial, are none the less irritating to a woman who has undertaken a life of work. There is her hair, which always requires time and attention, however early she may be obliged to rise and attend to the claims of her profession; her clothes must always be neat and pretty, for the more thorough a working woman may be, the more determined is she not to abandon the niceties of her sex. These same clothes are often a drawback to her work, but she is obliged to wear the conventional style, owing to our prejudiced state of society. Imagine having to add to this the claims of a household, the production and care of children. Indisputably it is impossible to do both; her work must be suspended, and work which is liable to interruption can never be very successful.

Yet these very women who have courage, independence, originality, who work hard, eschewing luxury and idle comfort, opening up new avenues of progress and labour, who are willing to take some of the burden of work on to their shoulders, instead of always accepting the reward of work from the hands of those who earned it, these women are more than often the ones who will produce a hardier, more character-full offspring. There are, of course, exceptions among them, but as a general rule they are higher principled, more enduring, less hysterical than the average woman who marries, and does not work. Are they not, then, more suited to be intrusted with the care and upbringing of the future generation; they have a more cultivated intelligence; a higher sense of honour (of necessity acquired by contact with working men and women), and a stronger character to bequeath to their children—of course, this is speaking of the best among them. The average working woman is certainly more selfish, and less inclined to self sacrifice than her idler sister; but surely any woman of principle can acquire unselfishness in proportion to the claims upon her, and the love she bears towards her husband and family. The woman who works may be the wife of the future, but how her position, economically and domestically, can be arranged is a question which still awaits an answer. If she shares the burden of earning the income there seems no reason why her husband should not share the cares of house and family more than he does at present. With division of labour the home might be made as refined and comfortable as it now is in cases where the wife's part is confined to the circumscribed duties of the household, and the husband alone has the interests and freedom of an outside life. Sooner or later a solution must be found for this social problem. C. M. B.

Queen 1900

Queen 1900

The sudden death of Mr. Lawson Johnston, which took place on board his yacht, "White Ladye," in Cannes Harbour last week, removes from our midst a very remarkable man. He was known to the world chiefly as the inventor of "Bovril," and as Chairman of the Company bearing that name. He was a Scotchman, and enjoyed the privilege of an Edinburgh education, and his predilection was for the study of dietetics, in which he soon became so well-known that after the Franco-German War he was chosen by the French Government as its Commissioner to proceed to Canada and investigate the subject of food concentration and preservation. This led to the discovery of Bovril, which, with the co-operation of Lord Playfair, Sir Edmund Frankland, Dr. Farquharson, and other scientists, was soon recognised as one of the most valuable foods of the century. In private life Mr. Johnston will long be remembered for his unostentatious philanthropy. An instance of this was the organisation of the War Employment Bureau, the entire expenses of which throughout were defrayed by him.

The Lady 1900

RECENT BOOKS.

It took a century or two to produce in the person of Mr Kipling a popular writer on the subject of India. There seems to be the same difficulty about Egypt as a subject. The latest writer of an Egyptian novel is Mr James Bagnall-Stubbs, author of " Ora Pro Nobis," whose "The Order of Isis," a story of mystery and adventures in Egypt, has just been brought out by Messrs Skeffington and Sons, Piccadilly. It has plenty of incident and adventure, but it misses being a good book.

PERILS OF THE ROAD.

At the Westminster Police-court, before Mr. Sheil, a young cabman, named Francis W. L. Taylor, was charged by the police on a summons with wanton and furious driving.—On the night of the 19th inst. the Defendant, according to the evidence of two police-constables, whipped his horse into a canter along the Brompton-road, and knocked down a gentleman, who narrowly escaped being run over. Taking no notice of the shouts of the constables to stop, Defendant drove off as fast as he could go. His number was eventually traced from the back plate of the cab.—Mr. Frederick William Crawley, retired civil servant. deposed that he was knocked over, and as the police had testified, the Defendant did his best to get away.—The Defendant made excuse that his horse took fright, but Mr. Sheil said he did not believe that, and fined him 40s. and costs.

Evening Standard 1900

VICTORIA MEMORIAL IN INDIA.

CALCUTTA, Wednesday.

The fund for the erection of a memorial to the late Queen Victoria in Calcutta now amounts to 26 lakhs and 52,806 rupees. Among the later subscriptions are included 50,000 rupees from Maharaj Rana of Dholpur and 12,000 from the Maharajah of Orchha.—*Reuter*.

A meeting convened by the Lord Mayor was held at Birmingham yesterday, at which a committee was appointed to consider the question of a Victoria National Memorial, and to report their recommendations to a future meeting. During the proceedings a letter was read from the Lord Mayor of London, stating with reference to the national memorial in London that the central figure would be a statue of her late Majesty flanked and surrounded by architectural work for which the most eminent artists were to be invited to send in designs. It was expected that half a million of money would be required, but he understood it was preferred that the nature of the memorial in all its magnificence should depend on the sum voluntarily subscribed by the public rather than that an estimate should be made up to which donors would be invited to contribute.

Daily Telegraph 1901

THE WOMEN WORKERS' UNION.

The Conference of the Women Workers' Union was resumed to-day at Brighton, when the subject which attracted the most attention related to domestic servants and management of modern householders. The servant question gave rise to an animated debate, in which many mistresses and an ex-domestic took part. Other topics included the training and supply of Poor Law officials, the treatment of the epileptic and feeble-minded, and the improvement of the condition of laundries.

Evening Standard 1900

BADGES OF COURAGE.

OUTPUT OF THE MINT FOR 1900.

The Medal Department was fully employed during 1900 on acount of the supposed "early termination of the South African war." Of the medals struck 46,941 were supplied to the War Office, 921 to the Admiralty, 4,000 to the Canadian Government, and 30 to the India Office. In addition 12,974 clasps were issued.

So many medals were wanted that the Mint was unable to cope with the work. Outside firms had therefore to assist, with the result that by the end of last year 102,043 medals had been issued to Woolwich to be engraved with the recipient's name.

Among the interesting figures given in the annual report of the Comptroller of the Mint is a detailed account of the number of coins struck during the year.

It appears that the coinage for 1900 consisted of—

10,846,741 sovereigns.
4,307,372 half-sovereigns.
353,356 crowns.
4,479,128 half-crowns.
5,528,630 florins.
10,987,590 shillings.
8,984,354 sixpences.
10,661,874 threepenny-pieces.
31,778,109 pence.
13,805,190 halfpence.
5,969,317 farthings.

The total number of all Imperial coins is placed at 107,689,518, the nominal value of which was £15,273,992 11s. 4½d.

Although there was a loss on gold coinage to the extent of £5,516, the profit made by the Mint was £989,992.

Daily Express 1901

THE MARQUIS OF HEADFORT.

We are desired by the Marquis of Headfort to announce that he is engaged to be married to Miss Boote. His lordship, who is in his twenty-third year, is at present a lieutenant in the 1st Life Guards, and Miss Boote is now playing at the Gaiety Theatre.

Daily Telegraph 1901

THE GOVERNMENT DEFEATED.

COMMONS REFUSE TO SUPPORT MR. RITCHIE.

EXCITING SCENES.

MINISTERS ACCEPT THE DECISION OF THE HOUSE.

The Government were defeated last night in the House of Commons, amid a scene of great excitement, on a clause of the Factories Bill relating to Saturday half-holidays in the textile trade.

Mr. Ritchie opposed the reduction of working hours from one o'clock to twelve o'clock, declaring that the trade could not afford the loss entailed by this reduction in the hours of labour, and appealed to the House to support him in this matter.

A number of Unionists, however, spoke in favour of the clause, and the House divided—

For the Government 141
Against 163

Government defeated by 22

The figures were received with loud cheers from the Opposition and derisive shouts from the Irish benches.

Mr. Ritchie then announced that the Government would accept the decision of the House in the matter, and accept the clause.

A PLEA FOR WORKERS.

The division which led to the defeat of the Government arose out of an amendment to the Factory Bill moved by Mr. Renshaw, and backed by a number of Unionists, to do away with the clause compelling early closing at twelve on Saturdays in the textile trades. Mr. Renshaw argued that if the clause passed, the trade would be severely handicapped.

But Mr. Harwood made an eloquent appeal for the half-holiday. He drew a moving picture of the women and children operatives in the cotton trade, who worked for some fifty-six hours a week in an atmosphere that ranged from 80 to 110 degrees.

"Give them the extra hour for their Saturday dinner," he pleaded, "and the quality of the work will improve." This appeal coming from a cotton manufacturer had great weight, and was supported by Mr. Kenyon, a Unionist.

Daily Express 1901

British Monthly Brevities

REV. JOHN GOULD, of East Anglia, gives a striking instance of a poor man's devotion to the Wesleyan Church. In one circuit £50 were required to complete the promise to the Twentieth Century Fund. A farm labourer, who spoke in the quarterly meeting when additional payments were being asked, said that he had not another sovereign in the world, but he would give the gold coin which he had worn on his watch-guard for many years.

British Monthly **1902**

Cardiff and District Notes.

Sickness is still playing havoc in the town. Mr. W. J. Travers is the latest victim, and has had a very severe attack of influenza. I am pleased to say he is much better, and is about again. The president (Mr. Huxtable) is also far from being well, and no doubt the hard work entailed by his office has been very trying. Mr. Bugg, of Crwys Road, has not quite recovered, but I understand is better than he has been, and we all hope and wish he may soon be himself again.

British Baker **1903**

THE directors of Messrs. Chapman and Hall report that the past year has been singularly prejudicial to the publishing trade. Nevertheless, the company is able to show a net profit of £2,812 8s. 2d. on last year's trading.

The Academy **1902**

MR GEORGE LICHTENFELD'S NEW TRIUMPH POMPADOUR FRAME.

IT is not always that the natural *chevelure* lends itself to the production of the full Pompadour effect, which is almost a necessity in the present style of hairdressing. Very fine hair, or an inclination to thinness of growth on the temples, present an absolute veto to the desired arrangement unless extraneous aid of one sort or another is called in. Often this is most convenient in the form of one of the Pompadour frames which have of late come so much into use, but here another difficulty is apt to arise; the frame is mounted on a wire which, though ever so slight, still causes a certain amount of pressure and consequent discomfort. This drawback is entirely obviated in the Triumph Pompadour frame, a recent invention of Mr George Lichtenfeld, of 93, Great Portland-street, and 79, Regent-street, which consists of a tubular network composed wholly and solely of woven hair without so much as a cord by way of foundation. The result is that one of the Triumph frames, round, for the front and sides, or only for the front, as the case may be, can be inserted beneath the natural hair without the slightest weight or pressure being felt. The elasticity and spring of the woven hair constitute another special advantage, the frame offering a natural resistance which ensures its preserving the light, raised appearance of the hair under all circumstances. The new frames, as shown in the accompanying sketches, can be used alone as a simple foundation for raising the natural hair, or are to be had mounted as a novel style of *toupet*. In the latter case, the device possesses the recommendation of making no line of demarcation whatever between hair and forehead. The yielding, elastic frame simply serves to give the Pompadour effect; the hair, which is mounted from beneath it in an upward direction, being adjustable in whatever way is most becoming to the wearer, with a softness and irregularity of line rendering the addition perfectly imperceptible.

Queen **1901**

Cook's Excursionist **1901**

A Denmark Hill tradesman, over seventy years of age, boasts (so a correspondent states) that he has never crossed the Thames.

Daily Mirror **1904**

BUSMEN PAY FOR THE FOG.

For arriving at the terminus two hours' late in the thick fog last Saturday night the London General Omnibus Company demanded 1s. 6d. from several conductors and 1s. 10½d. from the drivers "for being late."

On the top of this the directors have now passed a resolution to the effect that when journeys are lost through bad weather, drivers and conductors are to be paid for journeys done instead of the usual weekly wages.

Daily Express **1901**

This picture was sent in as a copy for a triumphal car in the Lord Mayor's Show. It would be interesting to know why it was refused.

Justice 1903

A LONDON COMRADE writes that his son, a lad of 15 was in the habit of being sent by his master to take bets to a bookmaker, resulting in the lad betting himself. He advised his son to look out for a fresh place, which he did. His master hearing of it, discharged him without notice. Upon being sued for a week's wages the County Court judge non-suited our comrade on the plea of the defendant that the boy had sought another situation without his knowledge, and that his father was a " Socialist." Our comrade is naturally incensed at the proceedings of the judge, whose decision aids and abets gamblers, and helps to bring boys to ruin. We sympathise with our comrade, but there is no remedy for such a case of hardship under which he and his boy is suffering. We, however, commend the conduct of our comrade in removing his son from the contamination of the gambling spirit which is fast becoming a curse to the rising generation.

Justice 1903

HOSPITAL ROMANCE.

Ward Sister and Dean's Daughter Marries Hospital Porter.

Miss Kate Lynch-Blosse, a daughter of the late Dean Blosse of Llandaff, had risen to the rank of sister at Cardiff Infirmary. Middle-aged, of medium height, untiring in her devotion to duty, Sister Lynch-Blosse was among the most faithful servants of the hospital.

Possessed of a private competence, her salary had always been returned in the form of subscriptions to the charity to which she had given so many years. A week ago, amid general expressions of regret, she left the infirmary, and it is now known that some months back she had married the hospital porter, Mr. Lewis Price, a well set-up man who had gone through the South African War.

Mr. and Mrs. Lewis Price are understood to have settled in Somerset, just across the Bristol Channel, where they have taken a farm.

Daily Mirror 1904

Charles Hammond, who had been employed as grave digger at Norwich Cemetery since 1857, had between that year and 1900, when he retired through infirmity, dug over 15,000 graves. On Saturday he was laid to rest himself. Hammond was a Crimean veteran.

*

Crusader 1904

THE LIFE AND WORK OF THE REDEEMER.
By EMINENT DIVINES.

With 8 Full-Page Illustrations. 352 pp.
PRICE **2s. 6d.** NET.

" In this work a commanding body of contributors discuss various aspects of our Lord's life and ministry. The Bishop of Durham has two striking chapters, which are marked by all his careful treatment of Holy Scripture, appositeness of illustration and practical application. The volume cannot but appeal to a very wide circle of readers."—*Record*.

British Baker 1903

THE COOK'S VIGIL.

FIGHTING THE COCKROACHES.

JURY DISAGREE.

The story of the cook and the cockroaches was resumed before Mr. Justice Phillimore in the King's Bench yesterday. Mr. G. Walton, an artist, claims £78 from the Rev. L. J. Percival, being a quarter's rent for No. 44, Holland-street, Kensington. The defence is that the house was dirty, and therefore uninhabitable.

Mrs. Emma Shorter, the cook, said she took up her residence in the basement before the family came in. She first saw the beetles when she began to prepare her tea. She found them in the cups and sugar basin. Shortly after she had got into bed she saw beetles pouring out in all directions. (Laughter.) She got out of bed, went to an oilshop and purchased Keating's powder, carbolic soap, and some night lights, with the object of driving the beetles away.

Mr. Justice Phillimore: You must have dressed?

Witness: Oh, yes, my lord. (Laughter.) She added that she sat up all night, and as the beetles became stupefied she brushed them up and put them on the fire. In order to catch more in different parts of the basement she put down two bowls in the kitchen, one outside the kitchen, and one in the scullery. These were in addition to the two bowls she had put down in her bedroom. The bowls were three-parts full of beetles.

Daily News 1905

MESSAGE IN A CHEESE.

GROCER'S UNIQUE EXPERIENCE.

Mr. B. H. Sheepwash, grocer, of Old Brompton, has had a unique experience.

In cutting a Canadian cheese he discovered a small glass phial containing a sheet of paper neatly folded, bearing the following message: " Whoever gets this write to me, and I shall answer. Tell me all interesting facts about yourself, and the place where you live, etc."

The note was in a lady's handwriting, and was evidently written by a well-educated person. A name was given, the lady notifying that she was a " Miss," and address, " Newbliss, Ontario."

Daily News 1905

Mr. John Lessels, Edinburgh, has handed over his branch shop in Canongate to Mr. Millar, who has for many years been foreman in his employ. The reward of a good and faithful servant, the kindly and thoughtful act of a generous employer.

—o—

Ex-Provost Gillespie appears among the batch of the newly-appointed Justices of the Peace for Fifeshire. It is so seldom that the honour of J.P. comes the bakers' way, we are pleased to note it in this case, and congratulate the recipient, who has spent many years in the public service.

—o—

THE UNEMPLOYED.

EFFECTS OF THE FROST.

The frost has practically put a stop to all outdoor labour in the Metropolis, builders, painters, and other outdoor workers being seriously affected. It is estimated that between 20,000 and 25,000 men have been thrown idle. Work has been suspended on the new Government offices in Parliament-street, the War Office buildings, several new Government buildings in Westminster being erected on the sites of demolished areas, the vast building of the Royal College of Science, South Kensington, and the extension of the Victoria and Albert Museum.

BARNET LABOUR YARD.

Barnet Union authorities yesterday opened a labour yard to cope with the distress prevalent in the neighbourhood. There were about forty applicants, and that number is expected to be at least doubled to-day. Single men are paid 1s. 6d. per day for four days per week; married men, 2s. 6d. per day, from three to five days per week, according to the size of their families. The labour yard is open from 8 a.m. to 4.30 p.m., with half an hour interval for dinner. The Local Government Board has been asked to remove the franchise disqualification from men in receipt of relief for work done in the labour yard.

WORKHOUSE ACCOMMODATION.

At a meeting of the unemployed held at Norwich yesterday a resolution was passed urging the corporation to provide work, and a committee of seven was appointed to wait on the Mayor. One of the speakers suggested that if the Corporation would do nothing for them as many as possible, say seven hundred or eight hundred, should apply for tickets of admission to the workhouse, a procedure which, since there is not room for so many in the institution, would compel the authorities to do something. Before the meeting dispersed another resolution was adopted, urging the Government to take steps to assist the local authorities in dealing with the problem of the unemployed.

DISCHARGED SOLDIERS.

In consequence of communications from Poor Law authorities throughout the Kingdom as to the number of discharged soldiers applying for relief, the War Office has issued an order that men entitled to do so shall re-enlist in Section D of the Army Reserve. This applies to men who have been discharged during the past two years, and who hold a parchment certificate containing a promise to re-enlist, if required, within two years or any shorter time from date of discharge, and they should immediately apply to their late commanding officers.

KETTERING.

A remarkable scene was witnessed at the gates of Kettering Workhouse yesterday morning when the members of the Board of Guardians, assembling for the fortnightly meeting, found upwards of a hundred of the unemployed, chiefly shoe operatives, awaiting them. At the suggestion of the chairman of the board, the men appointed a deputation of three to represent them. These stated that all the men were destitute and many were starving. They wanted work, not charity. The chairman pointed out the impotent position of the Guardians in the matter. Digging will, however, be found for a number of the men at the rate of fourpence per pole, taking about an hour to do.

NOTTINGHAM.

A meeting of the Nottingham City Council was held yesterday to devise means for dealing with the exceptional distress at present prevailing. There are about three thousand men out of employment, the building trade being principally affected. The council decided to put in hand immediately certain public works, for which Government sanction has been already obtained, at an estimated expenditure of about £15,000, and to supplement this by grants in deserving circumstances to workmen resident in the town, the money for the purpose being drawn from the profits of the gas undertaking.

ASTON.

The Mayor of Aston yesterday evening opened a relief fund for the unemployed. Considerable destitution prevails in the district.

BELFAST.

The Lord Mayor of Belfast yesterday received a deputation urging the corporation to do something to relieve the present distress. One speaker, a well-known doctor, said in twenty-seven years' experience he had not known of such universal want as at present existed among people who were not paupers and did not want to become paupers. The Lord Mayor, in promising every assistance, mentioned that five soup kitchens had been opened that morning.

Morning Post 1904

OLD ARTIFICIAL TEETH BOUGHT. — Persons wishing to receive full value should apply to the manufacturing Dentists, Messrs. K. Browning, instead of to provincial buyers. If forwarded by post, value per return.—Chief Office, 133, Oxford Street (opposite Berners Street), London. Established 100 years. No. 1502.

Chic 1904

THE FIRE BUZZER.—At a meeting of the Carlisle Gas and Water Committee on Wednesday night it was resolved that the sounding of the buzzer at the Gasworks for the purpose of summoning the members of the Fire Brigade to drill on the first Thursday of each month be discontinued: and the Town Clerk was requested to intimate the resolution to the Fire Brigade Committee. The Gas Committee decided to alter their hour of meeting from seven o'clock to half-past four on Wednesdays.

Carlisle Patriot 1904

"But who hath seen the Grocer
Treat housemaids to his teas,
Or crack a bottle of fish sauce
Or stand a man a cheese?"
G.K. Chesterton

The Need of Ambition.

Doesn't it grip your heart-strings to chance upon a man well along in years, toiling at some lowly task that could be done by a lad fresh from school? Is any failure so tragic as the failure of grey hairs to command respect and place in the world?

Look among your acquaintances in business, and you will find men past the meridian of life, holding places that are mere clerkships. The spark of ambition in such men has flickered and gone out. They are haunted only by one fear — that of losing their berths. There they cling, tooth and nail — afraid of a fall, yet too feeble to climb any higher. The stamp of the underling is upon these men, and underlings they will be until the bugle blows.

To be entirely satisfied with one's job, is the curse of the young man. To be content to get a mere living, just enough for daily wants, is the philosophy of the spineless incompetent. He exclaims blithely: "As long as I have enough to live on!" And so he saunters through life until the frost powders his hair and age crooks his shoulders. Then he wonders vaguely why others got ahead, while he was left behind.

The man with the soul of a clerk, will always be a clerk. The man without ambition to stir him, will never break into a trot, even much less a gallop. He'll stand still, dry up, shrivel, petrify.

Business Help 1906

WORKHOUSE INMATES AT BROUGHTON CASTLE.

On Friday, by the kindness of Lord and Lady Algernon Gordon Lennox, about 100 of the inmates, all who were able to attend, went to Broughton Castle, where they were hospitably entertained. They were driven in vehicles supplied gratis by the White Lion Hotel, Messrs. Sheasby and Sons, Messrs. Hunt, Edmunds and Co., and Messrs. Dunnell and Sons. The weather was showery, but a very enjoyable afternoon was spent in the beautiful grounds and in boating on the moat. The Rev. Maurice Maltby was present, as also were Mr. and Mrs. J. Humphris and Mrs. T. Warren, who assisted in entertaining the visitors, and Mr. Barrett, the butler, and the Castle staff did all in their power to make the outing enjoyable. Mr. Barrett arranged racing for the children for small money prizes. A capital tea was served in the large hall by the firm of E. W. Brown, of Parson's Street, Banbury. Mr. Maltby had to leave early owing to an engagement elsewhere and before departing Mr. Humphris said he was sure the Guardians were very pleased to sanction the inmates coming there that day and accepting the kind invitation of Lord and Lady Algernon Gordon Lennox. He thought they were all pleased to attend and partake of such splendid hospitality, and he asked them to accord their noble host and hostess a hearty vote of thanks for their great kindness. This was heartily responded to, and Mr. Humphris then, on behalf of the visitors, thanked Mr. Barrett and others who had assisted in seeing to the comfort of the inmates during their pleasant stay at the Castle. This was also received with great cordiality, and Mr. Barrett thanked Mr. Humphris for his kind remarks and all who had helped in the pleasures of the day. Before leaving packets of tea and sugar were given to the women, tobacco and beer to the men, and sweets to the children, and shortly before seven o'clock the work of re-loading the vehicles was commenced, and cheers were given as the party left the historic grounds. On Saturday morning Mr. Humphris, on behalf of Lady Algernon, distributed tea and sugar to the women, tobacco to the men and sweets to those inmates at the workhouse who could not attend the Castle the previous day.

Banbury Guardian 1905

FRINGE NETS.

HORN, CELLULOID,
and
FANCY COMBS.

Naumann & Co.
120, WARDOUR ST., OXFORD ST.,
LONDON, W.

Sole Agents for

MEHN'S PORTABLE

ELECTRIC

HAIR DRYER.

£3 5s. & £5 15s.
Nett.   Nett.

Messrs. Cammell's New Works.—It is announced that Messrs. Cammell, Laird and Co. have definitely decided to build their extensive iron and steel works on the Crumlyn Burrows, near Swansea. What this decision of Messrs. Cammell, Laird and Co. means to Swansea may be gauged by the statement that the firm proposes to spend £1,000,000 on the construction and equipment of the new works, and these, when completed, will give employment to 10,000 workmen. The site of the new works is the property of the Earl of Jersey, and the fact that his lordship is largely interested in the firm of Cammell, Laird and Co., has doubtless been a potent factor in its final selection. It is believed that the firm propose at once erecting several blast furnaces, and that they will import about 1,000,000 tons of iron ore a year, and turn out 100,000 tons of pig iron. The announcement has not been officially confirmed, but there is reason to believe that negotiations have now reached a stage of finality.

Labour News 1906

Hairdresser and Toilet Requisites Gazette 1909

THE RHODES' SCHOLARS AT OXFORD.

An undergraduate has written to the *Express* his experiences of the Rhodes scholars at Oxford. The public has, he says, been told a good deal of nonsense about them, especially about their isolation. He knows them well and has had their confidences and quotes several conversations to show that the foreigners and Colonials are quite at home. A muscular representative of one of the most remote American States gave a pull at his pipe, re-arranged his cushions, and thus summed up the last hour's conversation. "At Oxford you learn to live. A man keeps his body in a downy bed till ten o'clock, in snoozing comfort. After a cold bath he has a huge breakfast. After a period of torpor and smoking, he does some mental work. In the afternoon a good dose of exercise, either on the river or up at the ground—hard, healthy English sport. . Tea-time arrives, the delightful restful meal, with just a few cronies. A good dinner precedes bridge or a visit to the theatre. You men do not always do this, but you all learn to exercise your own capacities for enjoyment. And this is a better plan than our system of nine months' work and three months' slack. Better slack in company." This is, says the writer, an extreme point of view. But it proves that the man was not lonely. He had mixed with us. He appreciated the fact that the majority of undergraduates do not do a full day's work in the sense of keeping their noses in their books. Oxford life is not congenial to real study. More important lessons are learnt in seeming idleness. Another Colonial illustrated the general law of Bohemianism in term-time by the example of his professor, who is "a fussy little man, full of ideas and dodges, with the habit of leaving his cigarette ashes among my chemicals." Up in North Oxford, the land of the ladies, the "Rhodester" is a success. The real reason of this is his interesting conversation. We try to open conversation with stale criticisms of the latest novel or the most insane musical comedy. He gives the lady credit for intelligence, and starts to talk about something interesting without wasting words or inaninities. At many of the most literary and scientific houses of North Oxford you may find him interesting the guests with dissertations on abstruse subjects, though afterwards he is quite capable of pulling the family boat up the river. It would be rash to speculate as to how far Cecil Rhodes's ideas of thus uniting the Empire will be realised. It is evident that our Colonies could teach their Motherland a good deal in matters of national importance. This had been proved by certain speeches at the Union last term, where Colonials have put a plain common-sense view of the question before the House, and have driven in a nail of practical experience without any irritating epigrammatic flourishes, the favourite vice of the English juvenile orator.

Banbury Guardian 1905

A SHAW-T RESPITE.

LONDON, *December 29.*

I am informed that Mr. G. Bernard Shaw has made a New Year resolution not to write to the newspapers during the whole of 1907.

Later.

It is stated that Mr. Shaw has withdrawn his resolution in deference to the objections of his friends, who argued that he would be compelled to take to a meat diet to carry out such an act of martyrdom. He said he preferred vivisecting human beings in the Press to carving baked corpses of animals. He will go on writhing 'em.

Clarion 1907

ARTIST AND HER SALARY

Reynold's Newspaper 1907

Miss Alice Lloyd, Miss Marie Lloyd's sister, who is said to have signed a contract with Messrs. Klaw and Erlanger to tour the music halls of the United States. In five years she will earn the enormous sum of £75,000.—(Hana.)

A VETERAN BOOKSELLER.—Mr. Harvey Pearse, of Rochdale, one of our oldest subscribers, is the acknowledged senior among the Associated Booksellers. He was apprenticed at his native town of Plymouth as long ago as 1844, went to Manchester nine years later as principal assistant to one of the largest booksellers there, and thirty-six years ago started for himself at Rochdale, where he is still in daily work. In the "Rochdale Observer" he has given some interesting recollections of bookselling in a former generation. The coming of the publisher's traveller then was a great event. One of them represented about thirty firms, and travelled in his own coach, which was, as might be expected, well laden with samples. In the old days Longmans and Murray were the chief London publishers, and at that time Longmans had a great wholesale bookselling business. He recalled the issue, while he was at Manchester of the third and fourth volumes of Macaulay's History at 36s., of which his firm gave a first order of 150 copies, nearly all bespoken. Among early attempts at cheap books he remembers the "Parlour Library," which unfortunately, however, was not successful. He is a firm believer in the net system, in cheap reprints, and first editions of works at prices within the reach of the average man. At Manchester, which as a bookselling centre is said to be next to Edinburgh, three-volume novels were rarely sold except to book clubs, of which at that time there were a good many. While congratulating Mr. Pearse on his long and fortunate career we may mention that the oldest bookseller in the United Kingdom is probably Mr. S. W. Simms, of Bath, who at the great age of ninety-five still remains at the head of his business, though he does not take a very active share in its management.

Bookseller 1907

THE WELSH COLONY IN PATAGONIA.

The Rev. J. R. Jones, the pastor of the Ruabon and Cefn Calvinistic Methodist Churches, who has just returned from a preaching tour in the Welsh colony in Patagonia, where his father, the Rev. Robert Jones (Tryddyn) has for many years laboured as a Welsh missioner, gave a correspondent some impressions of his visit. He found the territory in a very flourishing condition ; almost all the farmers were doing well, and money was never so plentiful before. "A huge business," he says, "is done with 'alfalfa' (hay and seeds), wool, skins, and wheat, although there is less wheat raised of late. There is a great improvement in the shipping facilities. The Hamburg-American Company have an excellent line of steamers calling every fortnight or so from Buenos Ayres : also several Government steamers call, together with sailing vessels. All the cargo boats of the Pacific Steam Navigation Company, Liverpool, call on their way to and from the West Coast. The first batch of Chubut horses were brought over on the "Galicio" to Liverpool a fortnight ago. This is only an experiment, but Mr. D. M. Evans, of Llanrhaiadr, Montgomeryshire, is hopeful of a successful issue. In that event a regular business is very likely to be inaugurated. The Welsh find in the Germans—who are increasing rapidly in the territory—very keen competitors. Their splendid business tactics are displayed in every direction, and it is to be hoped that the great and prosperous Chubut Mercantile Company—the largest and wealthiest Welsh Company in the world—will show no signs of relaxation in this most critical time, but will fight on with increased sagacity and tact. It is a fight for supremacy in a country which has been opened to the world through the hard labour of the Welsh in the past, and which, according to the leading men out there, has a bright future before it. The Welsh could be masters of the situation if they liked, as the advantages are on their side. The population is rapidly increasing, and the Welsh number about 5,000.

London Welshman **1906**

PRIVATE TUTORSHIP OR MASTERSHIP desired; age 30; unmarried; long experience; good disciplinarian; conversational French; athletic; Socialist and Rationalist.— S. R., 406, Kennington Road, S.E.

Clarion **1907**

EATON SOCON.

While working a circular saw on the estate of Mr. W. A. Briscoe, Longstowe, Mr. Jno. Bedford, carpenter, residing in Eaton Ford, had the misfortune to cut off the top joints of the first two fingers on his left hand, the third finger being also badly cut. He was taken at once to Addenbrooke's Hospital, where his injured fingers were promptly attended to. Unfortunately it is not long since Mr. Bedford lost the tops of two fingers on his other hand.

Ampthill and District News 1908

Reynolds Newspaper 1907

The Peers and the Old Age Pensions Bill.

By a vote of 123 to 16, that is by a majority of 107, the House of Lords has agreed to the second reading of the Pensions Bill. The Peers have followed not their wishes but their discretion. To reject the Bill might have made their House more objectionable, and would have certainly distressed the hopes of Unionists at the polls. So the Lords took Mr. Balfour's advice, smothered their consciences, and voted as he directed them. But they indulged in much preliminary wailing. It was a spectacle to move tears in gods and men to behold one Peer arguing that the passing of the Bill would demoralise the working classes and do away with thrift. It moved mild men to satire as they listened to Lord Cromer, who has only just got a grant of £50,000 from the public purse, lamenting the necessity of giving five shillings a week to tired old toilers who manage to live to be seventy years of age. And Lord Rosebery was acutely sensible of the fact that the money for these pensions would come from some hitherto untapped source, and in any case would be absorbed from its preferable purpose of purchasing armaments. His speech undoes for ever any chance of his return from the Conservative side. As a Liberal he is no more. He opposes Home Rule for Ireland, he resists land legislation for Scotland, an I grieves, while he votes for them, that these Old Age Pensions will probably be paid by increased drafts on the resources of unearned income. Why cannot the poor earn their own pensions ? It is outrageous to draw the money for them from the stores of millionaires who never earn anything. Lord Ripon, we are glad to note, bluntly told him to vote against the Bill. But the interest of the House of Lords was paramount, and to save the legislative status of the Peers, the Lords generously consented to accept the Old Age Pensions Bill for the poor.

Catholic Times **1908**

HEROIC HOTEL PORTER.

DRAMATIC SCENE AT STRAND FIRE

Thrilling deeds of heroism took place during a serious fatal fire which caused much excitement early yesterday morning in Surrey-street, Strand. The scene of the outbreak was at Brook's Hotel, an unpretentious building of four floors, frequented, for the most part, by tradesmen, and particularly by visitors from the North.

The fire was discovered by one of the visitors shortly after four o'clock, but it had doubtless been burning for some time previously.

Exciting Rescue Scenes.

A man, named Walter Horsley, a night watchman at the adjoining Strand Station now in course of erection of the Piccadilly and Brompton Railway, lent a valuable hand in the work of rescuing the unfortunate inmates.

Meanwhile, the proprietor, Mr. H. G. E. Goult, aroused the other inmates, all of whom were able to escape in their night attire from the back of the premises.

The staff consisted of a porter named Jack Payne, a cook, and two housemaids. As soon as Payne was roused from sleep, he rushed off, regardless of his own safety, to the women's apartments on the top floor. He succeeded in getting the cook and one of the housemaids safely out of the house, and would have faced certain death in search of Rosie King, the other servant, had not he been forcibly restrained.

Teaching a nature study class at an Elementary School, April 1908.

LOCAL & DISTRICT NEWS
ELGIN.

In Elgin the dulness of trade during 1907 is, generally speaking, without a parallel in the course of the last score of years at least. The building trade, on which so large a percentage of the community is dependent, has been deplorably slack. The only works of any extent which have given employment during the year have been the additions to Dr Gray's Hospital, the Joint Smallpox Hospital, and the Sewage Purification Works. The new block at the hospital, which is expected to cost upwards of £6000, is practically complete so far as the mason work is concerned, but most of the other tradesmen have yet to fulfil the major part of their contracts. Three stories in height, the additions will provide space for 28 additional beds, besides augmenting the general domestic accommodation. The Smallpox Hospital which has been completed at Hardhillock is a stone building of simple construction, erected at a cost of about £1000. The Sewage Purification Works, for which Mr James Newlands, West Road, is contractor, are now well advanced, and it is hoped that the system—the total filtering capacity of which is 500,000 gallons per 24 hours—will be in operation in the spring. The estimated cost is about £5000.

The general business of the burgh has only been of average briskness. Shopkeepers, it is true, have done fairly well in comparison with tradesmen, and in this connection housewives have numerous complaints to make about the rise in price of certain articles of domestic use. The increased cost of coal, in particular, is a fruitful source of grumbling, and now that milk has gone up since the new year opened—on account, it is said, of the increased cost of feeding stuffs—housewives will hardly feel surprised should other articles of diet follow suit.

Northern Scot 1908

OLD-AGE PENSIONS
AT BIDEFORD.

150 PENSIONERS ENTERTAINED.

Speech by Mr. Soares, M.P.

At Bideford on Friday, the inauguration of Old-Age Pensions was celebrated by a public tea and social evening in the Public Rooms. For the admirable arrangements the Men's and Women's Liberal Associations were jointly responsible, with the respective Hon. Secs., Mr. F. Slee (Westleigh) and Mrs. Colwill, and the successful function will long be remembered with pleasure by all those who were privileged to attend. For the occasion, the walls and ceilings of the Public Rooms were bedecked with flags and banners, whilst the platform was treated with evergreens and foliage plants and flowers adorned the tables, the building presenting a very pretty appearance. Mrs E. J. Soares, of Upcott (who was accompanied by her husband, the popular member for the Division) presided at the capital tea, to which between 700 and 800 sat down, there being two sittings. Through the kindness of the Committee and friends, about 150 Old-Age Pensioners of the district were presented with complimentary tickets, and practically the whole availed themselves of the opportunity to be present. The leaders of Liberalism in a wide district also attended. The ladies who poured tea were Mesdames Banbury, Wilson, Bellew, F. Heywood, Clarke, Boyle, H. Cox, A. D. Adams, Ash, Bennett, H. Heywood, Tucker, Vincent, Sanguin, Lamerton, Davey, Jewell, and Miss Cadd.

*   *   *

The persistent influence of a comparatively small but growing number of citizens who are denied remunerative occupation seems to hypnotise important sections of the community who in ordinary life and in their private affairs are sensible and clear-headed. Both the Majority and Minority reports of the Royal Commission on Unemployment and Poor Law show confusion of thought amounting to positive illusion. If the essence of reform is getting rid of the unfit, then the first and principal factor of British progress is not the increase of taxes, the provision of pensions, or insurance against unemployment, but the factor of selection for parenthood. All the administrative reforms in the world may be passed unanimously and endowed lavishly, but unemployment will continue to increase so long as the increase of the unemployable is endowed, fostered, and encouraged. Unemployment is described by the Minority Committee as "a disease," but the Majority Commissioners notwithstanding declare in set terms that there is not work enough to go round; that under-employment is chronic, affecting tens of thousands of men at all seasons and in all years. Was hungry and defenceless Friday's plight on Robinson Crusoe's island an obscure "disease," or was it one of those chances and changes from which none is exempt in this mortal life?

Faith in the Untrue.

*   *   *

If the Minority's diagnosis of the "disease" of unemployment be correct, surely the way to cure the patient is not to administer a double dose of the poison that has laid him on his back. If there is not enough work to go round, why encourage improvident marriage by temporary measures of afforestation, new highways, or land reclamation? These operations will have no permanent effect other than to increase the number of children born into the world who must either perish like ephemera in the frost or add to the existing burdens of the fit. There is no escape from this dilemma. When the Children's Charter was passed with general joy benefit undoubtedly accrued to the existing child life of Britain; but the bare fact that a Children's Charter was necessary proved the existence of swarms of bad parents. These parents are not punished; they are relieved of responsibility by the State. Other parents in thousands consequently shirk their responsibilities. I recently investigated a certain Black Book kept by the Salvation Army at an institution of theirs devoted to the rescue and succour of little children, chiefly girls, who are the victims of their parents' ungovernable anger or insensate lust. On the day on which I visited the home, which is known as "The Nest," the newspapers were full of the wickedness and cruelty of the Belgians on the Congo. Considering the marked increase in the number of British fathers who criminally assault their girl children, and considering the amount of British brutality that is only partially kept in check by a powerful Society for the Prevention of Cruelty to Children, the question of taking Belgium to task for alleged ill-treatment of black men in West Africa is one that might be safely postponed until criminal and unfit British parentage is taken in hand.

Referee 1909

One of our contemporaries tells the following story:—"Just as the barber had lathered the customer, a man with the latest betting news entered the little shop, and the operator left his customer to discuss turf matters in the back room. After two minutes' waiting the victim, with the phlegm of the true Lancashire man, wiped off the soap and put on his hat. Twenty yards along the street he entered another barber's shop. 'Dun yo shave folk 'ere?' he quietly asked. 'Of coorse we dun, mestur,' replied the proprietor. 'Oh,' said the caller, taking the chair, 'they only lather 'em at Thompson's up street.'"

Hairdresser and Toilet Requisites Gazette 1909

North Devon Journal 1909

1910–1919

*The World and
his Wife
1910*

PAYMENT FOR WIVES

Should wives be paid? is the obvious question which occurs to the mind after having read of Sir Charles McLaren's drastic proposals in the House of Commons to secure for wives a share in the property of their husbands.

In brief, the proposals are to the effect that a wife who devotes her whole time to housekeeping and the care of the children shall, provided she has not received any other personal allowance, have a claim on her husband during life, and on his estate after death, for a sum calculated on a scale not exceeding the wages of a housekeeper in her station of life. Should a dissolution of the marriage or separation be obtained, it is suggested that a wife shall be entitled to payment for past services on this scale, should payment not have been previously made, and wives who work jointly in the same business as their husbands shall be regarded as partners.

Among other proposals contained in this "women's charter" are that all universities or institutions deriving money from the State shall be open to women; that women should have votes, and that brutal husbands should be more severely punished.

Gownsman 1910

Printer's Error.

We regret that by an accident in going to press at the last moment three lines were misplaced in Miss Kenny's article last week on "A Forged Canto in Dante. The paragraph, beginning at the bottom of the first column of page 291, thus became unintelligible. The passage should have read:—

The intervening Canto XI. opens with Dante and Vergil standing on the edge of a high rocky rampart, where there is a tomb inscribed: "I hold Pope Anastasius, whom Photinus led astray." Here Vergil calls a halt, till they shall become accustomed to the stench (puzzo) from below. But it was the Emperor Anastasius, not the Pope, who was led into heresy; and Righetti cannot reconcile this confusion with Dante's learning. Again, he finds "puzzo" (smell produced by corruption) incompatible with the "lezzo" (smell produced by neglect of cleanliness) of Canto X. And he thinks the tomb for a single man fits ill with the more than a thousand ("piú di mille") in Farinata's tomb among the Epicureans (x. 118).

Babyland 1910

The Postman as a Conveyor of Infectious Diseases. It has often been a matter of wonder in careful households where the children can have contracted the measles, and apparently now we may look to our letters as a possible source of infection, for according to a report of a Medical Officer of Health a postman is not taken off duty when his wife or any member of his family is suffering from the disease.

It appears the General Post Office has a rule: "That no Post Office employee can be absent from duty on account of his coming from a household infected with measles." The doctor pointed out that a postman whose clothing was infected with measles germs was a kind of peripatic incubator on a wet day, when wearing his regulation oilskin cape, and the recipients of letters would no doubt receive their quota of germs. Measles could not be considered trivial when the number of deaths from the disease in England and Wales alone had varied, during a period of thirty or forty years, from 6,000 to 14,000 in a year. Publicity may perhaps succeed in changing this rule.

TOO OLD AT FIFTY?

As representative of medicine, we may choose the veteran woman doctor, Elizabeth Garrett Anderson, who was born in 1836, and elected to the first School Board for London in 1870.

Photo by Illustrations Bureau.

Dr. Garrett Anderson, the veteran woman doctor, was born in 1836. She holds high medical degrees, and has had a most distinguished career. She has been twice Mayor of Aldeburgh.

Pearson's Magazine 1910

GREAT SCHEME OF INSURANCE.

HELP WHEN UNEMPLOYED, ILL, AND IN MOTHERHOOD.

A FUND TO FIGHT CONSUMPTION.

GOVERNMENT BILL WELCOMED BY ALL PARTIES IN THE HOUSE OF COMMONS.

"Then none was for a party, then all were for the State."
—*Macaulay.*

People 1911

The Government has now made known the details of its great scheme for grappling with the twin evils—sickness and unemployment. Never in the history of the country have such far-reaching proposals been laid before Parliament as those embodied in the Bill introduced by the Chancellor of the Exchequer.

As outlined by Mr. George they mark a new era in the social life of the nation, and all parties have extended to the scheme a hearty welcome.

Fifteen millions of people are affected by the scheme. The cost will be 24 millions on the first year it is in operation, and of this huge sum the State will contribute two millions and a half.

The Government proposals also embrace the endowment of sanatoria for consumption and State aid in maternity.

The Chancellor's Speech.

On returning to the Commons after his long absence through illness, Mr. George received a cordial welcome from all quarters of the house. On introducing the Government Bill the Chancellor spoke for two hours and 20 minutes, and before sitting down appealed to all parties to assist him in making the measure a success. "Fashion it, strengthen it, improve it," he pleaded; and the House assented. What more opportune time, he urged, to fight "the scourge of consumption, the shadow of poverty, of sickness, the tragedy of our poor." It was Coronation year. The Premiers from Overseas were coming. Let Parliament undertake this task to combat "the pestilence that walketh in darkness and the destruction that wasteth at noonday." It was a House of friends that cheered him as he sat down.

RAILWAY UNREST.

WILL THERE BE TROUBLE DURING THE HOLIDAYS?

Within the last 24 hours the situation in connection with the general unrest amongst railwaymen has assumed such a serious aspect as to give rise to the fear amongst the men's responsible leaders that we are on the eve of one of the biggest railway strikes ever known in the United Kingdom. The danger points are at Liverpool and Hull. In the one case the discontent exists amongst the men employed in the goods department of the L. and Y. Rly., and in the other the trouble arises from the fact that the men on the North Eastern at Hull, who have been in a state of considerable unrest for some time past, are determined to decline to handle goods from the G.C. Rly. because of a dispute in which that company is involved with its workmen at New Holland. In both cases meetings of the men of all grades will be held to-night, and one of the possibilities of the situation is that to-morrow morning will witness a general strike of the men on these two important lines, with a consequent dislocation of the Bank Holiday traffic. Seen yesterday afternoon, Mr. J. H. Thomas, M.P. for Derby, and Assistant Secretary of the Amalgamated Society of Railway Servants, admitted that he could not deny the gravity of the situation, and added: "All this trouble the railway companies have brought on themselves. They have been sitting on the safety valve ever since the conciliation boards were set up, and all the time the steam of discontent has been rising, and an explosion seems imminent."

People 1911

News of the World 1912

GETTING DRENCHED FOR A LIVING.

In the great water spectacle "The Sands of Dee" at the Bristol Hippodrome the actress who plays the part of Mary Stephen gets drenched three times a day, as she is tied to a post while the tide gradually covers her. (1) Basil Dean, the villain, threatens to turn out Rube Stephen unless his granddaughter will marry him. (2) Basil ties Mary Stephen to the post and leaves her to drown. (3) Rube laments the selling up of his cottage when Bill arrives and offers to pay the £100. (4) Polly removes the gag, but cannot untie the ropes. (5) The waters engulf Mary. (6) Left to drown. The tide is gradually rising.—(Daily Mirror photographs.)

Daily Mirror 1913

LONDON LETTER.

[FROM OUR LONDON CORRESPONDENT.]
The Constitutional Club, Wednesday.

In the Commons.

To-day, interest centres in the House of Commons, where, as I write, Mr. H. W. Forster is speaking, on behalf of the Opposition, to his amendment on the motion for the third reading of the National Insurance Bill. Mr. Forster is in fine oratorical form, and the tape machine tells me that he is not sparing the Government, but is rubbing it in in a way that should make them squirm— though I fear that with such a conscience-less lot as they have proved themselves to be in regard to this particular Bill sarcasm is as water on a duck's back. The amendment in question reads as follows:—

That, while approving the objects of national insurance, this House is of opinion that under Part I. of the Bill public funds and individual contributions will not be used to the best advantage of those most closely affected; and that, as the Bill has been neither adequately discussed in this House nor fully explained to the country, and would in its present form be unequal in its operation, steps should be taken to enable further consideration of Part I. to be resumed next Session, and in the meanwhile to have the draft regulations published.

It remains to be seen what affect this amendment—backed as it is with the full weight of Unionist opinion and indignation—will have upon the House. It is now an open secret that not a few of the Members on the Liberal side are seriously alarmed at the protest against the Bill which is being made in all parts of the country; and it is just possible, therefore, that when it comes to the vote at half-past ten to-night the majority may decide that it shall be further debated and amended next Session.

Bucks Herald 1911

DISCOVERY OF COAL IN NORTH BUCKS.

Considerable interest is being aroused in that part of North Bucks which adjoins Oxfordshire by the apparent discovery of coal. Several years ago the late Mr. A. W. Itter, of Peterborough, purchased some land from the late Rev. Mr. Pigott, of Grendon Underwood, for brickworks. They are close to Calvert station on the Great Central Railway on the south side. A large quantity of bricks have been manufactured, but a great drawback has been the scarcity of water. Finally it was decided to make borings for water, and on reaching a depth of 400ft. the men came across coal gas, which burst into flame, illuminating the whole district. It was then decided to sink another borehole on the north side of the railway station. This is on Thornhill Farm, occupied by Mr. D. Harris, and on the Claydon estate, belonging to Sir Harry Verney, M.P. They encountered 40ft. of water, and are now at 120ft. depth, on solid rock, the striking of which is plainly discernible from the public road. They are working at both borings day and night, and there is a rumour that borings are to be commenced near Verney Junction and on other portions of the Claydon estate, as Sir Harry Verney and the executors of the late Mr. Itter are convinced that coal will be found. Many years back, it is said, a seam of coal was discovered to the south of the Claydon estate. About thirty men are now employed on the borings.

Bucks Herald 1911

Home Secretary Winston Churchill with Chancellor of the Exchequer
David Lloyd George, Budget Day 1910.

A MYSTERY OF MONEY-LENDING AND BORROWING.

THE MORNING'S BATCH OF LETTERS OFFERING TO LEND YOU ANYTHING UP TO £10,000 WITHOUT ANY SORT OF SECURITY

WHEN YOU TRY TO BORROW HALF-A-CROWN

"IT'S ONLY TILL TOMORROW!"

W. K. HASELDEN.

How is it that, whereas hundreds of obliging persons offer daily by letter to lend the hard-up thousands of pounds, the said hard-up person finds, when it comes to the point, that he cannot even borrow half a crown?

Daily Mirror 1913

WORK OF WOMEN

Kew Garden Teahouse Burned Down.

TWO ARRESTS.

THE DESTRUCTIVENESS OF THE SUFFRAGETTES.

The tea-house at Kew Gardens was burned down early this morning, and it is supposed its destruction represents a further display of violence on the part of the Suffragettes. The tea-rooms were in the hands of the workmen in preparation for the re-opening at Easter.

The men would have resumed work at 7.0 o'clock this morning. At 3.30, however, the rooms were discovered to be on fire. The Richmond Fire Brigade was notified and proceeded to the scene.

Cotton wads soaked with paraffin were discovered in the vicinity. Two women were arrested. It was impossible to save any part of the building.

We have blown up the house of the Chancellor of the Exchequer. The authorities need not look for the women who have done what they did last night. I personally accept full responsibility for it, and if sent to penal servitude will "hunger strike." —Mrs Pankhurst at Cardiff last night.

North Eastern Daily Gazette 1913

ORANGE SELLERS "MOVED ON."

Since Day Of Nell Gwynne They Have Not Been Disturbed.

Orange sellers of Drury-lane, whose predecessors have plied their trade there continuously since the days of Nell Gwynne and Charles the Second, are being "moved on" by the police.

It is no longer the fashionable theatre-goers who buy oranges outside Drury-lane Theatre, and the modern orange-seller is no longer young and attractive, but old and poor.

One white-haired woman said with tears in her eyes to the *Daily Sketch*: "I've been 'ere over 47 years and me mother and aunt was 'ere before me. Wot 'arm do we do, I should like to know?"

Another woman who has sold oranges in Drury-lane since she was twelve years old told the *Daily Sketch* that before the order to move them on came, she was in the habit of selling 200 oranges in a day and night, but since the order, she hadn't sold more than ten a day.

The women are not allowed to stand still or approach the crowds and the chance of selling oranges is reduced to a minimum.

The Drury-lane management had nothing to do with the veto.

Daily Mirror 1913

Mr. Lloyd George has written a letter to Friday's papers in which he indignantly repudiates the monstrous accusation brought against him by Mr. Keir Hardie. Speaking at Norwich, Mr. Keir Hardie declared that workers who were putting in eighty-four hours a week had been "maligned and insulted, and the lying word—on the authority of Mr. Lloyd George—had gone round the world that the British working classes were a set of drunken wasters." Mr. Lloyd George has, of course, an easy task to show that not only did he never say anything of the kind, but that he was most careful to guard himself against misinterpretation, and used words which showed clearly that he did not mean to arraign a whole class, but only a minority.

Spectator 1915

The Wolseley Motor Company's works at Alderley Park, Birmingham, in 1914.

KING'S LONDON HOME.

BUCKINGHAM PALACE FRONT TO BE TRANSFORMED.

Buckingham Palace, the ugliest royal residence in Europe, as it has been called, is about to have a new face, and if all goes well, the work should be completed in 12 months' time. The new facade will be modelled from designs by Sir Aston Webb, who has been responsible for the general scheme of the surrounding improvements, of which the beautiful Queen Victoria Memorial is the principal feature. Not only is the design of the east front of the palace to be very considerably altered, but the new facade is to be built of Portland stone, which has been proved to be the best stone for the London climate. Sir Aston Webb's new design does not affect the palace structurally; it merely, if one may so express it, puts a new skin on the east front of the building. The principal feature of the new front will be 24 Corinthian columns rising from bases on a level with the first floor windows to a level with the windows of the top floor. Apart from the addition of these 24 Corinthian columns, the next most important change will be in the roof line. The ornate work on the roof directly above the archway in the centre will be removed and a plain, level stonework substituted. The remainder of the wall-front will be raised a little and all the chimneys will be concealed. Although the design is a considerable change from the existing front, it is by no means a complete transformation; but the introduction of Portland stone will be the chief agent in making the palace look like a new building. The alterations will be carried out during the absence of the Court, after the next London season. All the stones will be prepared and numbered in two London stone yards, and no chiselling will take place near the palace. It is expected that the men will have to work night and day to get the new front up in the short time at the contractor's disposal. The stone is already arriving, in two and three ton blocks, from Portland quarries. The present east face of the palace is from the designs of Blore, the architect, the remaining fronts to the inner quadrangle being by Nash. The architectural style of the new facade is described as English renaissance.

News of the World 1912

THE COAL STRIKE.

THE MINIMUM WAGES BILL.

COLLIERS TO BALLOT ON A SETTLEMENT.

DISTURBANCES IN NORTH WALES.

STARVATION IN THE POTTERIES.

THE HISTORY OF AN EVENTFUL WEEK.

A week of deep anxiety closes with a more hopeful feeling. It is impossible in the space at our disposal to do more than indicate in outline what has transpired since last week. On Monday the negotiations between master and men, the Government intervening, continued, and the Minimum Wages Bill was held up pending the issue. The men fought hard to have actual figures introduced into the Bill—in addition to the principle of a minimum wage, which the Government recognised. This could only be arranged by consent between the parties, and the masters flatly refused to give such consent.

On Tuesday, amid intense interest and with profound sorrow, the Prime Minister announced in the House the failure of the negotiations and the intention of the Government to proceed with the Minimum Wages Bill. The House sat till a late hour and carried the third reading by a large majority and amid cheers. It was immediately taken to the House of Lords, and between 2 and 3 a.m. on Wednesday it received a first reading, and before this issue of "The Chronicle" reaches its readers it will probably be the law of the land.

In the course of its progress through the House of Commons one of the miner M.P.'s said he put his patriotism above his trades unionism and would support the Bill—or at least use his influence to get it accepted.

Mr. Lloyd George, replying to another Labour M.P., who said the Bill was unacceptable, declared that all that the colliers asked for, when they went out, was the recognition of the principle of a minimum wage, and that the Government Bill gave them.

Meantime, the railways are curtailing traffic, railwaymen are being suspended by the thousand, the funds of nearly all the Trades Unions are exhausted, and starvation—actually from hunger—exists to-day in Crewe and throughout the Potteries, where thousands of men, women and children are suffering from lack of food and the means to procure food.

Chester Chronicle 1912

Mother and Home 1916

Masked clerks march from the Temple steps to Hyde Park for a rally,
on 13 September 1913.

THE COTTON WAR.

£300,000 A WEEK LOST IN WAGES.

The great lock-out in the Lancashire cotton trade has begun. One hundred and sixty thousand weavers in North and North-East Lancashire will be idle onward until the dispute is ended. The primary cause of the dispute is the fact that two non-unionists at Accrington and one at Great Harwood, Blackburn, have refused to accept membership of the Weavers' Association. The Master Cotton Spinners' Federation decided that all spinning mills affected by the dispute should be closed on Saturday, Monday, and Tuesday, commencing with next week. This will bring up the number of workpeople affected to over 300,000. Mr. Jno. Taylor, secretary of the North and North-East Lancashire Cotton Spinners and Manufacturers' Association, stated that the lock-out was being loyally carried out in the federated mills all through the area. No efforts had been made in the direction of mediation, nor had anything been heard of peace proposals, and the talk of Sir Geo. Askwith being invited to intervene was, he declared in vigorous phraseology "all rot."

People 1911

SHEFFIELD CHIEF CONSTABLE'S ANNUAL REPORT.

The annual report of the Chief Constable of Sheffield—the first issued by Major Hall Dalwood since his transfer from Leicester—is full of interest, and we regret that the exigencies of space will only allow us to publish brief extracts from it.

The first passage which calls for notice is an explanation of the methods employed in the Chief Clerk's Department for dealing with the heavy correspondence and complicated accounts. During last year 4,395 letters were written, 2,303 accounts received, and 700 despatched, and this is only a portion of the work undertaken by this department. The payment and despatch of pensions monthly alone involves three days' work per month for one man. In order to cope with this work it is necessary to employ the most modern office methods.

Office Equipment on Modern Lines.

This, says Major Hall Dalwood, is "especially noticeable in the compilation of the Record of Service Sheets, and in the Stores Department, both of which are kept and recorded on the 'loose-leaf' or 'Kalamazette' principle. This System obviates the laborious copying of documents, reports, and records of service, as the leaf can be detached and placed with other documents referring to the same subject. It will be adopted as soon as practicable throughout the Force. Every letter is indexed on the Card Index System, and filed so that it can be found at a moment's notice. During the year 5,274 new items of correspondence were indexed in this Department alone."

WOMAN POLICE INSPECTOR.

FIRST APPOINTMENT IN ENGLAND.

On the 30th ult., the Liverpool Watch Committee appointed Mrs. Hughes, matron of the main Bridewell, to be an Inspector in the Criminal Investigation Department of the city. This is stated to be the first appointment of the kind in England.

Her main duties will be the taking of evidence in charges concerning women and children. It is felt that women will more readily give statements to a member of their own sex than to men. Mrs. Hughes may also be sent out to obtain evidence in cases concerning women, but as the appointment is an experimental one her duties have not yet been strictly defined.

Mrs. Hughes is a widow about thirty-five years of age, and for two years as matron of the main Bridewell has been in charge of a number of wardresses. In other spheres of Corporation work she is also well known, her experience in this way being considerable, and likely to be of much practical use in her new duties. Before becoming matron of the main bridewell she was an assistant sanitary inspector, and in this capacity acquired valuable knowledge.

She has had the superintendence of all grades of female offenders at the main bridewell, and is well posted in the undercurrents of the lower strata in which they move. She knows alike their weakness, temptations, and their criminality.

An office is being prepared for Mrs. Hughes at the Chief Police Station in Liverpool, and on being transferred to the Head Detective Staff, she will have a telephone of her own, a clerk, and a typewriter, and she will be in direct communication with the Chief Constable.

Her new duties were defined by the Chief Constable in an interview with a "Daily News" representative. "Her principal work," he said, "will be the investigation of cases in which women and girls are concerned. She will not be sworn in as a member of the Force, and will not therefore be required to take the oath, nor will she be called upon to make arrests. She will make inquiries into these delicate cases and examine witnesses. It is obviously an easier thing for a woman to obtain evidence in cases of this kind than it is for a man."

Police Review 1914

Battle of the Somme.

During Tuesday night there was heavy fighting on the British front, and at certain points our troops made progress. In the course of yesterday the fighting, at times of the hand-to-hand order, was also continuous. It mostly consisted, however, in local struggles for the possession of particular points; and it resulted in our troops advancing slightly in certain sectors and losing none of the ground they had gained. The total number of prisoners now exceeds 9000.

Aberdeen Weekly Journal 1916

Police Review 1914

Making shells at Vickers, 1915.

The *Times* of Monday published from a neutral correspondent a curious account of how the Germans, as he has some reason to believe, are manufacturing a kind of "nebel-bomb," which is to be dropped from Zeppelins in order to produce artificial fog. The bomb is burst by a fuse at a regulated distance from the ground, and immediately a large space of air is filled with a fog which would hide the Zeppelin. One's first reflection is that such bombs are properly a weapon of defence, not of attack. To deliver an attack airships must risk themselves, as our gallant airmen have risked themselves and their machines when they swooped down to within two or three hundred feet of the ground in order to bomb with precision some point of military importance. If the Germans screen their Zeppelins to prevent them from being hit by anti-aircraft guns, they will also prevent themselves from aiming their bombs with any attempt at accuracy. Of course to the practitioners of frightfulness accuracy does not very much matter. All the Germans would want to know was that their fog-screened airships were floating above houses. It has been said that every German professor of science spends his day trying to invent some means of injuring England. That does not seem to be far from the truth. But, after all, the winds may serve England well as they did in Elizabeth's time. It is strange that in these days, when machinery seemed to have made us able finally to ignore the winds, we should once more be watching them as closely and anxiously as Nelson did when a shift of wind meant the triumph or failure of all his plans. Winds with some east in them bring the poison-gases drifting irresistibly across our lines in Flanders. But the same wind would make the crews of the Zeppelins anxious lest they should not be able to return from a raid on England. Winds with some west in them blow the gas back in the faces of the Germans, but they would cause no anxiety to the Zeppelins. If only they were not too strong to prevent the Zeppelins from reaching England, they would make the return journey easy.

Spectator 1915

Photo by Hills & Saunders.

THOSE IN AUTHORITY.

Mr. E. PERCIVAL SMITH (Gonville and Caius College),
President of the Union.

He is amazingly agile with his feet, and Caius gave him his Rugger Cap in recognition of the fact : unfortunately he overworked them, so they have had to desert football boots in favour of a wonderful pair of patent leather shoes, in which they sit every Tuesday night and beam upon the assembled politicians.

Last term he did five minutes' honest work, and took a very reputable classical degree as the result. He then decided that he really must work for a History Tripos, so he became President of all the societies he could think of and Secretary of all the ones he could not. Amongst others, the New Carlton and the Peace and War Society owe their present prosperity largely to him.

Granta
1913

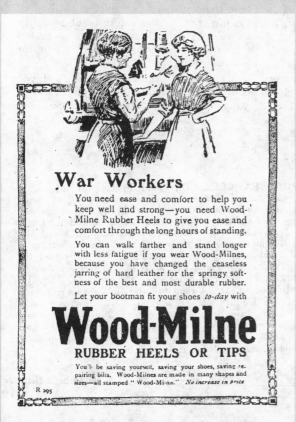
Mother and Home
1916

Pall Mall
Gazette
1915

Spectator
1915

We are very glad to be able to record the growing success of the new Welsh Guards. The life of the regiment formally began last Saturday, when more than five hundred men recruited for the Grenadiers took up their quarters at the White City as the nucleus of the Welsh Guards. On Monday, which was St. David's Day, the Welsh Guards were on duty at Buckingham Palace for the first time. Some of the spectators wore the rival badges of the regiment—the leek, the daffodil, and the red dragon on a white ground. The new regiment marched to St. James's Palace playing that magnificent marching tune, "Men of Harlech." On Wednesday it was announced that it had been authoritatively settled that the badge of the regiment was to be the leek. The dragon will be borne on the King's standard, and "Cymru am Byth" ("Wales for Ever") is to be the regimental motto.

WOMEN PESTS AT ABERGELE

Abergele Visitor
1916

Police-Constable W. H. Williams, Pensarn, gave evidence as follows :—"At 9-30 last night I was on duty on the St. Asaph road, near Kinmel Camp, accompanied by Special - Constable Thomas Leigh. Having watched prisoners for some time, I saw them stopping soldiers on the road. By Tai Tertyn Cottages we came up to them. They were then with seven soldiers. On seeing us they went away and picked up with two other soldiers. We again followed them, and eventually got up to them. They were then with the two soldiers by themselves. I asked prisoner Fanny Jones what she was doing there that time of the night, and she replied that she was out for a walk, adding that she was a native of Colwyn Bay, and had no home in Abergele. Prisoner Whittaker I knew as a native of this town. I took both of them away and locked them up." That was the evidence in chief, and witness continued :—"I may add, your worships, that Fanny Jones has been down in the vicinity of the camp for a long time, and she is one of the women against whom so many complaints have been made in various quarters. The Camp, for observation purposes, is very awkwardly situated, being partly in Flintshire and partly in Denbighshire. Fanny Jones has been about there for many months, including the whole of the summer. On Saturday night I saw her on Rhuddlan-road with seven or eight men. We have tried our best to get her to reform, but all to no purpose. She is known by the soldiers as 'Fanny Fourpence.' Special-constable T. Leigh and myself have also cautioned Susie Whittaker several times."

Special-constable T. Leigh, having been sworn, said :—" I have heard the evidence of P.C. Williams, in whose company I have been for three months, and I corroborate every word he has said. We have warned these two women several times."

Police-Sergeant Worthington said that he had cautioned Susie Whittaker and had called at her house and tried his best to get her to change her mode of life. He asked the magistrates for substantial convictions. The officer added that Fanny Jones was convicted at Conway in August, 1914.

The Chairman : I may say that it is most unpleasant for us to sit here to listen to cases of this kind. But we are here to do justice, not only according to the law, but in the interests of morality as well. Fanny Jones must go to prison for a month, and Susannah Whittaker for fourteen days.

Mr. Pierce : And take warning; if you come before us again it will go bad with you. Your conduct has been shocking.

STAFFORDSHIRE.
FARMERS HANDICAPPED BY LABOUR SHORTAGE.

Staffordshire farmers have done everything that lay in their power to carry out the recommendation of the Board of Agriculture that, to meet any deficiency in over-sea supplies of grain consequent on the war, they should put more land under wheat. Unhappily they have not been able to comply with the request to do anything like the extent they desired. The reason for this is that they have been greatly handicapped by the scarcity of agricultural labour. The young men have gone to the front, leaving behind the men unfit for military service to carry on the work of the farms, with the consequence that the farmers have had to get along as well as they could. Notwithstanding this serious handicap, the farmers have done well in the circumstances of the times. Many of them have sown more wheat this year, but enquiries made at Stafford go to show that the extra wheat acreage is not of any great extent. One farmer is making arrangements for bringing into use all the labour-saving machinery he can, and if other farmers are driven to the same determination there should be good business in agricultural implement manufacture.

*Crewe
Chronicle*
1915

LIVERPOOL PARCELS.—On Good Friday an interesting event took place at this office, all the postmen on duty being gathered together to honour our comrade, Mr. J. W. Morrison, on his retirement from the service after having served for forty-one years. Mr. Valentine, on behalf of the branch, asked Mr. Morrison to accept a case of pipes and an umbrella. He also presented Mrs. Morrison with an umbrella, and expressed the pleasure it gave him to make the presentation, seeing that he had worked with Mr. Morrison for over thirty years. Mr. W. Potter ably backed up Mr. Valentine, and in a few well-chosen words stated the feelings of the branch. Mr. Morrison, in a nice speech, thanked the branch for the gifts, and Mrs. Morrison also said a few words. We hope that Mr. Morrison will long be spared to smoke the pipe of peace and to enjoy the pension that he so richly deserves. Good old Joe !

Postman's Gazette
1919

Mother and Home 1916

LABOUR NEWS.

WOMEN'S EARNINGS.

Can a woman earn more than £3 a week in a business office? If she can there will soon be opportunities for her to prove it. At present women complain that the employers will not give them a chance in the higher paid and more responsible branches of the business. Very soon the drafting of Lord Derby's older classes into the Army will bring the need and the opportunity.

"Men have very exaggerated ideas of the importance of their work," said one of the new recruits to the business world. "They have wrapped it up in so much mystery that a woman is naturally a little afraid when she undertakes it. I thought I should make mistakes when I began, but I comforted myself with the knowledge that my mistakes could not be worse than those of any beginner, and I have since learned that they have actually been fewer than the man who formerly held this position.

"Women are a little afraid of themselves. When they get more confidence they will naturally take the better positions. If a woman can drive a car surely she has sufficient courage to manage a handful of men and girls in a bank or insurance office?"

MUNITION SLACKERS PLAYING CARDS AND SLEEPING.

At Barrow Munitions Tribunal on Tuesday, Messrs. Vickers brought charges against various workmen of absenting themselves from work, leaving work before time, and sleeping and playing cards during working hours. It was stated that the men who were engaged in shell departments were in the habit of leaving off work half an hour before the proper time in order to change their clothing and get to the gates before the buzzer sounded. This was a serious matter where so many thousands were employed, involving a large reduction in the output of munitions. Altogether it meant a loss of days or even weeks.

The Chairman warned the men to stick to their jobs until the proper time for knocking off, and said the penalties would be imposed in future.

Several men discovered sleeping were fined 10s. or 20s.

The Chairman remarked that the mischief of all the slacking was that men were getting in some cases £3 a week more than usual, and were more independent. They should remember their pals at the front, where if a man was found asleep when on guard he would be shot.

Crewe Chronicle 1915

What the Business Girl Thinks

A business girl said to me the other day: "Do you know, I am glad that little saucy coats are the spring fashion. I don't feel as if I had to rely so much on a tailor now, and as I really can't afford to pay five or six guineas for coats and skirts for which I formerly paid three and four, I must have my clothes made according to my purse."

I asked what she intended to do, and discovered that a dressmaker was to receive her next order. All her friends were doing the same thing, she told me, the heavily increased charges at the tailors driving them to this device. I congratulated her upon her good sense and practical economy. The tailors have more than enough to do making khaki clothes, and it is time the woman tailor, more especially the one living in the suburbs, got a fair chance.

Personally, I never could understand why the suburban dressmaker of late years should be regarded so superciliously. The majority of them nowadays come from exclusive Court dressmakers, and they do not fail to keep up-to-date even after starting a suburban business.

What the Dressmaker Says

One, whom I had previously known at a big well-known Court dressmakers, once complained to me bitterly after she had started a business within the four mile radius.

"People come to me and talk as if I know nothing of my business, just because I live here. Yet when I was in the West End, earning a salary that ran into hundreds a year, my advice was received thankfully. They seem to think that I have come here to vegetate, whereas every new season I see, through the kindness of friends, models of which they never dream. Besides, if they can keep up-to-date through fashion books and shop-gazing, don't I have the same opportunities? It's purely snobbery on their part."

I am afraid it was, but we are learning differently now.

THE CARDINAL AND THE BRITISH RED CROSS BRANCH.

On Monday, February 12, His Eminence Cardinal Bourne was able to pay a visit to the British Red Cross Branch in Rome. The ladies have excellent workrooms, very kindly lent them by the Poor Servants of the Mother of God, in the Via San Sebastiano, near the Piazza di Spagna. They occupy the whole of the top flat of their well-known convent. His Eminence was taken round by Mrs. Gaisford and Miss Howard, who explained the lines on which the work was carried out, and introduced the various members, who were all hard at their different tasks when the Cardinal arrived. There is an English hospital at the Italian front, under the care of the Embassy doctor, Mr. Brock, and it is this institution that the English ladies in Rome undertake to supply with all that is necessary for the efficiency of its work among our Italian Allies.

The Tablet 1917

WOMEN'S NATIONAL SERVICE.

THE Women's National Service Department issues the following notices:

Agriculture.

Required strong, vigorous girls and women from eighteen years of age to enrol for service on the land as milkers, carters, general farm workers, milk and stock women, and market gardeners under the Board of Agriculture's conditions and terms for the Women's Land Army.

Go to the nearest post office for application form, which fill up and post. Applicants may expect a call to present themselves before the selection committee within a few days, but are requested not to leave their employment even when approved until definitely summoned to join a training centre.

Aircraft.

Six thousand women required for work on aeroplanes. These include motor drivers, technical storekeepers, fitters mates, detail assemblers, sand blasters, &c., instrument repairers, and sail makers.

Timber Felling.

Strong, healthy girls and young women are required to work on timber felling and cleaning, for pit props, trench poles, &c. Colonial women with experience of this kind of work please note.

Queen 1917

On the buses, 1917.

GORDONS' GLORIOUS CHARGE.

—

Through an Inferno of Fire to Victory.

—

Wounded officers and men of the Gordon Highlanders who have returned to this country after taking part in the first days' fighting of the Allied offensive on the Western Front speak with enthusiasm of the struggle and the prospects for the future. A non-commissioned officer said—"On the morning of the advance we awoke with great expectations in our minds. It is curious that most of us went about the usual morning preparations humming,—'Now's the day and now's the hour.'

"It was half-past seven to the tick when we scrambled out of our trenches and went across into the shell-swept area. We pressed quickly onward, dodging shells, shell holes, and traps of all kinds strewn about for the feet of the unwary. Our losses were light enough until we came abreast of the village of Mametz, which we had to carry in concert with two supporting battalions—the Manchesters and South Staffords. As we approached the village the only sign of life was a thin streak of smoke issuing from a solitary chimney. Still we went warily, and in a few minutes our caution was justified. There was a blaze of rifle fire, a sheet of flame, and a perfect din of noise, gradually rising into one prolonged roar, as though a million mountain torrents were set agoing at once. Above the roar could be heard the cries of our officers, 'Steady, the Gordons,' 'Not so fast, my men,' and other calls all designed to restrain our impetuosity rather than to rally us, for we were eager enough to get into it.

Aberdeen Weekly Journal 1916

DELICATE SUBJECTS IN MIDWIFERY.

A Paper read by MISS VALERIE GRAHAM.

MIDWIFERY itself is a delicate subject, which in the past has been treated very much with bated breath, but is now being brought much into the daylight; and, if treated in a tactful, delicate manner, there is nothing indelicate or horrible in Midwifery. I think, as teachers, we have the opportunity of making our pupils see the beauty and interest of Midwifery far overshadows anything horrible about it.

Now, unfortunately, in the subject I am dealing with, the horrors, overshadow any beauty. But the more they are left in the dark, the more a thousandfold will the horrors increase. They are:

THE SINGLE PREGNANT WOMAN: THE WOMAN WHO HAS CONTRACTED VENEREAL DISEASE: AND ABORTIONS.—These three subjects are greatly before the public to-day, and it behoves the coming midwife to be fully armed, to tackle them, because, owing to her sex, and calling, she will come into contact with, and be appealed to, over them more than any other member of society; and, according to the manner with which she treats the subject, and the patient, so will be her influence for good or bad over an enormous number of the community. For her influence and treatment in one case may spread, like the circle round a stone, cast into the water.

Nursing Notes
1918

Is One Hour Enough?

WITH the introduction of Summer Time to-day, the few remaining muddle-headed sceptics who have extravagantly declared that " it is impossible to regulate the sun by Act of Parliament," will receive their quietus.

It needs little courage to predict that the extra hour's sunshine—or, at the worst, day-light—will be enjoyed not only with benefit to the community but to the individual, and without a trace of that " pandemonium of dislocation " which has been foreboded in certain quarters.

Summer Time will be a success—on that the authorities agree. But if it is a success, why should not the idea be extended? If one extra hour's daylight will save us such-and-such an amount of artificial light, two extra hours would save us twice as much. That is simple arithmetic.

If one extra hour's daylight will make us healthier, two would save us twice as much in doctors' bills. And so on, through the whole gamut of " benefits."

The only argument against Daylight Saving was that it wouldn't work. If it will work, there can be no possible objection to carrying the idea through to its logical conclusion.

We want all the daylight we can get, and now that we find it to be so easily within our reach, it would be the height of imbecility not to get it.

To-day the Government has but to say the word and it can get any measure passed that it wishes. Why not, therefore, go one better than the Germans, and advance the clock another hour the first Sunday in June?

Sunday Pictorial 1916

The N.A.G. Braille Watch Fund

Further donations in response to the appeal of the Executive for the Braille Watch Fund are acknowledged in this issue. Over £500 has been subscribed as yet. This is a splendid gift from the jewellery trade, for which the Executive express their most cordial thanks to every subscriber. The fund will be closed at the end of this month. Any member of the trade who has not yet subscribed is invited to give this Fund his consideration. The whole of the subscriptions will be used to pay for watches. These are being specially made, with dials of the design which has proved to be the one most readily and accurately " felt "- by blinded men.

The needs of St. Dunstan's Hostel grow week by week. At present there are 550 men there who are adapting themselves with remarkable courage to their new mode of life. Over 300 men have already been trained at St. Dunstan's, and there are over 200 blinded soldiers and sailors in various hospitals. These figures will show that your gift to the Braille Watch Fund, if not already sent, will be utilised in a practical way that has the sympathy of every man of feeling.

In reply to some correspondents; the Editors of " The Watchmaker " and " The Jeweller and Metalworker " were supplied with copies of the appeal on October 22nd as it appeared in this journal on November 1st, with a direct invitation to them to assist by giving publicity to the matter, but the invitation was not accepted or even acknowledged.

British Retail Jeweller
1918

Nottingham Evening Post 1917

RACE HORSES AND OATS.

MR. BOTTOMLEY'S REBUKE TO LORD RHONDDA!

THE OLD BOGEY ONCE MORE.

The following correspondence has taken place between Lord Rhondda and Mr. Bottomley on the subject of winter racing:—

My dear Bottomley,—I have carefully considered the question of allowing a ration of oats for horses to be trained for racing this winter. In view of the urgent necessity of conserving all cereals for human consumption, I do not feel justified in sanctioning such a ration without a decision of the War Cabinet on the subject, and I have written to Messrs. Weatherby and Sons to this effect. I propose to bring the matter before the Cabinet at an early date.—Yours very faithfully, (Signed), RHONDDA.

My dear Rhondda.—On my return from the Grand Fleet I have received your letter—which, I confess, amazes me. Whoever is responsible for reviving this old bogey of home rations? Is it anything to do with Sir Arthur Yapp, your assistant, or the Young Men's Christian Association? What has happened since you told me, a few weeks ago, that your Department was not the stumbling-block, that the moment we have overcome the railway difficulty, our old friend, Mr. Oats, pops up again? I suppose donkey racing on the sands will next be prohibited, owing to the shortage of thistles!

Do you seriously mean to say that the difference between the oats required for a few hundred horses in training and what they would consume out of training—for that is the whole " problem "—would in any way affect the food position? And remember that, as against even this infinitesimal increase, must be set the saving on the large number of flat race horses now turned out of active training. Surely you will not be party to such nonsense—on the strength of which thousands of persons, unfit for military service, would be thrown out of work, many absolutely ruined, and a fatal blow struck at one of the oldest and grandest of British sports, and at the breeding of a class of horse more essential than any other to army purposes.

I do hope you will not force the Racing Emergency Committee, of which I am chairman, to drastic action. But I see no alternative to another active campaign unless matters are satisfactorily adjusted during the present week. You seem to have no idea of the strain and anxiety, financial and otherwise, which the delay is imposing upon one of the most patient and patriotic sections of the community.—Yours sincerely.

Gallipoli and Compulsion.

THE end of our disastrous adventure in the Gallipoli Peninsula has at last been reached. The campaign began with the bombardment of the entrance forts on the 19th of February last, and yesterday it was announced that the Peninsula had been completely evacuated—

> Now a' is done that man can do,
> And a' is done in vain.

Of all the troubles, anxieties, and disappointments of the war, Gallipoli stands out by reason of the appalling loss of life, for the heroism and endurance of the troops, for the incapacity of leadership, and for the blunders of the Government. Sir Ian Hamilton's dispatches, vivid, painful, tragic in almost every line, demonstrated that the chief need in the Gallipoli campaign from first to last was men, and more men. While the echoes of that cry are ringing through our ears, the country is being asked to enact a small and simple measure of compulsion, and the demand is meeting with some opposition.

* * *

The obvious lesson of the katabasis of Gallipoli is that if we had had compulsion we should have had the men, and that glorious success instead of ignominious failure would have attended the campaign. If we are to profit from our experiences; if we are to support the men who have volunteered to fight for us, compulsion is now absolutely necessary, and any man who opposes the Military Service Bill is, under the circumstances in which the nation is placed at present, assisting to bring about repetitions of the Gallipoli catastrophe, with its gigantic record of 211,237 casualties. Labour conferences, Irish Nationalist M.P.'s, and extreme Radicals may vote against compulsion, but the working-classes at large, the middle-classes, and the upper classes are solid for the Military Service Bill. It has been stated that the Labour Conference vote against this Bill represented 1,215,000 individuals, but the majority vote for the Bill in Parliament, which is much more representative, aggregated 4,345,530 individuals, calculating the average constituency at 10,688 electors.

Aberdeen Weekly Journal 1916

Crusader 1919

Domestic Servants.

Writing with reference to a paragraph which appeared recently in THE CRUSADER, Rosa Hobhouse says:—

" The ' servant,' we know, usually lives in the least comfortable part of the house, whilst those who engage her live in the most comfortable part—the two never breaking bread together in the experience of a common meal. And these girls are mostly the daughters of the working people—the very people we want to influence in the direction of a deeper understanding of Christ! Can we really deceive ourselves to the extent of believing that we can become their illuminators so long as such customs prevail in our own homes, setting their kith and kin in the inferior position—at a disadvantage in almost every aspect of life, including such things as conversational opportunities, and initiative?"

Voluntary Aid Detachment (VAD) fitters at work on a car at Etaples, July 1918.

SEX EQUALITY

GOVERNMENT BILL IN THE LORDS.

WOMEN AND THE UPPER CHAMBER.

WESTMINSTER, TUESDAY.

In the House of Lords the LORD CHANCELLOR moved the second reading of the Bill of the Government to amend the law with respect to disqualifications on account of sex.

It provides that a person shall not be disqualified by sex from the exercise of any public function or from being appointed to any civil or judicial office or post, or from entering or assuming any civil profession or vocation. Women, however, are to be excluded from the Civil Service in any of his Majesty's possessions or in any foreign country. The Bill further provides that a person shall not be exempted by sex from the liability to serve as a juror, but gives discretion to the Judge to accede to the request of a woman not to be asked to serve in a case on account of the evidence to be given or the issues to be tried.

The Bill, as the LORD CHANCELLOR pointed out, was intended to fulfil the pledges given by Mr. Lloyd George and Mr. Bonar Law at the General Election that the existing legal inequalities between men and women should be removed; and, in the opinion of the Government, it did so more fittingly than the Bill of the Labour Party for the emancipation of women, agreed to by the House of Commons, against the wishes of the Government, and now before the House of Lords in the charge of Lord Kimberley.

WOMEN AND THE LORDS.

The debate showed a general agreement among the few peers present that, as the Lord Chancellor said, the time had gone by when it was possible to justify the exclusion of women from the various fields of activity opened to them by the Bill, but there was some difference of opinion as to the admission of women to the House of Lords. Under the Bill of the Labour Party all peeresses in their own right would be entitled to sit and vote. The Government proposal is that the King may, on the advice of his responsible Ministers, include in the letters patent for the creation of any new peerage a provision to the effect that where the holder of the peerage is a woman she shall be entitled to "a seat, place, and voice in the House of Lords." LORD BRYCE recalled that the Government had promised to bring in a Bill next Session to reconstruct the House of Lords, or at any rate to create a new Second Chamber, and he was supported by LORD CREWE in thinking that the better course would be to postpone till then any decision as to the right of peeresses to sit and vote. Not only that, but Lord Bryce was also of opinion that it would be wise to wait and see what the electors did in the way of returning women to the House of Commons.

The Bill was read a second time.

The Times 1919

1920–1929

Illustrated Sunday Herald 1921

FALL IN MINERS' WAGES.

2/- Comes Off the Advance Secured for January.

LOSS OF OUTPUT.

For the month of February the miners will suffer a reduction of wages varying from 2s. to 9d. per shift, according to grade.

That in effect is the decision of the Secretary of Mines in accordance with the settlement of November last. He announces that under that agreement the wages advances payable to colliery workers during February will be:—

1s. 6d. for workers of 18 and over.
9d. for workers of 16 and 17.
6¾d. for workers under 16.

The respective figures for January were 3s. 6d., 1s. 9d., and 1s. 3¾d.

It will be recalled that the basis of the November settlement was that a sliding scale should operate during a test period pending a permanent wages agreement being adjusted between the Miners' Federation and the colliery owners. The test period results were to regulate wages during January, February, and March, the men meanwhile to receive advances of 2s., 1s., and 9d. respectively.

Recoil Follows Boom.

The first finding of the test period came into force in January and proved highly satisfactory, as it substantially increased the advances which had been given prospectively. The second period has, however, reversed the process, and actually reduced the advances prospectively given.

The test consists of a four weeks' average of the return made from the export of surplus coal. Output, therefore, very largely affects the result.

On the September return, the basic figure of the scale being maintained, the men are entitled to advances of 1s., 6d., and 4½d.; if that return is exceeded the men receive an additional 6d., 3d., and 2½d. respectively on every completed £288,000 of excess.

For the four weeks which fixed earnings for January there was a very substantial excess, and wages advanced accordingly. But though an adjustment was made for loss of output during the Christmas and New Year holidays, the succeeding four weeks proved disappointing, mainly owing to idle time on account of trade depression.

Oswaldtwistle Council.

THE LATE CLERK.

The Chairman said he regretted that since their last meeting death had removed from their midst the very familiar figure of their late Clerk, Mr. Westwell was Clerk to the Council for a period of about 23 years. That was no small portion of a man's life. During that time a great amount of business of a public nature passed through Mr. Westwell's hands. He had known the deceased gentleman for eleven years and in all his dealings with, and knowledge of him, he could say he had always found him courteous, kind and generous. He was a gentleman of a most kindly disposition and one felt deeply the loss of such gentlemen from their midst. The circumstances attending his death were very distressing. Up to a few days before his death he was able to carry on his daily work and he was stricken down without being able to speak a word to his relatives and friends. That must have been very distressing to his relatives. He moved that a vote of condolence be passed and forwarded to the bereaved relatives.

Accrington Observer 1921

" Ladd wanted daily, to supervise maids."
Provincial Paper.
He will probably need that extra " d."

Punch 1922

Sir Jeremiah Colman

A GREAT and successful man of business ; the chief of a vast manufacturing concern ; a keen sportsman and cricketer —he was captain of the St. John's College, Cambridge eleven, and is now President of the Surrey County Cricket Club ; and with a love of country life, Sir Jeremiah Colman, Bart., D.L., J.P., M.A., belongs to a type of Englishman of whom we are justly proud, a type to which the country owes much.

Born in 1859, his sixty-one years have been full of many and varied activities ; he has worked strenuously for his country, and the great business to which he succeeded and which has developed into a concern employing many thousands of people and with world-wide interests. Nor have his business activities been limited to his own company, for he has frequently been Chairman of the Commercial Union Insurance Company, and has during his 35 years directorship seen it advance to phenomenal prosperity and world-wide influence.

Educated at King's College School, and St. John's College, Cambridge (passing out in honours), Sir Jeremiah Colman has always been a supporter of secondary and commercial education, and his connection with the Skinners Company, of which he was Master, brought him governorships of Tonbridge School and other schools ; for the Skinners Company is one of the great city companies which, like the Merchant Taylors and the Mercers, did much for education in days when the need was not so well understood as it is at present.

Sir Jeremiah's home is at Gatton Park, one of Surrey's historic homes. He has there an estate of some 3,000 acres where he has established a famous flock of Southdown sheep. There, too, are his celebrated orchid houses in which hybridisation is conducted on skilful and scientific lines. Many are the fine novelties originating in his collection, including the famous one which captured the cup for the best orchid in the New York International Show.

Although by descent an East Anglian, Sir Jeremiah Colman has always been more closely identified with London and Surrey. He was High Sheriff of the latter county in 1893, and has been Chairman of the Reigate County Petty Sessions Court for nearly twenty years, while his war service in the county was great and included a seat on the Surrey Appeal Tribunal, under the Military Service Act, and he was Chairman, Organising Member and Chief Special Constable of the Defence of the Realm Committee for the South-Eastern area of Surrey, established to make all civil arrangements in case of a hostile landing. The area under Sir Jeremiah's control comprised 12 parishes and extended to upwards of 60 square miles.

Mayfair 1920

Evening News 1922

WOMEN BARRISTERS.
Significant Feature in the Trinity Examination List.

"The Trinity Examination list of Bar students," writes a legal correspondent of *The Daily Mail*, "indicates an increase in the number of women qualifying for the Bar. Three women students have passed the final examination, but none of the three obtained a first class.

"In the preliminary subjects, taken separately, there are 4 firsts—2 in Criminal Law and 2 in Real Property and Conveyancing. One of the firsts (Criminal Law) is Miss Cornelia Sorabji, the Indian woman counsel and author.

"The total of 16 women in the lists is the significant feature. It shows that there is no slackening off of the flow of women students along the path now completed by one of their number, Dr. Ivy Williams, the first woman barrister."

Land Worker 1920

COLLINGHAM—NOTTS.

A member of the above branch writes :—
"It may interest and be a stimulus to others to know that a member of this branch, 49 years of age, has travelled 156 miles on foot, 392 miles on bike, and spent just over £6 in railway fares to attend meetings during the year. If half a century can accomplish so much, what could the young do if they only would try !"

Veteran 1922

CRITICAL SITUATION OF LEGION IN BIRMINGHAM.

BIRMINGHAM COUNTY COUNCIL SCRAPPED.

Influence of Haig visit. Crucial dissension must be overcome.

FROM OUR SPECIAL CORRESPONDENT.

The position of the British Legion in Birmingham is rapidly going from bad to worse, and notwithstanding the efforts made in certain quarters to put things right on lines diametrically opposed to those which have existed in the past, there seems to be grave doubts as to whether unanimity amongst the Branches can be brought about. It is hoped that the visit of Earl Haig to the city will be beneficial to Birmingham in bringing the Branches into line.

DEATH OF MISS MARY MACARTHUR.

Miss Mary Macarthur (seen on right in the first picture with her little daughter), the foremost woman trade union leader in this country, died yesterday at Golders Green. The well-educated daughter of a prominent Ayr Conservative, she took up trade union work when scarcely out of her teens. Her husband, Mr. W. C. Anderson, M.P., died in 1919.

Illustrated Sunday Herald 1921

Accrington Observer 1921

THE COTTON SLUMP.

Lancashire's Short Time Working.

India's Rapid Progress.

The International Federation of Master Cotton Spinners' and Manufacturers' Association issued yesterday the half-yearly report dealing with short time working in the European cotton trade together with figures of cotton consumption and the world's spindleage.

Mr. Arno Pearse, the secretary, states that no country on the Continent except Denmark and Belgium has had as much short time as Lancashire. Holland has had none. Germany had less than half our amount of short time in the six months ending July, and Italy less than one third, India and China also had no short time.

From the elaborate and carefully compiled tables it is seen that short time in Lancashire has been twice as large in the second half of the season as compared with the first. Virtually the whole industry was suspended for the equivalent of 12.92 weeks of 48 hours out of 26.

In this particular Mr. Pearse points out that more than 2,000,000 spindles have gone out of existence in the whole of the trade.

The figures dealing with the consumption of cotton show that in the first half of the season the world's consumption of all kinds of cotton averaged 59.64 per spindle but in the second period it dropped to 56.83. Europe with its 99½ million spindles used 1,660,039 bales as against the United States total of 2,451,000 bales.

One feature arising out of the above conclusion is that the Far East is steadily making headway, the India mills taking 21,330 bales of American cotton as compared with 587 in the previous six months. Japan's intention to extend its trade in the finer fabrics is seen in the consumption of Egyptian cotton, the figures being 8,760 bales against 5,751 bales.

The table dealing with the estimated number of spindles of various kinds in the countries of the world do not show much change, the total being 152,317,054. Great Britain shows a decline in the half-year of about 200,000, some of the principal figures being as follows:—

Great Britain 56,140,738 spindles.
United States 36,478,000 spindles.
France, 9,600,000 spindles.
Germany, 9,400,000 spindles.
Russia (no returns received but previous return) 7,100,000 spindles.
Italy, 4,506,294 spindles.
India, 6,763,076 spindles.
Japan, 4,128,000 spindles.
China, 1,800,000 spindles.

A pointer to remember in the above list is that Japan has increased its spindleage by 22,903.

The "Bournville Works Magazine" contains a picture and description of Hafod-Wen, the new Convalescent Home at Harlech. The home has now been open for nine months, and the experience of the working, and the benefits derived by the men who have been visitors to the home, show that a need has been met. The beautiful situation, overlooking the sea, the healthy, invigorating atmosphere, and the kindly treatment meted out by the Matron to those who go there, all combine to build up the health as well as to renew the vitality of visitors. Most of the visitors report that their stay has been so enjoyable that they are prepared to be ill again for the pleasure of spending a period of convalescence at Hafod-Wen.

Business Man: Birmingham 1923

DAME MELBA IN RARE FORM.

Special Message to Old Friends in England.

"IN RIPPING SPIRITS."

"If you want a message for dear London here it is:

"Tell everyone I'm in ripping spirits and looking forward to facing thousands of old friends with more pleasure than I can describe.

"Milsom Rees has given me a last run over. He says my vocal chords are perfect."

Melba gave this message to the *Illustrated Sunday Herald* yesterday in her room in Dover-street.

A dark-haired boy was sitting at the piano.

"Haven't you met Lindley Evans?" asked the singer, as I sat trying to get a story from her (writes an *Illustrated Sunday Herald* representative).

"Minnetonka."

"I've brought him with me from Sydney," he said, "because he is an Australian, and a jolly clever one, and as Melba's accompanist he ought to have a good chance for making a name for himself in London."

She stepped again to the piano. The liquid ripples of "Minnetonka" rang out, the accompaniment beautifully played.

"Oh! how I have to work," declared the singer; "art has no leisure moments. But when 10,000 people come to hear you sing you kind of forget what you have had to go through in order to be able to please them."

Melba will delight a mighty Albert Hall audience with a wonderful programme this afternoon.

Illustrated Sunday Herald 1922

CHANDELIER CLEANERS' BUSY TIME.

Illustrated Chronicle 1922

SOCIETY'S CRAZE FOR CHANDELIERS.

Business Romance Of A Woman Expert.

TREASURE HUNTS.

The fashionable craze for antique furniture and fittings includes glass chandeliers, on which Mrs. M. E. Crick, whose business premises are at 148 and 166, Church street, Kensington, is one of the leading authorities in London.

Mrs. Crick told a "Star" reporter that glass chandeliers are largely used in Mayfair, where she said she held contracts to clean them twice a year.

A Buyer of Books.

The story of how Mrs. Crick became an expert on glass chandeliers is a romance.

"Twenty years ago I was a buyer of books, and once I was compelled to take a large chandelier as well as the books.

"I did not want it, but I paid 9s. for it, and when it arrived we scarcely knew where to put it in the shop. A lady came in one day, and my husband, not knowing what it was worth, asked £20, and she bought it.

Treasure-Seeking.

"That's how I came to start buying, making and cleaning glass chandeliers," said Mrs. Crick, a vivacious woman possessed of humour, and with a twinkle in her eye.

Since then Mrs. Crick has searched for glass chandeliers and ornaments used for lighting, and has found them in the cellars of mansions, in town houses in all parts of London, and in Caledonian market, and has bought much glass from rag and bone men.

At the back of her shops are stored vast quantities of glass diamonds, pendants, arms, brackets, all arranged in periods — Napoleonic, Georgian, and Victorian.

Most Valuable.

Chandeliers of Georgian design are the most popular," said Mrs. Crick. "Old Waterford glass dating back to 1750 is the most valuable; then is Empire, which lasted until gas came in, up to which time all the arms were solid.

"There are straight cut, thumb pressed, barley sugar, and other patterns in glass.

"I am overwhelmed with orders Only the other day I refused a big order for export to America. A lady comes and asks me to design a chandelier, having described to me the style and period of her furniture. Suppose there is an Adam's ceiling, well, I design the chandelier to preserve the Adam's style.

Not Cheap.

"Chandeliers are not cheap, but the cost depends on the size, number of lights, decorations, and the quality of the glass used—from £20 to £100, with small pyramids costing a few pounds."

Star 1922

Punch 1922

DECEMBER 13, 1922.] PUNCH, OR THE LONDON CHARIVARI. 573

THE MAID WHO WAS BUT HUMAN.

It amazes me that people cannot keep their tempers at political meetings and debates, and indeed at all sorts of functions. The behaviour of some of the people who gained admission to the Town Hall to hear the declaration of the polls was shocking. There has always been decorum in previous years. But there are influences at work in politics to-day that know nothing of decorum. The sheer vulgarity of the women at the Town Hall, where everyone is supposed to be impartial, was revolting. And the vulgarity all came from one party; I am bound to say that.

Business Man: Birmingham 1923

Sir Edward Hulton, formerly the owner of several newspapers, has died at his home at Leatherhead at the age of fifty-six. Sir Edward's father built up in Manchester a large group of popular newspapers, which became associated with the family name. Coming to London, Sir Edward acquired the *Evening Standard* and the *Daily Sketch*. Nearly two years ago his health became seriously affected, and his newspaper interests were sold to a company controlled by Lord Rothermere and Lord Beaverbrook for £6,000,000.

British Weekly 1925

BOYS AND GIRLS GROWING SCARCER

One of the most vexatious results of the trade depression since the war has been the large number of young people among the unemployed.

We have refused to keep them at school, we have been unable to find them work, and they have loafed. So it is startling news (not altogether unwelcome) that the Government is expecting a shortage of juvenile labour during the next few years. The Ministry of Labour estimates that the number of juveniles at work in Great Britain is likely to fall from 2,175,000 in 1927 to 1,756,000 in 1933, a drop of 20 per cent. This, of course, is largely due to the lower birth-rate.

Naturally, the employment open to boys and girls differs very much in different parts of the country. In some places the shortage of labour has actually begun, while in others it is expected there will still be a surplus five years hence.

Children's Newspaper 1923

Burnham Scales.

Schoolmistress
1923

GETTING READY FOR THE 1925 REVISION.

(By Our Special Correspondent.)

Last Friday there was a meeting of the Burnham Committee. These meetings are, of course, private, but there is no harm in saying that the real business of the committee was to make some preliminary arrangements in view of the revision of the standard scales which will have to be made before April, 1925. The formation of the scales, in the first instance, took a very long time, during which only the provisional minimum scale was in operation as a compulsory payment. It is not expected that the new revision will take quite so long, but difficulties are sure to arise, and it is, of course, very unfortunate that the revision should have to be begun at a time of slump in trade and rigid economy in public affairs. Still, that revision is beginning, and it will be just as well for teachers to be thinking about the problem, so that they can make their views known to the people who will represent them on the revising committee.

Women's Salaries.

As I have previously warned the readers of this column, there is a distinct hardening of opinion among the local authority members of the committee regarding the salaries of women. How this will come out in the end nobody can say as yet. But there are men there with a fixed determination already to bring down the scales so far as the women are concerned, no matter what happens to the men. There are two schools of thought amongst these—those who would reduce the salaries of all women, and those who would confine the main part of the reduction to the younger women teachers. There is a specious argument being used that in the public service a difference ought to be made between those who make teaching a life's occupation and those to whom it is what the political economists call a " waiting occupation," that is, an occupation only intended to fill up the years between training and marriage. How anybody is to tell when a young lady comes out of college whether in her case it is to be a waiting occupation or a permanent occupation, I don't profess to know.

Women's Work.

INTERNATIONAL FEDERATION.

At the fifth annual council meeting of the International Federation of University Women, held in London last week, distinguished women from the universities of fifteen countries met in conference. Questions such as the foundation of international fellowships, the exchange of students and lecturers, and, in general, the promotion of understanding between the university women of different countries came under discussion. A visit was paid to Crosby Hall, where it is hoped to establish an international hall of residence for women graduates working in London, and an "at home" was held at Bedford College by the British Committee on International Relations.

BARRISTERS AT WORK.

Miss Helena Normanton, in wig and gown, took her seat among counsel at the Old Bailey last week. She is the first lady barrister to occupy this position. Miss Edith Hesling, of Heaton Moor, held her first brief last week, appearing on behalf of the Crown at the Manchester Sessions. Scotland's first woman advocate is Miss Margaret Henderson Kidd. She is M.A. and LL.B. of Edinburgh University, and has just been called to the Bar at the Edinburgh Court of Session. The daughter of the ex-M.P. for Linlithgowshire, Miss Kidd takes a great interest in politics, and it was on her motion that Mr. Stanley Baldwin, the Prime Minister, was adopted as Conservative candidate for the Lord Rectorship of the University.

Schoolmistress
1923

A TALL STORY

An American millionaire decided to import a ghost to heighten the antiquity of his mansion, and, after a prolonged search and the expenditure of a considerable sum of money, a satisfactory specimen was picked up in Devonshire and shipped to Chicago in cold storage. It walked by daylight and had every appearance, both as regards garb and figure, of having just missed the sailing of the " Mayflower." The millionaire and his friends were delighted with its old-world looks and solemn deportment. But—on the third day, alas ; it was unfortunately, discovered chewing gum.

Wall Paper Magazine 1925

COURIERS FOR TOURISTS.

We have on our staff first class Couriers who can be engaged to accompany individual passengers, or private and family parties, to relieve them of the many difficulties so often inseparable from independent travel. They attend to the reservation of train, steamer, restaurant-car, and hotel accommodation, deal with baggage registration and Customs examination, arrange transfer of passenger and baggage between station, steamer, and hotel ; pay all gratuities to railway and hotel servants, and make arrangements for sightseeing, etc.

COURIERS FOR COMMERCE.

Many Commercial men proceeding abroad have found that our Couriers have been of great assistance to them, not only by acting as Interpreters in trade negotiations, but also in effecting numerous economies in connection with their travel and hotel requirements. Relieved of the details of transportation, the principal is enabled to concentrate his energies on the object of his journey.

Our Couriers are men of education, speaking Continental languages fluently, and by long experience have obtained an intimate knowledge of the principal cities of Europe. They, of course, are always in civilian attire, being quite a distinct staff from our Interpreters in attendance at railway stations, ports, etc.

Traveller's Gazette 1924

MASTER OF THE KING'S MUSICK.

AN HISTORIC OFFICE.

The King has appointed Sir Edward Elgar, O.M., Master of the Musick.

The appointment of Sir Edward Elgar to the post of Master of the King's Musick, left vacant by the death of Sir Walter Parratt, will be universally welcomed. There has been some doubt whether the office, which is quite distinct from the organistship of St. George's Chapel, Windsor, would not be allowed to lapse, since from the time of King Edward VII.'s accession its duties have fallen largely into desuetude. Formerly the holder conducted the Royal Orchestra, which of late years has been replaced by one or other of the regimental bands when music has been required at Court functions.

The office has an interesting history. In a letter published in *The Times* recently a correspondent wrote :—

The first Master of the Musick was appointed in 1660, but from very early times the Kings of England have included in their households a band of musicians. Of Edward IV.'s 13 minstrels, "some be trompets, some with shalmes and small pypes." Henry VIII. rang the changes on "15 trumpets, three lutes, three rebecks, three taborets, a harp, two viols, ten sackbuts, a fife, and four drumslades," and "16 trumpets, four lutes, three rebecks, three taborets, a harp, two viols, nine sackbuts, two drumslades, three minstrels, and a player on the virginals."

In 1548 Edward VI. had eight minstrels, a player on the virginals, two lutes, a harper, a bagpiper, a drumslade, a rebeck, seven viols, four sackbuts, a Welsh minstrel, and a flute-player. Elizabeth enlarged and possibly improved this troup. Hautboys made their appearance under Charles I., with "recorders," violins, and 15 "musicians for the lute and voice." Nicholas Laniere was then master of the band, and he introduced "wind instruments" and "25 musicians for the waytes," besides a serjeant trumpeter and 18 trumpeters. At the Restoration came a band of 24 performers on violins, tenors, and basses, commonly known as the "Four and Twenty Fiddlers." They played during dinner and even breakfast (!), while in the Royal chapel anthems were especially composed with symphonies and ritornels between the vocal movements.

Formerly, besides its ordinary duties, the King's Band of Music was used, with the Gentlemen and Children of the Chapel Royal, in performance of the odes annually composed for the King's birthday and New Year's Day. The most famous holders of the Mastership were, perhaps, Thomas Purcell (1672) and Dr. William Boyce (1755).

Times Educational Supplement 1924

THE HOT IRON CURE

An old-fashioned, but still effective remedy, is to be found in the hot iron.

The ordinary flat iron used for home laundry work is made as hot as possible. The affected part of the body is then stripped of clothing and covered with a thick piece of brown paper. The hot iron is brought close to the brown paper, at the required spot—so close that the heat strikes right through.

The patient must bear all the heat he is capable of up to the point at which the whole region feels aglow and the pain less acute. From five to ten minutes of this thrice daily goes a long way to drive off an attack of lumbago, sciatica, stiff-neck, and certain forms of muscular rheumatism.

Health News 1925

Daily Express 1924

DEATH RAY SECRETS.

AIR AS CONDUCTOR OF ELECTRICITY.

SMALL RANGE.

EXPERIMENTS THAT HAVE BEEN MADE.

ALTHOUGH scientists have not yet been able to form a definite conclusion regarding the "death ray," they have formed certain preliminary opinions.

"As far as one can gather," said an eminent physicist to a "Daily Express" representative yesterday, "Mr. Grindell-Matthews' invention consists in making, by means of radiation, a pathway through the air that will conduct electricity.

"The only types of ray known at present which will cause the air to conduct electricity are the X rays and the ultra-violet rays. It is impossible to concentrate X rays in a beam that will not scatter. Ultra-violet rays, on the other hand, though they do not go through ordinary glass, can be concentrated into a beam by a quartz lens.

"The effect of ultra-violet rays in rendering air a conductor of electricity is well known, but so far as the leading physicists in this country are aware this cannot be done on a large scale.

WASTAGE.

"Air is only made to conduct electricity by ultra-violet rays when it stops them, just as a ray of ordinary light produces an illumination in foggy air or muddy water, which stop it, but not in clear air or clear water. A fairly typical ultra-violet ray which causes air to conduct electricity is reduced to half its original intensity after traversing two yards of air, to one quarter its usual intensity in four yards, one-eighth in six yards, and so on.

"Such a ray as this would be quite useless for long-distance work, but even if we had a ray whose intensity was halved in two hundred yards instead of two, we should need to multiply our source of power by a number with fifteen figures in it to make it carry six miles—the extreme practicable height for aeroplanes—instead of two hundred yards.

THE COMMON SENSE COOKER
FOR COOKING
MEAT AND VEGETABLES
IN THEIR OWN JUICES

Daily Sketch 1924

"NO NORMAL JAWS"

British "Worst Fed People in World," Says Harley-st. Doctor

"There is not a normal jaw in Great Britain, and there are 200,000,000 rotten teeth in the country," remarked Dr. Harry Campbell, a well-known Harley-street physician yesterday, when asked his views regarding the British Medical Association attacks on modern diet.

"The British public," he added, "are the worst fed people in the world, but they have also got the most deplorable teeth. And it is all due to our faulty diet."

Dr. John Wynne Yorke-Davies, who for years has been preaching against overfeeding, expressed himself very satisfied that at last the country was waking up to dangers of modern diet.

"Ninety-nine per cent.," he said, "eat three times too much food, and in addition to that our present-day food is not properly prepared. It is all too rich and too varied. If people could only be persuaded to get back to the plainly-cooked old English diet many of our troubles would disappear.

"Probably one of the most obvious examples of the results of the two different kinds of fare can be seen by studying the plain-living tramp, who is usually a sturdy, bronzed, almost perfect specimen of manhood, in comparison with the motor-car lounging, overfeeding magnate."

LAYING INFORMATION

"Daily Express" Correspondent.
BIRMINGHAM, Tuesday.

While a charge of fowl-stealing was being heard at Worcester Quarter Sessions one of the "exhibits," a Rhode Island Red, laid an egg, which was held up for the admiration of the Bench.

The case had no sooner been resumed when another hen followed suit.

Daily Express 1924

PROSTITUTION AND THE YOUNG GIRL.

While in Cairo in the early part of 1924, the Secretary came into contact with a young French woman—a professional prostitute of the better class and extremely intelligent, with a good knowledge of the various European Capitals. She discussed her mode of life and its conditions from a purely business point of view, and repeatedly expressed her regret that she had been unable to pursue her avocation in London. When asked for particulars she said that, having heard much of the generosity of Englishmen, she had come to London a year or two previously, and had taken a small, well-furnished flat in the West End (giving the exact address). After nine months, however, she had returned to France, as, owing to the vigilance of the London police—from whom, however, she said she had received much kindness and many warnings—she could not exercise her profession with any comfort, and had been arrested three times. It was sympathetically suggested to her that perhaps that difficulty might have been overcome, but she emphatically repudiated the idea, saying that it was no use offering money to the English police; they were not like the police in some other countries, where women such as she could always arrange to carry on their business without fear of arrest.

"DO'S" FOR FRESHERS

(With the usual apologies.)

Do always address your Tutor as 'Sir' (never 'Madam'). Neglect of such little courtesies may often lead to a long sojourn in Chesterton.

Do take in all the Cambridge journals. Some of them are quite funny unintentionally, and they are at least useful for hiding the bare patch in your green rep sofa.

Do try and treat your Head Porter with the servility that he expects. Remember that he is the one purely ornamental object of this utilitarian age.

Do join the Heretics. Your parents would like you to attend a University Sermon on Sunday evening as well as on Sunday morning.

Do attend lectures. Remember that the cinemas aren't open in the morning, and besides, the lecturer expects the men's colleges to provide a few chaperons.

Do buy a bright orange tie. It will enable your enemies to refer to you as an 'aesthete,' and the athletes may possibly mistake it for a Leander.

Do, if you own a bicycle, knock down old ladies in Senate House Passage. All the fragile ones have already been killed, so it is merely a question of the survival of the fittest.

Do stick to the gown you have stolen to wear in Hall. The owner is sure to get it back again sooner or later, by the law of averages.

Granta 1924

THE NEW MINISTRY.

MR. RAMSAY MACDONALD MAKES A GOOD START.

Mr. Ramsay MacDonald, after an audience with the King, became Prime Minister yesterday, and Great Britain's first Socialist Government came to power and responsibility. Thus we made a landmark in the continuing and age-long history of our race, and found, despite all panic-mongers, that the historic occasion was uncommonly like any other Tuesday in the workaday week. That is the fashion of a great and composed people, and it illustrates the spirit by which greatness is maintained.

Daily Express 1924

Vigilance Record 1926

The Casualty Department at St Thomas' Hospital, c. 1920.

The documentary maker and his subject at work, in a production shot from John Grierson's 1929 film *Drifters*.

Daily
Mail
1926

ARTIFICIAL VOICE.

ORGAN PIPE MADE TO SPEAK.

At the Regent-street Polytechnic, W., last night, Sir Richard Paget, Fellow of the Physical Society of London, made an organ pipe speak literally. It said, " Hallo, London, are you there? " to the audience at a lecture on behalf of King Edward's Hospital Fund, and then announced, "Oh, Lila, I love you," enunciating the words as loudly and clearly as a toastmaster.

Sir Richard had equipped himself with a foot bellows connected to a short length of organ pipe. The tongue of the organ pipe represented the vocal chords of the human voice, and with his fingers Sir Richard cleverly imitated the varying resonances in the cavities in the human mouth formed by the throat, the palate, and the tongue.

A NASAL VOICE.

Another organ-pipe, with a short length of pipe on top at right angles to represent the relation of the nasal cavity to the mouth, was made to say " Minnie." Then the nasal pipe was stopped with a cork, and " Minnie" spoke as though with a cold in her head.

Sir Richard said that with the spread of the telephone and broadcasting, the spoken word is coming into its own again. The man who could speak clearly, artistically, and musically had a real advantage over the man who mumbled.

Chaucer and Shakespeare, he said, would have been ashamed to spell as we did now. We had 14 vowel sounds in our language and only 5 vowels.

THE KING'S WOMAN CHIROPODIST.

ROYAL WARRANTS FOR QUAINT TRADES.

The list of Royal Warrant holders in the New Year " London Gazette " reveals the fact that the King is attended by a woman chiropodist named Miss Kelly.

Members of quaint trades and callings are in the service of the Royal Family. King George, for instance, has three tartan makers, but only one maker of kilts and one Highland ornament manufacturer. Mr. Sandow is the King's instructor in physical culture.

The Queen's list includes an antiquary, two shawlmen, a fan maker, two cleaners and dyers, two sewing-machine makers, and twenty-five jewellers and silversmiths.

Makers of lambs' food, gates and fences, wine-corks, fireworks, lamprey pies, Edinburgh rock, typewriters, and chimney cowls are in the household list.

Four posting masters, one job master, a horse milliner, and a stable linen manufacturer are retained by the royal mews.

Daily Express 1924

Daily
Mail
1926

FEDERATION ABANDONS THE MINERS.

LEADERS AGAIN SHIRK RESPONSIBILITY.

5 YEARS' PEACE IN ONE COALFIELD.

The miners' leaders on Saturday once more dodged their responsibility by passing on to the men the task of settling the coal dispute in the districts. The miners, in return for their 29 weeks' enforced idleness and the misery it has entailed, have gained nothing, and their so-called leaders have escaped without having had to sign a single document of agreement.

The national conference of miners' delegates on Saturday decided to bring the coal dispute to an end by abandoning all idea of national negotiations or settlement and by instructing each district to make terms locally for a general resumption of work. The various owners' associations will forthwith meet the men's representatives in an effort to formulate district agreements.

The pretence that the Miners' Federation still retains national authority is to be kept up until next Friday, when another delegate conference will be held to hear reports on the progress of negotiations in the districts.

An ominous remark was made by Mr. A. J. Cook, the secretary of the Federation, immediately after Saturday's delegate conference broke up. He said :

I am still as strongly opposed to district settlements as I was on May 1, because I know that permanent peace cannot be secured in the coalfields this way.

GUIDING PRINCIPLES.

This statement has to be read in conjunction with one of a series of "guiding principles" which have been framed by the federation executive for the negotiation of district agreements. It stipulates that they shall be terminable by one month's notice. The federation leaders deliberately refrained from laying down any period for the duration of the agreements, the object being to restore to the federation the power to launch at any time a further offensive against the industries of the country.

Such an obvious trick is not likely to succeed with the owners, who will insist on long-term agreements—three years in some cases and five in others.

Each district has been given freedom to fix the length of its own working day.

A meeting of Cabinet Ministers will be held early this week, but in well-informed quarters it is not anticipated that the Government will now attempt to set up any central arbitral coal tribunal since the owners are opposed to it and the miners no longer appear to demand it.

WANTED.

ROOMS, OR HOME IN A FAMILY, by a Lady. Experienced teacher, linguist—French and German—good reader; companionable, needlewoman, travelled, fond of children. Would supervise homework, some teaching; help with W.I.s or Adult School. Dry soil, good elevation, within 50 miles of London preferred. Could furnish own rooms; good references.—R., c/o " HOME AND COUNTRY," 26 Eccleston Street, London, S.W.1.

Home and Country 1925

SMITHFIELD SHOW.

The Smithfield Club's fat cattle show, with its history of 127 years, opens to-day in the Royal Agricultural Hall, Islington, N.

The show has the biggest entry of stock since the war- nearly 1,000 animals. For the first time for some years, owing to the incidence of foot-and-mouth disease, the champions of the previous shows will meet at Islington. Major Morrison's crossbred heifer Lily of Basildon was champion at Norwich and Birmingham, and Lord Durham's crossbred steer at Edinburgh. There will be close competition for the London honour.

One of the heaviest animals is a Hereford bullock exceeding a ton, though under three years old. The King has about 30 cattle, sheep, and pigs from Sandringham, and the Prince of Wales also is an exhibitor.

Daily Mail 1926

VICTIMISATION.

THE POSITION OF THE RAILWAY COMPANIES.

Sir Felix Pole, the General Manager of the Great Western Railway, contributes the following message on victimisation to the G.W. bulletin :

"The word victimisation has often been used in connexion with strikes. In the experience of the G.W.R. it has usually been imported at the end of a strike, the trade unions invariably asking that there should be no victimisation. The present strike not only differs from previous strikes in that it is not associated with any dispute or labour question affecting the company, but because of the fact that victimisation started with the strike, the victim in this case being the G.W.R. Company.

"It is, indeed, true to say that the country as a whole is being victimised by a strike which is the blackest spot in the history of labour in this country. That thousands of men with no grievance against their employers should have been 'instructed' to leave work and that so many of them should have done so passes all comprehension. It can only be explained on the ground that there was a deep conspiracy against the State. Thank God such a conspiracy cannot succeed and can only result in the discrediting of its promoters and the disillusionment of those who have been used as pawns in the game."

Observer 1926

£3 A WEEK RISE

Not for Edinburgh Unemployed : An Official's Reward

FROM A WORKER CORRESPONDENT.

The Edinburgh Parish Council recently refused to receive a deputation of the unemployed to protest against the cuts in relief. It was afterwards learned that the business which the Council was engaged on was proposals for the increase of officials' salaries.

And, just as the Council had decided to reduce the excessive pay of the workless, so naturally it decided to relieve the underpaid officials. The Parish Clerk got an advance of £150 a year, bringing his total pay to £1,000 a year.

Worker's Life 1927

PRINCE'S HUSTLE.

RECORD DAY OF ENGAGEMENTS TO-MORROW.

NORTHAMPTON AND PARIS.

The Prince of Wales is accustomed to very full days of engagements, but to-morrow will surely approach a record in these matters.

At about 9 o'clock in the morning the Prince leaves London for Northampton. After spending many busy hours there he will return to London in the evening, and at 9 a.m. will leave Waterloo by the boat train for Southampton, where he will embark for Le Havre on his way to Paris.

At Northampton, where he arrives at 10.19 a.m., he will be given a civic reception, and before lunch he will somehow contrive to make an inspection of a leather works, the Northampton School for Boys, the County School for Girls, and the General Hospital. After luncheon with the Mayor and a large party of invited guests at the Guildhall —less than an hour is allowed for this— the Prince will lay a wreath on the war memorial, inspect a boot works, and watch 4,000 schoolchildren at physical training, leaving Northampton by motor car at about 4.15 p.m.

After reaching London the Prince will have a short respite before setting out for France.

Bath and Wilts Chronicle 1927

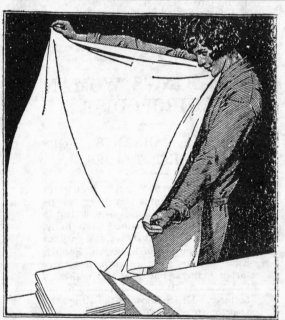

PERFECT WHITENESS

As you fold up the white things washed with Omo— as you smell and handle such fragrant white clothes, you cannot help remarking "Omo is indeed a wonder." White things washed with Omo are *really* white, not *nearly* white. Omo provides the most effective way of taking out stains which ordinary washing fails to remove.

Bleacher **OMO** *Cleanser*

You only need to boil

E. S. HUDSON LIMITED, LIVERPOOL, WEST BROMWICH AND LONDON

The Domestic Servant Situation in New Zealand.

DURING the last few years there has been a large influx of British domestic immigrants into New Zealand, but in spite of this there is still an urgent demand in the Dominion for really competent and reliable domestic help. Efficient cooks and capable "all-round" general servants especially need never be at a loss for situations in this young vigorously-growing country, and though the work is by no means light, and both energy and resourcefulness are required, on the other hand the conditions of life there are so much richer and fuller, and the standard of living is so much higher than elsewhere,

Colonizer
1928

MINERS' EIGHT HOURS' DAY.

Mr. James Welsh, M.P., at Belper.

The chief speaker at a public meeting organised by the Belper Branch of the Labour Party, and held in the Labour Hall on Saturday, was Mr. James Welsh, M.P. The gathering was presided over by Mr. G. B. Blount, who said the men that were sitting in the House of Commons under the banner of Labour were men who had their minds set on one thing—the deliverance of the people. The workers were demanding a better status, and the things that did for their fathers were no longer sufficient for the sons of these fathers.

Mrs. J. Lees (the agent and wife of the local candidate) remarked that there were still a million and a half unemployed in the country. Men were being asked to take still further reductions in their wages. She also spoke of the plight of many Derbyshire miners, who were only having one or two shifts a week. In conclusion, Mrs. Lees, who urged the people to do all they could for the benefit of the cause, spoke of the importance of the little details which should not be neglected.

Belper
News
1927

OVERCROWDED BUSES.

CLOWNE CONDUCTRESSES SUMMONED AT ECKINGTON.

Three conductresses employed by the Unity Service Company, Ltd., were summoned at Eckington last week for permitting overcrowding on buses. The defendants were Ivy Crooks, Clowne; Ida Owen, Clowne; and Beatrice Bird, Clowne.

Supt. Clarke said that previous cases, which he did not press in the hope that they would be a warning to the company, had apparently had no effect.

P.c. Stone said he stopped three buses in Station Road, Bolph, Whitwell. Owen's bus, which had a seating capacity of 26, was carrying 37 adult passengers and three children. The vehicle of which Bird was in charge had a seating capacity of 32, and it was carrying 56 passengers. The bus of which Crooks was acting as conductress was built for 20 passengers, but it was carrying 34.

A solicitor, who represented the defendants, said the Unity Service Company had adopted the suggestion of the Superintendent and had put more buses on the road, to cope with the traffic, but the demand was heavier than expected. New buses had also been ordered, and the company were doing everything they could to comply with the law.

In fining the defendants 10s. each, the Chairman (Col. Butler-Bowdon) said that any future cases would be severely dealt with.

Belper
News
1927

MICROPHONE AS HECKLER.

Speaker Greeted With Howls and Cackles.

When the President of the National Union of Manufacturers, Mr. George Terrell, rose to propose the health of the Home Secretary, Sir William Joynson-Hicks, at the annual dinner of the Union in London on Tuesday night the amplifiers installed in the hall began to emit weird crackling noises.

Mr. Terrell began by urging the Government to make the Factories Bill as flexible as possible. The microphone responded with a loud cackle.

Manufacturers, said Mr. Terrell, had come to look upon factory inspectors as "brass hats" (the microphone emitted a loud peal of laughter), and he suggested that all decisions of inspectors should be submitted to a local committee. The microphone gave a long whistle.

At this point the Home Secretary stood up and threw his table-napkin over the offending microphone, which immediately gave forth an uncanny howl. Loud cheers greeted the Home Secretary's action, and loud laughter the howl of the microphone. Then somebody discovered a means of turning off the instrument, and Mr. Terrell was able to continue his speech without further interruption.

Bath and Wilts Chronicle 1927

THE BEAUTIFUL STRANGLER.

But Miss Ruby Miller Thinks That "Once is Enough."

Miss Ruby Miller, the stage "star," is recovering to-day from the effects of being strangled by Mr. Arthur Wontner in the screen version of "Mayfair," now being made for New Era at St. Margaret's (writes our Film Critic).

Mr. Wontner seized Miss Miller by the wrist as she lunged at him with a knife.

"Down," shouted a director, and Miss Miller fell over the wooden arm of a settee.

"Now scream." She did, but it became a muffled groan.

Ruby Miller.

"You're strangling her beautifully," was the next comment.

When the camera lights went out Miss Miller did not rise. Mr. Wontner rushed to her side. A doctor was sent for. Miss Miller complained of her back, and the doctor said she had sprained herself slightly.

Miss Miller tried to make light of the occurrence. "You strangle beautifully," she said to Mr. Wontner, "but once is enough."

Evening Standard 1928

THOMAS HARDY'S NOVELS·

When we say that the death of Thomas Hardy leaves the art of fiction in England without a head we are speaking the most obvious of truths. So long as Hardy lived there was not a writer who did not feel that his calling was crowned by the unworldly and simple old man who made not the slightest effort to assert his sovereignty, yet stood for more to this generation than it is possible for any single voice to say. The effect of such a presence is indeed incalculable. His greatness as a writer, his standing among the great of other ages, will be judged perhaps more truly by critics of a later day. But it is for the living to bear witness to another sort of influence, hardly less important, though bound in the nature of things more quickly to disappear. His was a spiritual force; he made it seem honourable to write, desirable to write with sincerity; so long as he lived there was no excuse for thinking meanly of the art he practised. His genius, his age, his distance might remove all possibility of intercourse; the plainness and homeliness of his life lent him an obscurity which neither legend nor gossip disturbed; but it is no exaggeration to say that while he lived there was a king among us and now we are without. Of no one, however, would it be more unfitting to write in terms of rhetorical eulogy. His only demand upon us, and there is none more exacting, was that we should speak the truth.

Times Literary Supplement 1928

"FATHER TIME" PARADES.

Brasenose College Servants Entertained.

The annual college servants' party at Brasenose College, Oxford, again proved an enjoyable gathering.

The servants met in the college hall last evening, the interior being seasonably decorated.

The evening opened with a whist drive, at which Mr. J. Stone was M.C., followed by dancing. The prizewinners at the drive were:—Ladies—Mrs. S. Smart and Miss E. Tomins. Gents—Mr. C. Weedon and Mr. W. Griffin. A special prize was awarded to Miss A. Selby.

Entertainment was provided by Mr. Bob Reynolds, Mr. T. Macknay, and the Rouge et Noir Concert Party.

The principal of the college (Mr. C. H. Sampson) and his wife were present, also Mr. H C. W. Wace, the bursar.

At two minutes to midnight Father Time (Mr H. Drew) entered the hall, and as the clock chimed 12 "Auld Lang Syne" and the National Anthem were sung. Following this, Master 1929 (G. Harvey) dashed into the hall with quite a lively air. Thus was 1928 banished.

The party concluded at 3.0 a.m. after a most successful time.

A luncheon for the servants and pensioners was held at noon to-day in the hall, followed by a children's party.

Oxford Mail 1929

WOMAN'S BOOK WITHDRAWN.

"Jix" and "The Well of Loneliness."

PUBLISHERS' ACT

Miss Radclyffe Hall and the "Sunday Express" Protest.

MR. JONATHAN CAPE, on behalf of Jonathan Cape, Ltd., the publishers, of Bedford-square, W.C.1, announces to-day :—

We have to-day received a request from the Home Secretary asking us to discontinue publication of Miss Radclyffe Hall's novel, "The Well of Loneliness." We have already expressed our readiness to fall in with the wishes of the Home Office in this matter, and we have therefore stopped publication.

Attention was first drawn to the unusual theme of "The Well of Loneliness" by the editor of the "Sunday Express" last Sunday, when he called for the book's suppression.

The book was recently published by Jonathan Cape at the unusual price, for a

MISS RADCLYFFE HALL.

novel, of 15s. net. The reason for the high price was explained by the publishers as being because the book was not issued for the general novel-reading public.

They stated that " it handles very skilfully a psychological problem which needs to be understood in view of its growing importance."

" In England hitherto," they added, " the subject has not been treated frankly outside the region of scientific text-books, but that its social consequences qualify a broader and more general treatment is likely to be the opinion of thoughtful and cultured people."

Evening Standard 1928

DAME M. FAWCETT

Champion of Women's Suffrage Dies at Age of 82.

Dame Millicent Fawcett, G.B.E., died in London shortly after 1 o'clock this morning, at the age of eighty-two.

Dame Millicent was the widow of the Right Hon. Henry Fawcett, the famous blind Postmaster-General, and she was the real founder of the women's suffrage campaign.

She was president of the National Union of Women's Suffrage Societies from 1867 to 1918, and she was present in the Commons when John Stuart Mill moved the Women's Suffrage Amendment to the Representation of the People Bill of 1867.

She belonged to a family of pioneers, for her sister, the late Dr. Garrett Anderson, was the pioneer woman doctor.

Dame Millicent Fawcett, who died in London early this morning.

Daily Mirror 1929

MISS GRACIE FIELDS.

Wife of Paris Manager who Settled Comedienne's Engagement.

Miss Gracie Fields, who can sing in nearly every dialect of the English tongue, is to go to Paris to sing in French at a Parisian music-hall (writes "Argonaut").

A contract has been signed between Miss Fields and the manager of the Apollo Theatre for the famous comedienne to appear in Paris for a fortnight's season, beginning next Monday.

Miss Gracie Fields.

Mr. Archie Pitt, Miss Fields's husband and theatrical manager, told me to-day:—

"The manager of the Apollo had seen Miss Fields several times before, but he could not make up his mind whether she would succeed in Paris. Last week he came over especially to see her again, bringing his wife with him. His wife was so pleased with Gracie's performance that she made up her husband's mind for him."

Evening Standard 1928

RECOVERING THE LIMBS YOU LOST

The Work of W. B. Hilliard & Sons for Upwards of three Quarters of a Century

We have many times in this Journal had occasion to emphasise the fact that the man or woman who is looking for sound service, will find no finer criterion of where to find it — all other things being equal — than that of the long establishment of the firm he proposes to use.

The old established firm has not, lived through many years of competitive business without a reason for its existence; for businesses do not succeed and remain by accident. On the contrary, the very fact of its long existence is proof that it has rendered sound service, and

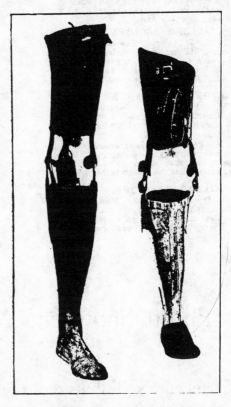

Left: A Hilliard Limb after 24 years of constant wear, still in use.

Right: Another make of Limb after 3 years of wear, now a discarded wreck.

so welded its connection together against all the wiles of its competitors; and it is usually safe to presume that those who have rendered sound service in the past will continue to render it in the future.

Town and Country Life 1929

£100 EACH FOR MINERS' WIDOWS.

Daily Mail
1929

WIDE SCOPE OF FREE INSURANCE.

The varied nature of the accedents following which *The Daily Mail* to-day pays benefits emphasises once more how wide is the protection afforded those who take the simple precaution of registering for its Free Insurance by using forms such as those in Page 8 to-day.

It will be seen that five of the fatal accident benefits, including two of £250 each, have been sent to widows. These claims have been admitted by the Eagle, Star, and British Dominions Insurance Co., acting for *The Daily Mail*.

DROWNED WHILE BATHING.

Mr. A. H. Dyer, Remoney, Moor Green, Moseley, Birmingham, was drowned while bathing in the sea. A cheque for £250 has been sent to his widow.

FATAL CAR ACCIDENT.

Mr. R. H. Walton, "Kenwood," 77, Halford-road, Hillingdon, Middlesex, was travelling as a passenger in a private car when it collided with a motor-van and he was killed. £250 has been sent to his widow.

STREET ACCIDENTS.

Mr. A. Fleet, 65, North-street, Bicester, Oxon, was knocked down and killed by a motor-car. His widow has been sent £100.

Mrs. M. Rodger, 8, Lothian-gardens, Paisley-road, Cardonald, Glasgow, died after being knocked down by a motor omnibus. £100 has been sent to her husband.

KILLED AT WORK.

Mr. E. D. McGhee, 88, Mossblown, Annbank, Ayrshire, was killed by a fall of stone in the mine in which he was employed. His widow has been sent a cheque for £100.

Daily Mirror
1929

LADY DORIA HOPE

Duke's Shopgirl Daughter Joins a Paris Firm—Marriage Rumour Denied

Lady Doria Hope

Paris, Monday

Lady Doria Hope, daughter of the Duke of Newcastle, who created a sensation in New York when she was discovered working behind the counter as a work-girl in the big Saks store in Fifth-avenue, has now joined the board of the New Sporting Kit Co., a British firm in Paris.

Lady Doria, when interviewed, denied stories published abroad that she was married and was the wife of a British aristocrat.

"I am not even engaged to be married," she said. Lady Doria earned a salary of £5 a week while working in the New York store.—Central News.

Daily Mirror
1929

LADY HOUSTON'S ULTIMATUM

Hull Tramway Victims' Case Before Council To-day

LAW COURT FIGHT

Dismissal Notices Not to Take Effect Before Christmas

FROM OUR SPECIAL CORRESPONDENT

Hull, Monday.

Assured of financial support from Lady Houston, the 113 Hull tramway "victims" have resolved on legal action against the City Council.

These men volunteered during the general strike and were given permanent employment. They are now being dismissed as the Socialists have a majority on the Council.

I understand that Lady Houston has given the City Council twenty-four hours in which to reconsider their "most unjust edict" in threatening to dismiss the men.

Early developments are expected, as the Tramways Committee are due to meet to-morrow, when the present situation and Lady Houston's offer to assist the men will be discussed.

Lady Houston, who contributed £30,000 to the Miners' Relief Fund last year, has offered to pay the wages of the volunteers until the new year, and if necessary to fight the decision of the City Council in the Law Courts on their behalf.

THE MEN'S THANKS

In a letter from Lady Houston, who is now at her Jersey home, to Mr. G. T. Gibson, the secretary of the volunteers' organisation, her secretary wrote:—

"Lady Houston wishes to know how much the sum she has promised comes to each week, so that she may send a cheque to you for the men, and if you will kindly arrange to pay them for her as it becomes due, she will be greatly obliged."

A resolution expressing heartfelt thanks and deepest appreciation to Lady Houston for her magnificent offer, proposed by the chairman, Mr. C. G. Fox, was carried.

"I have written to Lady Houston," Mr. Gibson told me to-night, "explaining that as Councillor Wokes has withdrawn his motion to rescind the council's proposals on hearing that they would extend our notice from one week to nine weeks, we do not expect to be suspended before Christmas."

Mr. Philip Snowden, M.P.

Chancellor's Tribute to the Savings Movement.

Saving
1929

A WORD OF WARNING.

Mr. Snowden then sounded a note of warning regarding the investments selected by thrifty working people. There were a great many attractions and temptations to-day and working people were sometimes tempted by the dazzling prospects of capital appreciation or of a high rate of interest to invest in issues or shares of a not very reputable character. He knew the struggles that working people had to make to put a little by and it was a terrible thing to see the savings of years swept away.

"I think," said Mr. Snowden, " that one of the great benefits among the many benefits which this Movement confers is that it gives security to savings for people who cannot afford to take any risks and, if it will not be regarded as an impertinence, I should like to give this word of warning to thrifty people—to be extremely careful about the investments they select for their hard-earned savings which they cannot afford to lose."

1930 – 1939

Guidance for Commercial Travellers.

Commercial travellers are not required to register, but they are required to pay heavy licence fees (in Spanish " patentes ") to the Federal Government for permission to work in Buenos Aires. There are provincial licences costing varying amounts for every province visited. The duration of the licence is for one calendar year, or what may remain of the calendar year when the licence is taken out, with the exception that on the occasion of a first visit a traveller need only pay for the remaining months in the year in which he arrives. The Federal licence is obtainable from the Administracion General de Contribucion Territorial de Patentes y Sellos, Calle San Martin, 561, Buenos Aires. The licence fee ranges from 500 to 20,000 paper pesos.

The penalty for contravention is immediate arrest, with detention for one month unless the licence fee and a fine of double the amount of the fee are paid.

South American Handbook 1930

The Church of St. Mary the Virgin, Monken Hadley, Middlesex, dates back to 1494. It has always been lighted by candles, but the Consistory Court of London has just granted the Rector permission to instal electric lighting. The petition was opposed by Mr. J. Percy Callard, of The Priory, Monken Hadley, who was supported by Dr. Walter Mercer. Their objection was on aesthetic grounds; the Rector's case rested on hygienic grounds (rebutted by the Doctor) and on financial grounds (which of course are always irrebuttable)—for candle-lighting costs the Church no less than £20 a year! Mr. Errington, the Chancellor of the Diocese, rested his decision on the ground that he must pay particular importance to the views of the congregation; but the proof of their views appears to have been the " almost unanimous vote of the Parochial Church Council." (*The Observer*, July 27, p. 16.) We hope that Mr. Callard will not allow the matter to rest there, and we suggest to any readers who agree with his action to write and tell him so. The destruction by fire of so many old country mansions recently ought surely to be a warning against the adoption of modern lighting methods. The Rector's health, and the health of his congregation, are not of supreme importance. Like candles, they go out one by one, and are replaceable. The fabric of this ancient church is irreplaceable.

New Age 1930

GIRL GENERAL MANAGER.

BIG POST AT 24.

"MEN ARE EASY TO WORK WITH."

At the age of only 24, Miss Laura Bowen, a slim brunette, has been appointed general manager of Messrs. Peter Jones, the drapery and furnishing store, Sloane-square, S.W.

A little more than three years ago Miss Bowen joined the firm as secretary to the buyer in the furnishing sec-

MISS BOWEN.

tion. She had just gained her degree of B.Sc. at London University, and settled down to learn all she could of administrative methods.

Soon her unusual abilities were recognised, and she became the general manager's assistant.

Miss Bowen said to a *Daily Mail* reporter yesterday:

My appointment as general manager was something of a surprise to me. I had been working and studying with that ambition, but I did not dream it would be realised so soon.

I do not find any difficulty in dealing with the men under my control. Most of the male staff have their own departmental managers, and these managers and supervisors are extraordinarily helpful and easy to work with.

I believe it is a good thing to have a woman general manager in such a store as this. The majority of the staff and nearly all our customers are women.

After a long day at the store Miss Bowen often plays a vigorous game of tennis to freshen her for the next day's work.

Evening News 1930

INSURANCE STAMPS USED TWICE.

BRISTON CARPENTER FINED £4

At Holt Petty Sessions, on Friday, before Lt.-Col. F. Watson-Kennedy and other magistrates,

Herbert George Whittred (55), carpenter, of Briston, was summoned on the information of John Harold Pegg, of Norwich, for fraudulently affixing two used stamps to a National Health Insurance card, at Briston, between January 20th and 27th, 1930. He pleaded guilty to the two charges.

Mr. A. Wiltshire prosecuted for the Minister of Health, and said that the proceedings were brought with respect to stamps placed on the first and third spaces of defendant's health insurance card for the first half of the year 1930. Altogether there were seven bad stamps on the card, to the total value of 10s.6d., but the more important feature was that the stamps qualified the man for the benefits such as a pension at the age of 65 instead of 70; a pension of 10s. a week for his widow, and also medical benefits. The defendant had said, when interviewed by the inspector, that his employer had given him the stamps and he had kept them in an old wallet, and they had become stuck, and he had removed them and had to use gum to fix them on the card. It was found, however, that the stamps had come from an insurance card, and a witness would be called to depose that the stamps had been cancelled and had been put on a card for defendant's son Alfred. The suggestion was that defendant removed the stamps from his son's card and put them on his own.

Reginald George Green, an executive officer of the Ministry of Health, deposed that he found the two stamps had been previously used on another card for the second half of the year 1929.

Defendant told the Bench that the stamps were given to him to put on and he did so, thinking it would be quite all right.

Whittred was fined £2 in each case, including costs, or in default of payment 14 days' imprisonment in each case, the sentences to run consecutively. He was allowed a month in which to pay.

Norfolk Chronicle 1931

THREE BOOKMAKERS FINED.

SEQUEL TO POLICE RAIDS AT YORK.

Following a series of raids by York City police on 31 March, three bookmakers appeared before the magistrates yesterday on summonses for having used premises for the purpose of betting on horse races, with persons resorting to them.

Fred Bell, of 38, George-street, was fined £20; Richard Francis Hodge, of 24 Nunnery-lane, £30; and John Saville Wharton, of 2, Montague-street, £10. The Chairman (Coun. Ben Dodsworth) said that all three had been convicted previously of similar offences, and as they thought it worth while carrying on, they were each fined higher amounts than they had been fined before.

Summoned for having resorted to Hodge's office in Nunnery-lane for the purpose of " betting on certain events and contingencies relating to horse races," Harry Bootland, Frederick E. White, Robert Simpson and Sarah A. Hardgrave were bound over on an undertaking not to resort to betting premises in future. Benjamin Thompson was similarly bound over on a summons for having resorted to Wharton's office in Montague-street.

CHILDREN VISIT SHOP.

Evidence was given in each case by Constable Thomas Capstick, who said that, following complaints, he kept observation on the premises of the three bookmakers between 25 and 31 March and saw numbers of people visit them and remain a short time.

In the case of Bell, who carried on betting at his baker's shop, a large number of children visited his premises, and the officer was satisfied that they made no purchases. When Chief Inspector Williams and other officers raided the premises and produced their warrant Bell said " It's all right. You needn't read it, it's all here," and handed over slips relating to bets on horses running at Nottingham.

Bell denied that all the children went to his shop with bets, and said some called for things which were being baked but were not ready.

Northern Echo 1931

In Defence of the Dole.

Bank Chambers,
Sowerby Bridge.
Feb. 5, 1931.

Sir,—In his weekly article of Saturday last James Parker is very severe on some women who draw unemployment benefit at the Labour Exchange. He goes on to say that the butcher's boy, who came across their garden the other morning whistling " Happy days are here again," is unaware that it is quite a common practice for married women to get work for a few weeks, qualify for unemployment benefit, lose their work, and then draw unemployment benefit as long as it is allowed. Any woman who read that article and thinks the process of getting unemployment benefit is as easy as James Parker describes will have a rude awakening. First of all she has to get a job—not so easy in these days for a woman turned forty. Then when she loses the job, purposely, and goes to the Exchange to sign, she will have a few questions put to her as to where she has been working and why she is playing, and the woman will be surprised on her next visit to the Exchange, when they have got all the information about her case; and even if the woman has got enough stamps to qualify, she will find her benefits suspended six weeks, and if she goes with her case to the Court of Referees, she will still find herself without benefits if she loses her shop as James Parker describes. Before a woman can draw unemployment benefit at the Employment Exchange, she has got to satisfy the officials on that department that, normally, she works in an insured trade or occupation, and has got at least 30 stamps for the previous two insurance years, and that her unemployment for the rest of the period for which she has no stamps is due to the exigencies of the trade in which she is normally employed, or that she has been off work through accident or sickness (a doctor's certificate must be produced in this case to cover the period of unfitness for employment). We had a case before the local Court of Referees in January when a girl had worked in the factory from 14, became an insured person at 16, and is now within a month of 18, but has only 28 stamps, because since she was 16 the factory where she is employed has played off two-thirds of its time, and the young woman has not yet drawn one penny from the Employment Exchange.

Halifax Courier and Guardian 1931

UNEMPLOYMENT PAYMENTS.

To the Editor of the "Bexhill Observer."

Sir,—I note in your last Saturday's " Observer " a statement from the Hastings Employment Committee that during the period from January 28th to February 24th the sum of £275 13s. 8d. was disbursed at Bexhill in unemployment benefits. I think, in all fairness to employer and employed, they should also state how much is received by means of the unemployment stamps contributed by the employer and employed for that period.

Yours truly,
COMPELLED TO PAY.

Bexhill-on-Sea Observer 1930

England's Detroit

If one looks at the recently issued volume of Census figures one will notice in it a list of large towns with a population of over 50,000. One may be impressed with the growth of several of these towns, but easily the most impressive is that of Dagenham. Within ten years its population has increased from 9,000 persons to 89,000. Dagenham is the home of the Ford Motor Company's new works in England and if it is American in nothing else it is certainly American in its springing up, like Topsy, in a not very long night.

A little over eighteen months ago the works consisted of 500 acres of marshy land on the banks of the Thames. To-day, the marsh is no longer visible—vistas of concrete, of steel and of glass have replaced it. The building of the works has been an epic of constructural engineering : like so many of the epics of this country, very few people are aware of it.

ISMA 1931

Saving Money on Clothes

Any woman can save half to two-thirds of the cost of her clothes—and her children's—by making them herself. The Woman's Institute can teach her to do so with skill equal to that of a professional dressmaker. There are no difficulties in the way.

All the instruction is by correspondence. You learn in your own home at your own time. Friendly teachers guide you every step of the way. Soon you are able to make all kinds of smart garments, and then on can effect large economies every year.

IF YOU WISH TO TAKE UP DRESSMAKING AS A PROFESSION

the Woman's Institute can be of invaluable assistance to you.

Send us your name and address, a post-card will do, and we will forward you full information about our Dressmaking and Designing and Millinery Courses.

WOMAN'S INSTITUTE OF DOMESTIC ARTS AND SCIENCES, LTD.
(Dept. 32), 71, Kingsway, London, W.C.2.

Modern Marriage **1932**

TATE AND LYLE, LTD.

SPLENDID RECOVERY IN PROFIT: CONSERVATIVE DISTRIBUTION.

In a season of almost unalleviated gloom, the report of Tate and Lyle, Ltd., stands out with an even greater clarity than its inherent excellence would have commanded for it during a period of normal trading. A year ago the company returned what, for it, was a poor result, and about one quarter of the ten per cent. dividend to ordinary shareholders had to be taken out of profits previously accumulated. The chief cause of the severe decline in profits during 1929-30, it may be recalled, was the slump in raw sugar, the latter falling in price from about 9s. 9d. to 4s. 9d. per cwt. Against some fall in values the company had been holding itself in readiness for a number of years, but the fall when it came was so far-reaching that it involved a scale of prices never previously within experience. To put the stocks on a sound basis in the light of this experience required such heavy provisions from revenue that profits fell to the lowest level experienced by the business since the Tate and Lyle amalgamation of 1921.

Investor's Guardian **1931**

Girls In Demand

Girls are more in demand than boys in the Labour market. Girls, according to a report issued by the Ministry of Labour, are displacing boys in many of our lighter manufacturing industries and in clerical and commercial work.

This, of course, is due to the fact that employers are finding out that the average girl is of far more use than her brother in many directions in the modern factory. She is a better machine-minder, her fingers are more deft for the handling of small apparatus, and her ability not to let her mind wander from the job is greater than a boy's because she is less restless.

Owing perhaps to their lack of originality as compared with boys, girls, according to psychologists, can much more easily adapt themselves to dull routine work of machine-run factories and offices

Gloucestershire Echo **1932**

SIR WILLIAM PRYKE DEAD

Sir William Pryke, Lord Mayor of London in 1925-26, died at his home at Wanstead on Wednesday. He was 85, and had been ill for some time.

For nearly 50 years Sir William had been prominent in the life of the City. During his year as Sheriff in 1921-22, he was knighted. In 1926 he received his baronetcy. Lady Pryke died in 1925. His daughter, Miss Ethel Pryke, who acted as Lady Mayoress, was married in St. Paul's Cathedral during her father's year as Lord Mayor. This was the first wedding to take place in the Cathedral for 16 years.

Sir William had for twenty-two years been a member, and for nine years chairman, of the Wanstead Urban Council. For eight years he represented Wanstead on the Essex County Council, and during the war was chairman of the local tribunal and of the Food Control Committee. He began his business career as an office boy at 5/- a week, and rose to be chairman of Pryke and Palmer, Ltd., iron and hardware merchants.

He is succeeded in the baronetcy, which was conferred in 1926, by his son, William Robert Dudley Pryke, who was born in 1882.

Essex Herald **1932**

Should Married Lady Doctor Resign?

The Public Health Committee reported that Dr. A. E. Rowlands, assistant medical officer, had married, but that a proposition that she be asked to resign was lost.—Mr. A. Jones, Holywell, proposed that the minutes be not confirmed. He said he had nothing against the doctor but was opposed to the principle. A school teacher who married had to resign. Here was a doctor getting £11 per week, married to a county school master, and between them they got £20 per week from the county.—On a vote, an amendment that the doctor be asked to resign was lost, and then a ballot was demanded, and this resulted in favour of the doctor by 26 votes to 24.

Rhyl Journal **1932**

COTTON SPINNERS.

Deadlock In Wage Cut Negotiations.

EMPLOYERS MEET.

Ministry of Labour Watching Events.

THE Wages Committee of the Federation of Master Cotton Spinners' Associations met in Manchester to-day to discuss the position arising out of the deadlock which has arisen in the negotiations over a wage reduction in the spinning section of the Lancashire cotton industry.

The negotiations had been carried on with representatives of the two operatives' organisations—the Operative Spinners' Amalgamation and the Cardroom Workers' Amalgamation.

Originally the employers asked for a wage cut of 2s. 9d. in the £ off earnings, but this figure was reduced in the course of negotiations, and when the discussions ended the employers offered to agree to a settlement on the same terms as that which was arrived at in the weaving section. This was for a wage reduction equal to 1s. 8½d. in the £.

OPERATIVES' DEMAND.

The operatives refused to agree to any figure beyond approximately 9¾d. in the £, and attached to this concession certain conditions regarding the restoration of the 48-hours' working week.

At that point the negotiations broke down.

When the Wages Committee of the Federation met to-day it considered, among other aspects of the question, that of taking a ballot of its members on the issue of closing the mills to enforce the reduction.

The support of 80 per cent. of the members is required before the Federation can give instructions to that effect.

It is known that at least one important section of the spinning trade is extremely reluctant to go to the length of closing the mills.

Bournemouth Daily Echo 1932

Messrs. W. S. Whimster & Son

NINETY YEARS OF PROGRESS.

Established by William S. Whimster in 1844, this business was carried on by him and his son till 1902, when it was taken over by his grandsons, who still carry on. Incidentally, both present partners have a son in the business, this making a fourth generation. The firm has grown steadily until it is one of the most comprehensive in the north of Scotland. Messrs. Whimster & Son still continue to handle the heavies, such as iron and steel, etc., but have launched out in many other ways. Of course, being in an agricultural district, and Montrose being more or less an agricultural town, this industry represents quite fifty per cent. of the firm's activities.

Success to-day is still dependent upon the practice of those principles that have always proven quite efficacious to this end, viz., the supply of truly worth-while productions at the lowest reasonable prices. This policy will never fail! The photograph shown here is that of Mr. W. S. Whimster, the founder.

The late Mr. W. S. Whimster, Founder of Messrs. W. S. Whimster & Son

Town and Country Illustrated 1932

MONKEN HADLEY CHURCH.

Sir,—Your courtesy in sending me a copy of your issue of 31st ult. is much appreciated, and I thank you for the sympathy expressed in it. I deeply regret that my effort to save this beautiful and unique old church from being modernised and robbed of its quiet restful character has failed.

I am afraid I can do no more. For years I have fought this battle, both in and out of office as church warden, but it seems hopeless now, so blind are people to beauty in any form.

New Age 1930

SEEDS FOR UNEMPLOYED.

At Ecclesfield, on Saturday, the seed distribution, under the Unemployed Scheme, took place in the centre of the village, under the supervision of the secretary, Mr. Alfred Stringer. Nearly six tons of seeds and fertiliser were distributed in addition to nearly 100 gardening tools.

The village gardening scheme has under cultivation about seven acres of land.

Sheffield Daily Telegraph 1933

Daily Mirror 1932

NOBEL PRIZE FOR MR. GALSWORTHY

"I Am Very Proud," Says Famous Novelist

Mr. John Galsworthy, the noted novelist and playwright, was yesterday awarded the coveted Nobel Prize for Literature.

The value of the prize this year, states Reuter from Stockholm, will be about £9,000 at current rate of exchange.

The names of John Masefield, Maxim Gorky, and Paul Valery (the French poet and critic) had been mentioned as being in the running for the prize.

Mr. Galsworthy is widely read in Sweden, the message adds, and this is probably the most popular literature prize award the Nobel Commissioners have ever made.

Mr. and Mrs. Galsworthy are staying at their Sussex home near Arundel.

John Galsworthy.

"I am very pleased and very proud," was Mr. Galsworthy's comment on receiving news of the award from Sweden. Mr. Galsworthy now joins Mr. Rudyard Kipling and Mr. Bernard Shaw, who are the only two British writers to whom the prize for literature has been previously awarded.

The Nobel Prize for Medicine has also come to Britain this year, being shared by Sir Charles Sherrington, of Oxford University, and Professor Douglas Adrian, of Cambridge

DEVOTED SERVANT BURIED IN MASTER'S GRAVE

Served Rev. W. T. Hollins For 45 Years

Miss Clementina Jane Daguid (63), who for 45 years was in the service of the late Rev. W. T. Hollins, sometime vicar of St. James's, Clapham Park, was buried on Monday in the vicar's grave at Morden Cemetery.

The Rev. W. T. Hollins died a fortnight ago and the next day Miss Daguid fell ill and never recovered.

She was a student in Mrs. Hollins' bible class in Cumberland and when Mrs. Hollins married she entered the service of the family.

She brought up the eight children of the family and helped to rear their 11 grandchildren.

EVEN TO CANADA

One of the sons is a farmer in Canada and when his wife fell ill Miss Daguid travelled the thousands of miles to nurse her.

The three remaining sons of Mr. Hollins and his daughter were mourners at the funeral service in St. James's church on Monday.

Four clergymen took part in the service, including Canon H. M. Braithwaite, Rector of St. Michael's, Gloucester, a brother of Mrs. Hollins, who had travelled specially from Gloucester to deliver an address.

South London Press 1933

THE WATCH OF DEATH

GRIM AND GAY TALES FROM THE EAST

ROTARY ADDRESS

INTERESTING sidelights on police work in the East were given by Capt. E. W. Nell, of Gloucester, at the Cheltenham Rotary Club's luncheon at the Queen's Hotel yesterday.

He related many amusing experiences of his career in the East as a Chief of Police, Deputy Assistant Provost Marshal, magistrate, Officer Commanding Prisons, officer in charge of an Egyptian Battalion, officer in charge of an Italian contingent, Town Major, Chief Naval Officer, First Chief of C.I.D., and Judge of Assize.

Wounded in France in the Great War, Capt. Nell went out to Jaffa in 1917, where he became head of the C.I.D. and filled a multiplicity of duties for, as he remarked, "You have not only to be a policeman in the East but a good many other things."

In a droll, chatty and entertaining way, he amused the company by saying that although he had had no medical training it was nothing unusual for him to have in the town hall 60 or 70 patients in the morning waiting to be examined.

Of his success as a physician he did not speak. "But," he said, "I would like to tell the doctors that my maternity ward was quite up-to-date, and that I assisted in bringing quite a lot of children into the world during the time I was there—and I didn't lose a baby. I don't know whether that is a record, but it ought to be."

A QUICK FIST

He told some picturesque stories of his experiences as chief naval officer; and, speaking of the work of the police, he remarked, "You require a quick fist and a quick method of tackling anybody who looks like being unpleasant."

By way of emphasising this he produced from his pocket a curved sinister-looking weapon, used by the native for attack, and showed the method employed in defending oneself against it. "You go straight up to the man," said Capt. Nell, "get your knee to the stomach and as he falls forward bring your fist up to the jaw. That is how you defend yourself against a thing like this. It is useless to think you can draw a revolver, because he is quite as quick as you are."

Captain Nell also drew a colourful picture of the bribery and corruption of the East. "If," he said, "you are going to try a case in court, and you come out of your house in the morning, by the door you will probably find a goat, or one or two sheep, or perhaps a camel, tied to the door. They have been put there by people interested in the case you are about to try, and you are meant to accept them. Naturally, they are not labelled. You have to find out who put them there!

TALE OF A WATCH

After dealing with other phases of Eastern life, Captain Nell took from his pocket a watch, and told a dramatic story in connection with it.

"It was stolen," he said, "by a man called Mahmud, who was killed by an Arab named Isaf. Isaf had the watch, which was stolen from him by his brother Mohammed, and a Jew fought with Mohammed and killed him.

"The Jew claimed the watch, but Isaf killed the Jew because he killed his brother, and then came up for trial. Three men died for the watch, and Isaf eventually paid the penalty, and," said Captin Nell, "I have the watch!"

"That is the sort of thing that happens in the East," he concluded.

In proposing a vote of thanks to Captain Nell for his address, Mr. E. P. Bartlett said he did so with some diffidence, because his name appeared on the watch.

Captain Nell looked up in surprise.

"I have had no connection with it so far as I know," said Mr. Bartlett, amid laughter.

"I must say," remarked Captain Nell, "that the watch was put into my hands for safe keeping, as there was no claimant."

Gloucestershire Echo 1932

South London Press 1933

MINERS' WAGES.

National Conference on June 1st.

NEW AGREEMENT SOUGHT.

A national delegate conference of the Miners' Federation is to be held in London on June 1st to consider what action the Federation shall take following refusal by the owners to negotiate a new national agreement and the Government's refusal to fix a new standard wage rate by legislation.

The decision was reached by the Miners' Federation Executive, after they had given the matter several hours' consideration yesterday. There is still the old-standing rift in outlook by owners and the Federation, the owners adhering to their contention that regulation and supervision of wages must be carried through in the various districts.

Matters are fast drifting towards a climax, for the present wage agreement terminates in July, and the miners' Executive has received authority to end all district agreements

The Federation headquarters in London has been bombarded with resolutions that it is imperative that the existing wage standards should not only be maintained, but improved if possible.

A Fighting Stand.

In face of these resolutions the Federation is determined to make a fighting stand, but is looking to the Government to save the situation and prevent a crisis in July.

It was stated among the miners' leaders yesterday that only national negotiating machinery will satisfy the miners and avert another crisis. The position is viewed with considerable misgiving and anxiety.

Mr. Ebby Edwards, secretary of the Miners' Federation, at the conclusion of yesterday's Executive meeting, said: "We have offered the Government to meet at once on the question of establishing by legislation national machinery for the settlement of any dispute that may arise in the industry, and we are prepared to meet from day-to-day until satisfactory machinery has been agreed upon between the parties.

"Between now and June 1st, when the national conference will be held, there are, of course, possibilities of accommodation, although things at the moment look a little black.

"Matters may have advanced before June 1st, so that we can report favourably to the conference, and if possible prevent any disturbance in the industry in July."

Sheffield Daily Telegraph 1933

London University

Next Monday the King will lay the foundation stone of the new University buildings in Bloomsbury. During its life of not quite a century (it was born in 1836) the University of London has had three different headquarters, each of which it has outgrown in due course—first, some modest apartments in Somerset House, then the building in Burlington Gardens now occupied by the Civil Service Commission, and for the past thirty years the Imperial Institute at South Kensington. The Bloomsbury site, behind the British Museum, is not only more convenient, but it gives ample room for buildings big enough for the administrative staff and consonant with the dignity and importance of the University. These buildings, whose architect is Mr. Charles Holden, will comprise much more than offices. Here are to be a library and a great hall, a number of different University institutions, such as the Institute of Historical Research, the Schools of Oriental Studies and Slavonic Studies, the London Day Training College, and the Courtauld Institute of Art. So far as we can judge from plans and models, the scheme when it is completed should be one of the fine sights of London.

New Statesman 1933

The Saturday Book 1933

Unemployed Demonstration

GET RID OF WASH DAY

No modern household service has reached greater perfection than the laundry . . . Collected regularly at your door, returned to you fresh, clean, beautifully washed . . . The laundry frees you from the back-breaking, ageing toil of the washtub, makes your house healthier, because free from steamy clothes, your home and your appearance smarter. Get rid of washday with its ageing toil. Have new leisure, new comfort for yourself, new smartness for your clothes and house linen. Send it all to the laundry. Say—

How thankful I am for the Laundry

L.5

The Builder 1933

THE FIRESTONE FACTORY, GREAT WEST ROAD, BRENTFORD.

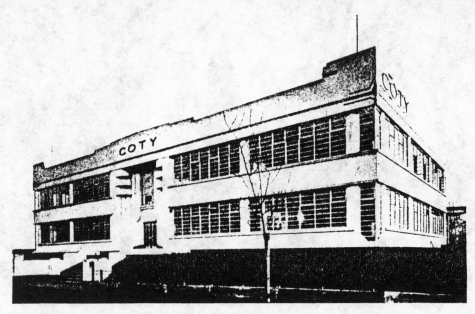

THE COTY FACTORY, GREAT WEST ROAD, BRENTFORD.

THE HOOVER FACTORY, PERIVALE.

Some Modern Factories.

MESSRS. WALLIS, GILBERT AND PARTNERS, Architects.

SIR J. ELLERMAN
TO START WORK.

AT HIS FATHER'S DESK.

Sir John Reeves Ellerman, who has just inherited several of his father's millions and now, at twenty-three, pays more tax than any other individual in the United Kingdom, is to take a part in his father's shipping business.

He is one of the very few who pay £70 in income tax and surtax out of every £100 he receives.

Sir John, who has literary tastes and cares little for social life, has been taking a course in accountancy under private tuition.

He will shortly join the directorate and thereafter will work daily at the London office desk at which his father sat for many years.

Sunday Express 1933

OLD AGE PENSIONS CLAIMS

Problems Before Newtown District Committee

The monthly meeting of Newtown District Old-Age Pensions Committee was held on Tuesday, when the Rev. F. J. Davies presided.

A pensioner in receipt of 4s. a week asked for an increase on the ground that his income was so small that he could no longer manage on it. It was stated that in return for some work he was kept with food and lodging and a little pocket money. The unearned portion of that was considered by the pensions officer to represent 7/8 a week and the earned portion 5s. and it was agreed that the pension should be increased to 10s.

A case was before the committee in which the claimant thought she would be 70 years of age in October and she made her application on July 3 to be in readiness. When the case was investigated it was found that she was 70 last October so the pension of 10s. was allotted to her from the date of the application.

A woman who has been in receipt of a pension of 4s. asked the officer to investigate to see if she were not entitled to a larger amount. It was stated that she had shares totalling £833 15s. 3d. in various companies and a banking account of £255, and also owned the house she occupied which was assessed at £12 5s. a year. The total income was considered, for pension purposes, to be £79 15s. 3d. a year and carried only a pension of 4s. It was agreed to make no change.

Montgomery County Times 1933

THE NATIONAL GALLERY

NEW DIRECTOR NEXT YEAR

The Lords Commissioners of his Majesty's Treasury have appointed Mr. Kenneth McKenzie Clark, Keeper of the Department of Fine Art in the Ashmolean Museum, Oxford, to be Director of the National Gallery in succession to Sir Augustus Daniel, K.B.E., whose term of office expires on December 31, 1933. The appointment is for a term of five years.

Mr. Clark, who is appointed to this important post at the early age of 30, has been Keeper of the Department of Fine Art in the Ashmolean since 1931, when he succeeded Mr. C. F. Bell. He was educated at Winchester and Trinity College, Oxford, where he was a scholar, and after taking his degree in 1926 he worked for two years with Mr. Bernhard Berenson, at Florence, the authority on Italian art. Mr. Clark will be remembered for his work on the committee of the Exhibition of Italian Art at Burlington House in 1930; he was part author and editor of the commemorative catalogue, and in recognition of his services received the Order of the Crown of Italy. He is the author of a remarkably able study of the Gothic revival, and of articles in the *Burlington Magazine* and elsewhere.

Sir Augustus Moore Daniel will be followed in his retirement by the regrets and good wishes of artists, scholars, and connoisseurs, among whom he has a high reputation for fine judgment, wide and accurate learning, and personal charm. When he succeeded Sir Charles Holmes as Director on December 31, 1928, he had just completed his sixty-second year, he was already a trustee of the National Gallery, and had been Assistant Director of the British School at Rome. He had also had much administrative experience, and during his term of office at Trafalgar Square he has shown not only taste and judgment but organizing ability.

The Times 1933

Englishmen for St. Sophia's.

A party of English workmen will soon leave London to clean the mosaics of St. Sophia's in Constantinople. Those mosaics, some made in Justinian's reign, are believed to be the finest in the world, and perhaps the greatest triumphs of Byzantine art, but when the Turks captured Constantinople the decorations of St. Sophia were plastered over, and so, till lately, the great mosaics only showed dimly through the whitewash. But the Moslem church no longer dominates the Turkish State, nor is Constantinople the capital of Turkey. Kemal therefore, has not been afraid to give Christian architects and archaeologists permission to uncover the Christian decorations of the great mosque or former cathedral which the western world still calls St. Sophia. Hence the dispatch of English workmen, fortified with passports and recommendations.

Sheffield Daily Telegraph 1933

Western Times 1933

THE MARRIED WOMAN'S RIGHT to WORK

Individual's Right to Sell Labour for Gain

OBSTACLE in WAY OF MARRIAGE

Two Incomes for One House

The right of married women to work was staunchly championed yesterday at the Conference of the National Council of Women at Torquay by Mrs. Eva Hartree, of Cambridge.

"In Germany," she said, "150,000 young women have been bribed to leave industry to get married. We claim, however, that it is a fundamental right of every individual, regardless of self, to sell his or her labour for gain.

EMPLOYERS ONLY BUSINESS.

"It is a private matter between a woman and her husband how they arrange their lives. It is no business of the employer. The only business of the employer is whether the work is well done and what payment should be given for it.

"It has been said that there should not be two incomes going into one house. But every man who is earning an income of more than subsistence level is taking two incomes into the house."

OBSTACLE TO MARRIAGE.

Mrs. Hartree declared that refusal to allow married women to work was putting an obstacle in the way of marriage.

"To make a woman give up her work on marriage leads to many secret marriages, and even to a great number of immoral marriages—of people living together," she said.

"We all know that young people are the worse for having to wait to get married. It has a shocking effect on young people that they cannot marry until the thirties."

THE NEW DIRECTOR OF THE NATIONAL GALLERY: MR. KENNETH CLARK TAKES UP HIS APPOINTMENT.

Mr. Kenneth Clark, formerly Keeper of the Department of Fine Art in the Ashmolean Museum, Oxford, was appointed Director of the National Gallery in September. He was then only thirty. His term of office began on January 1. He is the author of that delightful book, "The Gothic Revival," published in 1929.

Illustrated London News 1934

WIDECOMBE-IN-THE-MOOR'S NEW POST OFFICE.

Widecombe-in-the-Moor has a new Post Office, and it was opened on Wednesday.

According to a letter which we have received from Miss Beatrice Chase, the Dartmoor novelist, the village is thrilled at the prospect, not only of having the new office at the bottom of the famous Widecombe Hill, but at the arrival of a pillar box! A pillar box has not previously been known in the village. But there is just one snag. The colour of the box clashes violently with the colour of the rambler rose adjoining, and it is suggested that the Postmaster-General should be asked to see that either the pillar box or the rambler rose should be repainted!

Western Times 1933

Birmingham Mail 1934

PAYMENT FOR HOLIDAYS.

Sir,—Your correspondents on the subject of payment for holidays overlook the really vital point. In the case of staff workers holidays do not affect the volume of work accomplished; the lost time is made up either before or after the holiday by an extra effort from the individual concerned, or the work is carried on by colleagues during his absence.

The tradition of an annual holiday for staff workers is one of the finest examples of reciprocal effort in commerce.

When the manual worker is given a holiday, production must suffer unless additional labour is engaged. To pay a production worker when he is producing nothing would obviously involve the employer in a double loss.

COMPANY SECRETARY.

DRUNK IN CHARGE OF— ICE-CREAM !

A fine of £12 and his licence endorsed was imposed upon John Manno, 13 Leonard Street, Perth, at Perth to-day, when he was charged with driving a motor cycle combination under the influence of drink. It was stated that accused was of Italian extraction, and sold ice-cream from a motor cycle. A constable had to support accused all the way to the police station.

Edinburgh Evening News 1934

Maison Lyons at Marble Arch

Public Support for a Restaurant of Many Novel Ideas

MAISON LYONS Corner House, the fourth establishment of its kind, was opened near the Marble Arch on Monday, October 23. This latest addition to the big popular restaurants of Messrs. J. Lyons & Co., Ltd., seats over 2,000, being composed of three cafés—the "Quebec Café," with a capacity of 1,250, "Bryanston Café," seating 750, and "Park Café," to seat 80.

A staff of more than 1,000 is employed, most of whom have been transferred from the Maison Lyons, Oxford Street, which was closed on the Sunday night preceding the opening of the new Corner House.

Artistic Decorations

The establishment occupies two floors. On the ground level is a shopping hall, called "Park Court" with "Park Café" to one side, behind which lies "Bryanston Café," with the kitchens at the back.

Downstairs is "Quebec Café," with cloakrooms and a big telephone room.

The whole place has been decorated and furnished in a most artistic manner; the decorative themes being more restrained, though no less luxurious, than other Corner Houses.

Nippys ready to commence the first day's service in the Quebec Café at the new Maison Lyons at Marble Arch, London

Hotel Review 1933

WOMEN TEACHERS

MANCHESTER PROPOSAL TO DISMISS THE MARRIED.

The Manchester Education Committee yesterday decided to dispense with the services of women teachers upon their marriage.

A resolution to this effect was carried by ten votes to nine, and is subject to the provision that exceptional cases will be taken into consideration. It has to be submitted to the City Council before it can be enforced.

It is stated that there are 289 married women teachers in Manchester.

Councillor Jackson, who moved the resolution, spoke of the hardship imposed on many young women who could not obtain positions after they had passed through college owing to the number of married women teachers. It would be an encouragement to those young women if the barrier were removed.

He also pointed out that a new teacher had to spend many hours after school in study, and that it was detrimental for them to go home and have their ordinary household duties to do, which interfered with the preparation of their lessons.

Mrs. H. M. Iliff seconded, urging that a woman who had a home and a husband had a full-time job, and that the Education Committee ought not to encourage her to give up the time she should be devoting to her home to teaching. Young women teachers, she said, had come up against a blank wall through the employment of married women, and the committee would be able to deal with any special case of hardship on its merit.

Miss Annie Lee said she thought it would discourage young people to enter the teaching profession if there was to be a barrier in the way of marriage.

Councillor Wright Robinson said that education was enriched by the inclusion of married women.

Birmingham Mail 1934

THESE BOARDING-HOUSE HUSBANDS

Hard-Working Men Who Command Our Respect

Blackpool Gazette and Herald 1934

THE boarding-house husbands of Blackpool are out shopping again. You meet them all over the town, often with capacious baskets, always with long and detailed lists. For Whitsuntide has come and gone, and the men who help their wives to run boarding houses are in for a busy time these next few months.

You often hear the question: "What does he do?" And the answer: "Oh, his wife runs a boarding house," has a thinly-veiled contempt behind it sometimes.

* * *

And, yet . . . . .

And yet, no one would dream of sneering at an hotel manager and his wife.

Believe me, these boarding-house husbands are to be admired. They may not be in a big way of business, their daily toil may not have the status of a profession, but they work hard and with an enthusiasm worthy of the cause.

For when all is said and done, boarding-house keeping and hotel management is the real business of Blackpool, and few seaside resorts can offer such excellent all-round facilities in that direction.

FACTORY ACCIDENTS

INCREASE OF 7000 IN A YEAR

WHAT IDLENESS DOES TO THE WORKER

There was an increase of more than 7000 accidents in factories and workshops during last year when compared with 1932, the respective totals being 113,260 and 106,164. Fatal accidents increased from 602 to 688.

Commenting on these figures the annual report of the Chief Inspector of Factories and Workshops for 1933, which was published to-day, states that this increase was not only due to increased employment, but also to other and altogether exceptional factors operating at the present time.

"Workers are returning to employment often after long periods of enforced unemployment," it is stated. "Many of them are suffering from lack of nourishment, and physically and mentally are less alert and more liable to mishap than in normal times.

TOO EAGER

"Again, there is evidence that on re-starting work after a long spell of idleness some workers tend to over-exert their strength and energy, while others take some time to get accustomed to working conditions again.

"All these factors have to be taken into account, although it is also true that machinery is more efficiently fenced, plant of all kinds more safely constructed, welfare and working conditions of a much higher standard, and more precautions are taken by employers and workers alike than at any time in our industrial history."

Mr D. R. Wilson, the Chief Inspector, states that, in common with his predecessors, he had been chiefly impressed by the industrial accidents that yearly recur, and not so much by their frequency and severity as by the number that were avoidable. "The contempt for transmission machinery, for instance," he adds, "which is responsible for a wholly unnecessary toll of death and disablement, is almost incredible, considering that its dangerous character has been continuously emphasised from the very start of factory inspection. And yet there are still workers, and even factory engineers, who contend that smooth shafting in motion is harmless."

CARELESS BUTCHERS

Other three machines which were particularly dangerous are guillotines, in connection with which fingers and sometimes whole hands had been amputated; the careless approach to hydro extractors, which had led to arms being torn off at the elbow and shoulder; and mincing machines in food factories, butchers' shops, and restaurant kitchens.

With regard to mincing machines, states another part of the report, of about 10,000 butchers' shops visited, more than 7000 were found not to comply with the agreed standard for the use of these dangerous machines.

A series of deaths due to inhalation of vapour of diethylene dioxide—dioxan—at an artificial silk works was followed by an inquiry into the extent to which that substance was in industrial use, the result of which was negative. "Subsequent research," adds Mr Wilson, "has clearly demonstrated not only the toxicity of this substance—dioxan—but also the insidious nature of its action, and, unless suitable precautions are taken, there is nothing to prevent a similar catastrophe arising from the use of other compounds the properties of which are unknown."

Cardiff Transport Band.

At the Bridgwater Band Festival last Saturday, the Cardiff Transport Band (conducted by Mr. D. Carrie), came first out of 19 Bands in the competition for Uniform and Deportment, and thus they repeated last year's success in this event. Having won the cup twice for this competition they only have to win it next year to make it their own. The Band through its success last year was debarred from entering Class 2 section and they had to compete with some of the best bands in the country in the Open Championship Class A. The competition was much keener this year and there was a larger entry and the Band did well to come third. Cory's Workmen's being first and Camborne Town second. In the test piece "Z'ebreo" (Appolloni) the Band was the best. The Band greatly appreciates the help and assistance given to them by Mr. W. Forbes (the General Manager) and Mr. J. D. Dunning (The Traffic Superintendant) and this has been a big factor in the Bands' success.

Cardiff and Suburban News 1935

Traveller's Gazette 1936

Congresses in Holland.

THE International Refrigeration Congress will be held from June 16 to 27 in The Hague, which will also be the venue, from July 12 to 23, of the Technical and Chemical Congress of the Agricultural Industries.

At the neighbouring seaside resort of Scheveningen (" the Brighton of Holland ") the International Union of Producers and Distributors of Electrical Energy will meet in Congress from June 10 to 20.

Edinburgh Evening News 1934

RETIREMENT OF SERGT. R. ROBERTS.

Shrewsbury Officer Who Served With " Death or Glory Boys."

Sergeant Robert Roberts, chief clerk of the Shrewsbury borough police force, retires to-day after 31 years' service. He is well known, not only to every member of the force, but to everyone in Shrewsbury. He is the personification of the spirit of the force; sympathetic without prejudice to his duty, helpful and considerate.

He is one of those men who has always got to be doing something. He was born at Hookagate, and joined the 17th Lancers at the minimum age. He was promptly whisked away to the Boer War, and saw active service for two years there. The Lancers landed at Cape Colony, and fought their way from Johannesburg, via the Orange Free State and the Eastern Transvaal to Koomati Port, near Delagoa Bay. He admits to having enjoyed that campaign not a little. It was a more gentlemanly war than that of 1914 to 1918. The type of fighting was different. The Boers ensconced themselves in a range of hills—kopjes they called them—and fired on the Lancers from long range. The Lancers, having duly driven the Boers out of one range, went over the hills to find them, digging themselves into an exactly similar range just beyond. And so it went on.

"We all grew whiskers," says Sergt. Roberts, "and looked as bad as the Boers themselves!"

After the war he returned to Shrewsbury, and the very day of his arrival —it was the Monday after the Flower Show—he presented himself at the police station as a recruit. He filled in the appropriate form, and was appointed to the force just three weeks later.

Then in 1914 war again broke out, and Sergt. Roberts rejoined his old regiment at once. He went to the 17th Lancers, because, he says, "They are second to none in the British army." This incidentally was just after his promotion to the rank of acting sergeant.

He was appointed a yeomanry instructor in Ireland with the rank of sergeant-major. Unfortunately, he had his arm badly smashed in an accident in 1916, and spent fifteen months in hospital, being laid up at the time of the Irish rebellion. He recollects with regret the smashing and looting of the fine city of Dublin.

In 1917 he returned to the Shrewsbury police force as assistant chief clerk, and was promoted to chief clerk and sergeant a year later. He has held that rank ever since.

He has known four chief constables, Mr. Blackwell, Mr. F. Baxter, Mr. H. F. Harries, the honorary chief constable during the war, and the present chief, Mr. Frank Davies.

"Shrewsbury has never been bad as regards crime," says Sergt. Roberts. "Our chief cases were drunks, mostly local men. Things have improved wonderfully since then. In those days I could get a rough house any night I felt like it."

Shrewsbury Chronicle 1933

THE UNIVERSITY LIBRARY, CAMBRIDGE—I
Architect : Sir Giles Gilbert Scott, R.A.

The present year has seen the completion of two great libraries, each the finest of its type in this country. The Manchester Reference Library, which we illustrated last February, is a building on a confined site with the stack and reading-room in vertical relationship; the books are fetched to the reading-tables by attendants. The Cambridge Library, on the other hand, is a wide-spreading building, typifying the open-access system in an ideally developed form.

Plan.—The first floor is the principal floor, and steps lead up to it from either side of the entrance hall under the tower. From the lobby thus reached the long Catalogue Room leads through to the Reading Room; the catalogue is housed in a series of shelves with desks in front of them. On either side of the Catalogue Room are the under-librarians' rooms and editorial and revising rooms where the catalogue is kept up to date. As the library is obliged to receive a copy of every book published in Britain, the work involved is, of course, elaborate and continuous.

Architect and Building News 1934

"OLD KATE"

Death of London's Best Known Match-Seller

"Old Kate," the match-seller—Kate Lucille Foote was her real name,—has died in a London County Council institution. She was known to thousands who every day passed her pitch, just where the 'buses halt at the corner of Aldwych and the Strand. She was about seventy years of age.

She used to sit swathed in clothes, with a red flannel scarf round her neck, her face towards the Gaiety Theatre, which stood on the site of that theatre in which she had played leading parts.

During the eleven years she occupied her pitch she made many friends, and through them gossip of the theatre still filtered through to her.

She was the daughter of an American colonel, and first went on the stage when she was twenty. She was with George Edwardes in London for three or four years. She was married three times, and each of her husbands left her a fortune. Her last husband, Mr. Isidor Mass, a tobacco merchant, left her £25,000. Some time afterwards she went to the Monte Carlo Casino with a party of friends, won thousands of pounds, lost them again, and returned to London with little money but the bare fare. She sought work in vain, and at last, already grey-haired, she became a match-seller.

Manchester Guardian 1936

NOT GAS

False Alarm in Commons

Miss Wilkinson (Lab.—Jarrow) drew the attention of the Deputy Speaker (Captain Bourne), in the House of Commons last night, to what seemed to her to be an escape of gas in the Chamber.

Captain Bourne replied that he had detected a peculiar smell in the Chamber.

Mr. Magnay (L. Nat.—Gateshead) said that at high tide there was always an abominable smell from the river not unlike gas.

Manchester Guardian 1936

ULSTER PROTESTANT LEAGUE.

DERRY COUNCILLOR'S SPEECH.

Councillor James Gallagher, president of the Maiden City Ulster Protestant League, spoke at a meeting near Bally-money on the occasion of the opening of a new branch.

Mr. Gallagher referred to the employment of Roman Catholics in Londonderry, and said hundreds of Londonderry's Loyalist citizens were walking the streets of their native city in idleness, while inter-lopers, and treacherous, rebel interlopers at that, were given employment and a foothold in the city by the very men who should be keeping them out.

"History tells us," said Mr. Gallagher, "that Lundy stole away in disguise to save himself from the vengeance of the people he tried to betray. Unfortunately he left plenty of his breed to take his place.

"Derry and the Six Counties are being betrayed and lost through a weak and short-sighted policy. The process of welcoming and employing Donegal rebels has gone on so long and so freely in Derry that we are now outnumbered. You can have little idea of what it means to dwell in a border city. Our trade is being strangled, and ever since the betrayal of the cause that led to the establishment of the Free State there has been a consistent and definite attempt to boycott Derry to force us into the South. That they will never succeed in doing."

Mr. William Archibald, chairman of the Derry League, said the situation to-day was just as critical as it was in 1912 or 1920. Indeed, it was more so, because the present attack on Ulster was not so open. Ulster must stand or fall as a whole, and the Protestants on the border looked to the others further in for support.

Mr. H. J. Crawford, chairman of the Belfast League; Mr. Crossey, secretary of the Belfast League; and Mr. J. S. M'Connell, Belfast, also spoke.

Londonderry Sentinel 1935

Bringing in the catch; in 1932 there were 33,073 men employed in the fishing fleet.

Dover Express 1935

CIVIL SERVANTS' CLERICAL ASSOCIATION.

EQUAL WAGES CLAIM.

A meeting of the local members of the Civil Servants Clerical Association was held at the Grand Hotel on Tuesday evening, to hear addresses by Alderman Ross Wyld (President, C.S.C.A.) and Mr. W. A. Boddy (Secretary, C.S.C.A., P.O. section). The Chairman, Mr. E. P. Kidson, in his opening remarks, said that meetings of this sort gave all the different departments the opportunity of getting together to exchange their views, and also to hear what the headquarters of the Association was doing. This year they could congratulate themselves on getting Association officers down to speak to them.

Mr. W. A. Boddy discussed the need for the re-organisation of the Civil Service Association. In 1891 a strike of "jellyfish" clerks showed that conditions in the service were intolerable, and that drastic alterations were necessary. Their organisation was formed to bring these changes about and without it none of the changes that had been effected could have been brought about. One of the problems they had had to contend with was that of segregation. At one time, men and women worked in separate departments, at times with ridiculous results. Further progress could only be achieved if all in the service were members of the Association. Now there was the possibility of a change in the working of their organisation. By re-organisation they could have a much better chance of securing their aims and objects. In the Post Office they had reached a situation in regard to pay claims which could only be resolved by complete reorganisation. At present, writing assistants were doing work which could be done by lower grades and while these duties were performed by writing assistants so long would writing assistants remain at their present scale of pay. There should be a review of the limitation which conditioned their employment in the service. Writing assistants were employed in the ratio of one for every four clerical officers in the Service, but in some departments that ratio had been greatly exceeded. Mr. Boddy concluded his plea for the necessity for reorganisation, by pointing out that more than ever to-day was it essential that they should stand together in the organisation to which they were proud to belong.

Mr. Ross Wyld discussed in some detail the various points which they had put to candidates in the recent general election. Most important of these were the questions of equal pay, and of the Saturday morning holiday. Dealing with equal pay, Mr. Wyld said that there was a general demand in the Service for equal pay for men and women. It was ridiculous, he said, that women who were doing the same work as men should receive less remuneration. It hit the men just as badly as the women, because the tendency was to employ more women and fewer men. The Government had evaded the issue whenever they were approached on the matter. Of course, the Government realised that if they granted equality of pay in the Civil Service, they would have the women teachers making similar demands. It had been pointed out that women were able to marry, but as a matter of fact it was when a woman was passed what was usually considered a marriageable age that the discrepancies between men's and women's wages grew most marked. The Saturday morning proposal was that the four hours work should be spread over the rest of the week, so that except for a minimum staff, they would have two whole days in which to do what they liked. The Government had refused their demands, but if they worked together in a spirit of fellowship success would attend their efforts.

Beauty Culture as a Career

By W. E. C. COWIE

(Principal of the Institute of Health and Beauty).

THE cultivation of facial and bodily beauty has never had so many exponents as it has to-day. Its study and practice may be called a science, a profession, an art or a trade. That depends upon one's viewpoint. The quest of beauty is primarily a science which should express itself in highly professional and artistic practice and possess as its auxiliary a sound, well organized trade which is beyond reproach. Unfortunately, many people have reason to regret their connection with beauty culture, because so many of its practitioners are insufficiently trained for their work and quite unfit to practise, their aim being simply that of money-making.

It is the girl with good health, supple hands and a pleasing and sympathetic personality who should be encouraged to take up beauty culture as a career. Such girls will find this calling an interesting and profitable one, the training for which is comparatively inexpensive. There are many schools and institutes where training is obtainable, but great care should be exercised in selecting one that is really suitable, and in this direction Cook's Scholastic Agency can give invaluable advice.

Traveller's Gazette 1936

Inauguration

Official opening of Pinewood to-day—though of course the Studio has been working in mild form for some days now. 1,500 guests have been invited and a minimum of 1,100 are expected. It should be a great day in the history of Iver Heath and Fulmer. It is true that in the fruity days of the past when Pinewood was Heatherden Hall, there was some nifty entertaining, but I don't think Col. Grant Morden, or any of his predecessors did it on this scale.

*　　*　　*

Pinewood, of which I have written so frequently that I need hardly do it again, looks like being a great national institution and certainly one of the finest studios in the world. To-day will speed it on its way.

Cinema News 1936

Press Association messenger boys and their superintendent, c. 1930.

The signalman, from *Night Mail,* the 1936 film about the postal service.

PEMBROKE'S APPEAL TO THE KING

INVITATION TO VISIT BOROUGH

MAYOR AND TOWN CLERK BUSY

Pembroke Borough is making every effort to induce His Majesty King Edward VIII. to pay a visit to the town during his forthcoming tour of distressed areas in South Wales.

Immediately it became known that the King would visit South Wales on November 18th and 19th, the Mayor (Ald. W. J. Gwilliam) and the Town Clerk (Mr. R. D. Lowless) got busy.

On Monday letters were dispatched to the King's private secretary—this letter being in the nature of a personal appeal to the King—to Capt. Geoffrey Crawshay, Commissioner for the Distressed Areas, Major Gwilym Lloyd George, M.P., etc. No stone is to be left unturned in an endeavour to achieve the desired end.

Speaking at a meeting of the Pembroke Borough Council on Tuesday, the Mayor said that although the houses in the borough were not hideous and smoke-grimed but pretty and well kept, yet distress and poverty were just as acute as in the Rhondda.

DECEIVED BY APPEARANCES.

"It has not," he said, "been advertised as much and visitors are apt to be deceived by appearances, but make no mistake there is a dire necessity for this borough to receive help. People here have been fighting to keep up appearances. We have appealed and appealed to His Majesty's Ministers and we should now do everything in our power to get His Majesty personally interested in our plight and to visit us here. The Town Clerk has already been active and we intend taking every possible step to induce the King to visit the borough."

Pembroke County and West Wales Guardian 1936

ACTRESS FAINTS ON LONDON STAGE

PLAY DELAYED

Miss Victoria Hopper, the actress wife of Mr. Basil Dean, fainted last night while singing a song, with Miss Flora Robson at the piano, in the play "Autumn" at the St. Martin's Theatre. She had sung only one line when she slipped to the floor. Miss Hopper was carried off the stage by Mr. Wyndham Goldie, and the play was held up for about a quarter of an hour.

An announcement was then made that Miss Hopper was unable to carry on and her part was cleverly taken up by her understudy, Miss Betty Marsden.

Sunday Times 1938

WHAT JARROW WANTS

GOVERNMENT RECOGNITION—NOT INDIVIDUAL HELP

The March—A Successful Proof of Fitness

By "Catholic Herald" Special Representative

Jarrow has been in London all this week and if the dismal situation of this decaying town has not sufficiently impressed itself upon the national conscience before, two hundred marchers walking three hundred miles is publicity that cannot be overlooked.

Jarrow is very far from London, and London is the capital of our centralised semi-Socialist State. But Jarrow remains Jarrow, whatever London does about it, and though London may disregard it in the interests of the "greatest good of the greater number," no Christian may do the same.

For him the men and women of Jarrow, the tradition of Jarrow, the life of Jarrow are as important as the men and women of London and even England. The utilitarian and the Socialist will gladly scrap Jarrow; a true Christian can never scrap anything human, let alone a human being.

"We Don't Get Noticed"

"That's the whole trouble, Jarrow is too far away from London," a *Catholic Herald* representative was told by one of the marchers. "Not because I walked it do I say that" he went on, "but because somehow *we don't get noticed up there, we're out of the public eye, so to speak.*"

Catholic Herald 1936

More Colour in Posters of Tomorrow—
—Says ANNA ZINKEISEN

BELIEVING that no attempt to portray accurately the trend of poster advertising would be complete without a contribution from the expert who does the job, MARKETING consulted Anna Zinkeisen, the artist.

We chose her because only a portion of the work she does is commercial, and consequently she sees posters from the non-commercial artist's angle as well as from the poster artist's.

We asked her first of all how she thought advertisers could make better use of their poster appropriations than they do at present. "Firstly," she replied "by correcting the mistake which so many make of paying a great deal of money for space and then filling it with poor material. They should always employ the best possible artists. Many posters which were painted by famous artists many years ago are still being used.

"I wish that advertisers would allow the artists they commission a little more license. After all, an artist knows far more about art than the advertiser and just as much about his particular branch of selling. Why shouldn't artists be credited with some understanding of the public?"

Miss Zinkeisen spoke next of the trend of posters. "I think," she said, "that they are departing from the abstract type of design which has been popular lately, and going towards a more pictorial style. The trend seems to be towards a more colourful presentation."

Marketing 1937

Market Investigation
for
SALES MANAGERS

Marketing
1937

Speaker :

D. CAMERON SWAN

MARKET analysis is at the very root of a sales manager's job and unless he applies it either consciously or sub-consciously, a sales manager will not in any way justify his position.

The best definition I know of market analysis is this : *Mostly observation of many plain facts, accompanied by constant effort to realise the causes and effects in their due order of importance and time; and then a final effort to express the findings in such orderly manner that the explanation stands firmly and definitely as a guide for action.* If only business executives would learn and apply this definition, there would be much less loose thinking and much time saved.

There is no longer any need for guessing about the things that lead to business success. Achievement has been reduced to a science as exact as chemistry.

Club Life
1937

Finsbury Park Railway Club.

The old ladies' tea and concert, which took place Tuesday, January 5th, was another of the ladies' section successes, which they deserved.

All the dear old ladies, numbering about 57, arrived at about 5 p.m. to a meal which was a credit to the caterer.

The ladies in waiting, all ready to escort and tend to the wants of the elderly, never ceased in their efforts to see that all were well supplied, and I can tell you it was a sight not to be missed to witness the old ladies enjoying themselves after the meal. The hall was cleared and got ready for the concert, and what a show.

The artistes who gave their services free done all they could to make the old ladies happy, and I must say they succeeded, and to Ethel Wyman, Lionel Brook and Harry Hawkins, George Weston, Little Hazel, and not forgetting our little Ilene Roberts, our heartfelt thanks for the way they put themselves out, and as usual the evening closed with " Auld Lang Syne," the pres. wishing all a Happy New Year, hoping to see all their smiling faces next year.

As they all left the club each was given a parcel of groceries, which ended another grand evening for the pres. (Rosie Robinson) and her girls.

Saturday's concert was not supported as it should have been, as we had the pleasure of the company of Wally Viney and friends of the Snooker Boys (Tottenham Trades), and also the vice-pres. (Mr. E. Church), W. Newman and Tom Baldock (Harringay Social), hoping they enjoyed themselves as we enjoyed their company, also the concert, which was first-class.

The Cherry Boys are developing into a great sub-club, which will be an asset to the mother club, and also affiliated clubs, whom they will visit in the near future, so here's wishing them luck.

RUF MOT.

The Times
1937

49 MORE MILLIONAIRES

INCREASE IN NUMBER OF BIG INCOMES

After the number had fallen for some years, there were in Great Britain and Ireland last year 49 more millionaires, and 2,030 more persons with annual incomes exceeding £2,000 than in the previous year. The aggregate income of all such persons increased by £17,175,138.

The full figures, which are based on surtax assessments made at September 30 last on 1934-35 incomes, are included in the report of the Commissioners of the Inland Revenue for the year ended March 31 last. The number assessed was 85,449, with an income of £424,339,484. Those with annual incomes exceeding £30,000 number 824, compared with 775 in the previous year.

There were 60 persons last year with incomes ranging from £75,000 to £100,000, and 69 with incomes exceeding £100,000, the latter aggregating £11,485,300. In the previous year the numbers were 50 and 64 respectively.

FIREMEN HAVE GAS MASK DRILL

Wearing regulation gas masks, members of the Hexham Fire Brigade manipulated the hose and pump on Thursday afternoon under the conditions likely to be experienced during an air attack.

The fire engine was taken out of Hexham for the pumping practice, and the firemen were accompanied by Mr W. G. Landale, the Air Raid Precautions Officer in Hexham.

The object of the display was to get the firemen accustomed to the gas masks and to the operation of the fire-engine and fire appliances while wearing the masks.

The practice was carried out in accordance with the regulations of the Home Office in regard to Air Raid Precautions, which require firemen to receive this training.

MORE VOLUNTEERS WANTED

"The Local Authority desire further volunteers for training for enrolment as Air Raid Wardens, repair and rescue parties, decontamination parties, and messenger service. Particulars ..of ..the ..duties ..of members of these services may be obtained on application to W. G. Landale, A.R.P. Officer, Hexham House, Hexham."

Hexham Fire Brigade starting out for Gas and Fire Fighting Practice.

Hexham Courant 1938

LIABILITIES OF OCCUPIERS FOR DANGEROUS ACTS ON HIGHWAY.

Cellar Flap Dangers.

A RECENT decision, Daniel v. Rickett, Cockerell and Co. and Raymond, indicates that occupiers of premises may be responsible in law for the negligence of third persons, although not their servants or agents, in respect of dangerous acts done on the highway.

In the case in question a firm of coal merchants were delivering coal to the order of a householder. The latter, the occupier of the premises in question, gave instructions to the carter to deliver the coals into the cellar through the cellar opening in the pavement. For this purpose the removal of the cellar flap was necessary, and the carter removed the flap and thereby left the opening in the pavement exposed, while he went to the cart to take out a sack of coals. The plaintiff without any negligence on her part walked into the opening and injured herself. The occupier of the premises was nevertheless held liable in law for the damage suffered by the plaintiff in consequence of the carter's negligence.

Wine and Spirit Trade Record 1938

Hairdresser's Weekly Journal 1938

MODIFIED CONSCRIPTION

Sir Archibald Sinclair's Views

In the House of Commons on Thursday last, the Government's proposals for conscription for youths between the ages of 20 and 21 was carried by 376 against 145. It was approved in the House of Lords without a division.

The Prime Minister said :—Nothing could be more stupid and nothing more likely to lead the country into disaster than that the Government should refuse to change its mind if changed conditions should require it. The fact is to-day we no longer believe that the needs of the country can be met by the voluntary system if that system is to stand alone.

Continuing, Mr Chamberlain said :—It is important to my judgment not to belittle this great departure by this country from one of its most cherished traditions. I do not think anyone can read the papers of this morning and read extracts from the foreign Press without realising that the statement of the Government's intention has brought comfort, relief and encouragement to all our friends in Europe.

Sir Archibald Sinclair's Views

Speaking for the Liberals, Sir Archibald Sinclair said that while wide differences of opinion seemed to exist as to the merits of the Government's proposals, any foreigner who believed there was any real difference in the attitude of all parties on the question of the defence of this country, and peace, freedom and order in the world, would be making a profound mistake.

Caithness Courier 1939

Nevertheless we, shall continue. Our printers have given us the assurance of their support. The general feeling of the trade is one of optimism. We have at least as much right to crave the patience, indulgence and sympathy of our readers as the B.B.C. of their listeners, and I hope that in our own humble way we shall make less of a mess of it than the B.B.C. have made of broadcasting and that THE GRAMOPHONE will not assume the characteristics of a newspaper edited in one of the lower forms of a girls' school. The other day I had the opportunity of shaking hands with Mr. Fred Smith who has just taken on the direction of that grand centre of gramophonic life— Rimington, Van Wyck's. He urged me to write an editorial which would be an inspiration to everybody who lives by or loves the gramophone. I feel that I am letting Mr. Fred Smith down by this editorial, but words will not always obey the passion of the man who tries to handle them. Still, whatever my deficiencies, I know that the friends of this paper all over the world will be apostles of music all over that distracted world. I know that they will appreciate and shoulder their individual responsibilities. Advertisement will necessarily be curtailed, and we look to our readers to advertise the power of the gramophone to console distracted minds:

The Gramophone 1939

Private House Opposition

" DEAR 'MIDLANDER,'—I have cut-price opposition. The young lady responsible is dressing hair after business hours at her lodgings. Could you advise to whom I could write, or what lawful steps I could take to curtail this?—' Reader.' "

[If the house is situated within a Town Planning Scheme, under which businesses are restricted, the practice is illegal, and can be stopped by reporting it to the local Housing Committee. In the event of no protection being afforded in this way, you may report the matter to the landlord. He may take steps to stop it or increase the rent. If he refuses to take notice, you may approach the local Assessment Committee with a view to the premises being assessed as a business instead of a private dwelling.—"MIDLANDER."]

Hardresser's Weekly Journal 1938

Here is a true story. At the beginning of the war a certain Government Department suddenly needed a number of women secretaries. A friend of mine applied, and although she explained that she could neither type nor do shorthand, she was taken on. The first job she was given was typing, and when she again explained she could not type, she was told to get hold of a typewriter and learn. So she spent her office hours learning, and after some weeks she agreed to type a friend's book in order to practise. One evening she stayed late and her boss found her hard at it. "Working overtime?" he said, "I hope you are getting overtime pay." Rather shamefacedly she explained that she was doing her own private work and trying to make herself a competent typist : so she could not possibly claim overtime. "Nonsense," said the kind-hearted civil servant, "no overtime here without pay." And, believe it or not, she had to take it. I should add that my friend had not got her job by influence !

New Statesman 1939

Hairdresser's Weekly Journal 1938

1940
1949

GRANTS FOR MOLE-DRAINING

The Minister of Agriculture and Fisheries is prepared to make grants to owners and occupiers of agricultural land for the purpose of assisting them to carry out mole-drainage work. The rate of grant will be 50% of the net cost, with a maximum grant of £1 per acre.

Stratford upon Avon Herald 1940

Training for War Work

By the Rt. Hon. ERNEST BEVIN.

The number of civilians in training for war work at the Government training centres is now about 10,709.

This is a record number. It is nearly 1,000 more than a week ago and nearly 2,000 more than a fortnight ago.

In the last four weeks more than 6,000 men have been sent forward to training centres. This is also a record, but we need many thousands more.

Those awaiting entry into training wil lbe quickly absorbed.

A continuous flow of applicants will be needed to keep the centres at full strength and to fill the new places which are being provided.

Shift work is being introduced and new centres are being established, and greatly increased numbers, both of men for training and of instructors, are required.

York Star 1940

WORKLESS OBJECT TO WOMAN DOCTOR

EXAMINATION REFUSED

Because they refused to be examined by a woman doctor, a number of unemployed men lost the chance of jobs at a Government depot in Lancashire.

About 100 men sent from Employment Exchanges in the Oldham and Rochdale districts to fill posts as storemen and labourers, were told to attend for a medical test. The surgery was in the temporary charge of a woman doctor, and some of the men refused to submit to the test.

Daily Telegraph 1940

INDUSTRIAL REGISTRATION ORDER—1940

All men
who are or who have been
in these trades
must register

BY ORDER Men who are now employed in the following trades and who are over 21, must register at their local Employment Exchange between Monday, August 19th and Friday, August 23rd, whatever the nature of their employers' business. Men under 65 who, though not at present engaged in these occupations, have worked in them for one year since January 1929 must also register.

Brass, Bronze, Aluminium or other non-ferrous metals, Finisher, Fitter
Coppersmith
Core Maker
Die Caster
Draughtsman (Engineering, Jig or Tool)
Electrician, including Wireman
Fitter, Assembler, Erector, Marker-Out (Engineering and Kindred Trades including Electrical)
Forgeman, including Power Hammer Smith, Forge Hammerman, Forge Pressman, Hot Stamper, Hot Drop Stamper, Drop Hammer Smith, Drop Forger
Gunsmith
Inspector, Tester, Viewer, Examiner (Engineering and Kindred Trades including Electrical)
Instrument Maker or Assembler—All kinds including scientific, optical, surgical, dental, electrical, wireless, watch and clock, telegraph, telephone

Leadburner (Chemical Plumber)
Lens Worker, Prism Worker
Machinist, including Driller (Boiler, Constructional)
Metal Annealer, Hardener, Temperer
Metal Machinist, including Turret Lathe Operator, Capstan Lathe Operator, Miller, Borer, Grinder, Planer, Shaper, Slotter, Driller
Millwright, Maintenance Man (Metal)
Moulder (Iron, Steel, Brass or other non-ferrous metals)
Power Press Operator (Metal)
Sheet Iron Worker, Sheet Metal Worker, including Tinsmith
Toolsmith
Toolmaker, Press Toolmaker, Die Sinker (Cutter), Jig or Gauge Maker
Tool Setter (Machine or Press Tools)
Turner (Metal)
Welder (Gas or Electric)

THE ONLY EXCEPTIONS ARE (1) Men *wholly* engaged on Government work. (2) Men in certain industries specified in the Notice.

You must see the Notice posted in Works, Post Offices & Employment Exchanges

The Notice tells you when to register.

TO EVERY EMPLOYER

Every Employer of men who come under the Order, whatever the nature of the employer's business, MUST READ THE NOTICE to find out what is required under the Order.

Failure to comply with the Order is an offence under the DEFENCE (General) REGULATIONS, 1939.

ISSUED BY THE MINISTRY OF INFORMATION FOR THE MINISTRY OF LABOUR & NATIONAL SERVICE

Western Mail 1940

CONSCIENTIOUS OBJECTORS FOR RIVER WORK?

CONSIDERABLE NUMBER SHORTLY AVAILABLE

POINTS BEFORE CATCHMENT BOARD

The question of the employment of conscientious objectors on river clearance work engaged the attention of the Avon and Stour Catchment Board at a meeting at Bournemouth on Monday. Among the points brought out in discussion was the desirability of employing men not wanted on the farms during the winter, and it was urged that preference should not be given to conscientious objectors when the services of other men were available.

The matter arose on a communication from Mr. C. F. Hughes (Hampshire County Land Officer), who inquired whether the Board had any work on which conscientious objectors could be employed.

The ENGINEER (Mr. T. Ward Whitfield) stated that he discussed the matter with Lord Lymington and the Hants County Labour Officer early in September, and was told that the service of a considerable number of conscientious objectors, who would not be allowed to follow their normal occupation would shortly be available. The Hampshire County Council was anxious that these men should be absorbed on the land, and he was told that if the Board could find work for them the Council would be prepared to house them in the vicinity of the work.

Salisbury and Winchester Journal 1940

Queen Mary Called 'Missus' Delighted

QUEEN MARY, simply dressed and wearing an apron, has been helping lately in a West of England canteen and many of the men have been quite unaware that they were being served with a snack by Royalty.

Two Tommies entered the canteen recently and seeing the Queen behind the counter, hailed her: "Hi, mussus, two cups of tea, please."

They were duly served.

"Queen Mary was delighted." another helper in the canteen said to-day, "She said it was the first time in her life she had ever been addressed as missus."

Oxford Mail 1941

South American Handbook 1940

THERE has been no little stir among younger women in all parts of the country since they were compelled to realise that at last their turn has come—that they must line up beside the men for the essential services of the war. Up to now, though large numbers have undertaken war work from a compelling desire to help the country, in the main women have accepted employment in units attached to the fighting services, or in Government departments, or in munitions factories in much the same way as they would take up any other job: they were free to offer their services, and here were jobs convenient to them as well as congenial to their sense of patriotism. Till now there has been no mastering necessity. During the first year and more of the war there was still considerable unemployment among men. The defence departments refrained from drawing more men into the fighting services than they could adequately train and equip, and it is only recently that the industrial machine has acquired a momentum such that all or nearly all the man-power available is used up either in its own service or in the military services. But the further expansion of the war industries and of the forces which they will equip depends on finding more people to make munitions and more men to fight, and this if possible without starving the export industries and the services indispensable to civilian existence. By no means can these additional men be found except by releasing them from their present occupations with the help of women substitutes.

Spectator 1941

"TOO FAST" WORKER
CAUSES 2,000 TO STRIKE

Daily Express Staff Reporter

BECAUSE thirty-six-year-old Mr. Albert Lazenby, cutter in a Lancashire clothing factory of Montague Burton, Ltd., stayed at his bench yesterday and continued doing his job too fast, 2,000 men and women walked out.

Mr. Lazenby was censured, fined and expelled from the Tailors' and Garment Workers Union for being too efficient with his electric knife.

In one week he had cut 324 pairs of trousers above the limit set by the union. Instead of taking home £5 a week, it meant he was earning another four shillings a week for about three weeks.

Other cutters at Montague Burton's Worsley factory complained. He went with them for the morning break yesterday, and had a game of darts in the canteen. Afterwards, instead of re-starting work the 200 cutters marched out.

At Burton's factory in Walkden, not far away, 1,500 stopped in sympathy, although they were told that their strike was not official.

Mr. Lazenby was left alone in his section. His wife, a machinist in the same factory, could just see him bending over the tables and carrying on. At the end of the day he had cut 240 pairs of trousers, ninety-six jackets, and thirty-eight overcoats without much exertion.

Daily Express **1940**

Fred gets an important job

Mr. A:	Fred — you're just the man we're looking for. We want you to run the firm's War Savings Group.
Fred:	What's the idea? Why can't we each do our own saving?
Mr. A:	We all can, Fred . . . but a Savings Group makes *certain* you save regularly every week.
Miss C:	And it keeps you up to it, and gives you the feeling that everyone is working together to help to win the war.
Fred:	But aren't we too small for a Savings Group?
Miss C: *(quoting from advertisement)*	No, it says here that The National Savings Committee has Savings Schemes suitable for firms of all sizes. And they give you help and advice in starting one.
Fred:	But, won't it mean a lot of extra work?
Miss C:	A friend of mine runs her firm's Group and she says there's very little work involved. Besides, I'll help you.
Fred:	That will be fine. How do we make a start?
Miss C:	The first thing to do is to post the coupon to The National Savings Committee.
Fred:	I'll do it right away — then we'll get down to it and see what this firm can do " to save for Victory."

POST THIS COUPON
TO YOUR LOCAL SAVINGS COMMITTEE, OR TO THE NATIONAL SAVINGS COMMITTEE, LONDON, S.W.1

I/we wish to form a War Savings Group in my/our firm, factory, office, shop. The total number of people employed is approximately ....

Please send details of suitable schemes. *(Write in pencil and in block letters)*

Signature(s) ....

....

Name of Firm ....

Address ....

....

LEND TO DEFEND
THE RIGHT TO BE FREE

Stratford upon Avon Herald **1940**

MAN WHO CAN'T FIND WORK

WHEN a farm worker, Arthur William Edward Tilbury, declared at Sittingbourne County Court today that he could not find work, Judge Clements said:

" With all this work crying out to be done, this is a matter which cannot be overlooked.

" **Here is a man of 47, a healthy, fully-trained man, who tells me he has been engaged in farm work all his life, the very man the country so badly needs, and yet he cannot get work.**

" Nor can the Labour Exchange find him work. It would be, in my opinion, a public duty for someone from the Labour Exchange to come to the next court and tell me why. It may be the man won't work. I cannot bring them here, but it is their duty to come."

Star **1942**

Plans To Meet The Women's Response To War Work Call

P LANS have been made to meet the response to Mr. Bevin's call for women war workers.

It is expected that most of the volunteers will be taught in the factories where they are to work.

News Chronicle 1941

BOMB DEATH OF LORD SUFFOLK

ESCAPE FROM FRANCE IN CARGO SHIP

DAILY TELEGRAPH REPORTER

The 35-year-old Earl of Suffolk and Berkshire was killed by a bomb on Monday, together with seven other people, including his secretary.

Lord Suffolk acted as the Ministry of Supply's liaison officer between British and French scientific organisations until the collapse of France.

His journey back from Paris to England was a hazardous adventure. Carrying valuable scientific records, he eventually crossed in a small cargo vessel from Bordeaux to the British coast.

Lord Suffolk was only 11 when he succeeded to the 300-year-old earldom on the death of his father, the 19th earl, who was killed in action in Mesopotamia in the last war.

After two spells of sheep farming in Australia and service as a subaltern in the Scots Guards, he decided when he was 29 to farm scientifically on his estate of 10,000 acres at Charlton Park, Malmesbury, Wilts.

He entered Edinburgh University, studied chemistry for four years, and took his B.Sc. in 1937.

In 1934 he married Miss Mimi Crawford the actress, who is a niece of Lord Chalmers. They had two sons and one daughter, the heir, Viscount Andover, being born in 1935.

Daily Telegraph 1941

After quickly learning the preliminaries they will soon be busy on actual production. Many tens of thousands of women were employed on this class of work in the last war.

MISUNDERSTANDINGS

Although the drive in the North-West for the first hundred thousand is meeting with a satisfactory response in many centres there are many misunderstandings. Here are facts that clear up some of these:

The jobs are not all "dirty hands work."

Training in many jobs need last only a week.

Applicants need not visit an Employment Exchange. They can seek advice at demonstration centres.

They need not commit themselves at once; there is time to think it over.

Further, it was being pointed out yesterday that women with secondary school education would be welcomed.

"MUSIC WHILE YOU WORK": BIGGER PLANS

CONTRASTED "Music While You Work" is to be the order for seven days commencing July 6.

Employers have been asked to co-operate in an experiment designed to evolve the ideal type of workers' programme, and a report form, upon which they can express their opinion on audibility, rhythm, enjoyment of workers and effect of output will be sent to any employer on application to the Listener Research Director, Broadcasting House, Whiteladies Road, Bristol, 8.

This series, which attains its first "birthday" on June 24, has met with considerable success in relieving monotony, and consequent fatigue, in factories where the work is mainly repetitive.

The Medical Research Council has found that increase in output during a period of music ranged from 6.2 to 11.3 per cent., and in individual cases reached a figure of 23.1 per cent.

One firm stated that with suitable programmes they would be able to reduce overtime by half. A canning firm in Kent stated that a daily programme

of dance tunes stepped up production by 30 per cent.

Now it is the object of the B.B.C. still further to increase production through the right type of music, and there is every possibility that this experiment will result in considerable expansion of the type of programme, and, consequently, employment for a greater variety of bands.

Listed also on the questionnaire to employers is a suggestion that a third "Music While You Work" period might be introduced for the benefit of late or night-shift workers.

East Anglian
Daily Times
1941

Once again there is a great campaign for scrap iron and steel. In this country particularly there is great need of it. In the halcyon days that preceded the war our steel manufacturers made up for all sorts of other deficiencies by using scrap in the smelters. This did not quite enable us to hold up our heads against the mass production of the United States, nor even of Germany, but it helped. And because we have got used to the use of scrap it is perhaps more important to us to-day than to any of the other belligerents—except perhaps Japan.

Financial Times
1941

WAGE INCREASE FOR 2,000,000

SHIPBUILDERS AND ENGINEERS

The National Arbitration Tribunal has awarded a 5s a week increase in wages to male workers in the shipbuilding and engineering industry, beginning next week. About 2,000,000 men are affected.

The increase is for members of trade unions affiliated to the Confederation of Shipbuilding and Engineering Unions, of those unions represented by the Engineering Joint-Trades Movement, members of the Amalgamated Engineering Union and of the National Union of Foundry Workers employed by members of the Constituent Associations of the Shipbuilding Employers' Federation, and the Engineering and Allied Employers' National Federation. The men's claim was for "a substantial increase in wages."

The Tribunal, under the chairmanship of Mr. Justice Simonds, in arriving at its decision, states that it took into consideration, among other things, a comparison between the wage standards of this and other industries, both at the present time and in the period since the outbreak of war and over a period of years preceding the war. The Tribunal also took into account that changes in the amount of the so-called national bonus, which has existed since 1917, have been the agreed normal method of increasing or decreasing wage rates in the industries, and that the national bonus therefore stands on a different footing from bonuses in industry which have only come into being since the war and are related solely to changes arising out of the war.

PARLIAMENT AND WOMEN

Peers And Commons A.T.S. Critics

NEW METHODS URGED

The need for new methods in attracting women to war organisations was debated to-day in both Houses of Parliament. In the Commons a Conservative criticised Mr. Bevin, Minister of Labour, as a bellowing rhinoceros, while in the Lords young women were defended by Lord Trenchard.

Captain McEwen (C., Berwick and Haddington), resuming the debate on the Address in the Commons, suggested that the Government, and the Minister of Labour in particular, in their appeal to the women to join women's war organisations, were proceeding on an entirely wrong basis.

"It is no good the Minister of Labour going about the country bellowing like a wounded rhinoceros and threatening conscription and the rest of it for women and appealing to their sense of adventure. That is not the right approach at all," he said

"Some girls in one of the branches of the national effort are forbidden to have mirrors in their rooms," he said. "That's on a par with the proposed withdrawal of the glamorous A.T.S recruiting poster.

"ELDERLY CRITICS"

Lord Trenchard, opening a debate on woman-power in the Lords, to-day, defended young women from "the almost slighting references" to the fact that a large number did nothing but enjoy themselves, and were not coming forward to help their country.

These remarks were sometimes unfair

"I know of a young girl," he said, "who had been for six months in the A.T.S., and was in a West Country town She had two days' leave and came to London, where she put on mufti and went to look in shop windows.

"An elderly man told her she should be ashamed of herself for not being in uniform and that she looked like a picture on a magazine cover.

"There are too many people who think because they see places like big hotels crowded with young girls dancing in mufti that they are not doing their bit."

Liverpool Echo 1941

Oxford Mail 1941

MADELEINE CARROLL, the West Bromwich born film star, who announced last night at Hollywood that she has offered her services to the British Government and is coming here. She said, " I would be too miserable if I did not go back."

Waste Paper
A Compulsory Order

A new Salvage of Waste Materials (No. 2) Order, 1942, made by the Ministry of Supply under Regulation 55 of the Defence (General) Regulations, came into force on March 9. Under the provisions of the Order it is a punishable offence to

Burn or destroy paper or cardboard ;

Throw it away ;

Dispose of it otherwise than to a collector or buyer ;

Put it in a refuse bin or mix it with refuse.

Under the Order Waste Paper means "any waste, scrap, worn-out or disused material or article, being paper or cardboard or an article made therefrom, but does not include any secret or confidential document."

Mr. Ralph Assheton, Parliamentary Secretary to the Ministry of Supply, in a statement on the main points of the Order said :—

From now on we must no longer throw our cigarette cartons or envelopes or other scraps of paper on the fire—we must no longer make a bonfire of any waste paper or cardboard.

It is, of course, quite permissible for the public to continue to light fires with paper, though increasing numbers of housewives are, I am glad to say, finding ingenious ways of managing without even that.

NAAFI and ENSA

In any discussion of the discrepancy between civilian and Service pay, it is always claimed that the fighting man receives additional benefits which bring his total remuneration much nearer the level of the factory worker. One of these is free board and lodging ; and in the provision of food NAAFI plays an important part. As the Select Committee on National Expenditure points out in its fifth report of the session, before June, 1940, Army units used to receive a large part of their rations in cash, and were able to purchase that amount direct from NAAFI, which thus enabled messing officers to vary the diets of their men. This system is still followed by the RAF, but, since that date, the RASC is responsible for providing almost the whole of the army ration. NAAFI continued to supply the RASC with some of the goods, but they are issued at wholesale prices. Thus Army units have lost, not only the advantage of a more varied diet, but also the rebate of 6 per cent of the profits on the retail sales made to them. The Select Committee notes that a small cash element of $2\frac{1}{2}$d. a day, to be spent at the NAAFI, has been re-introduced into the soldier's rations, but it regrets that the change was ever made. To-day, therefore, the only benefit a soldier obtains from the NAAFI is from his own individual purchases. On these, his unit gets 6 per cent rebate, which is used for welfare purposes and the provision of amenities, but it is personal benefits which alone can alleviate his sense of grievance that in money terms he is far worse off in the Army than outside. The Select Committee agrees that NAAFI's policy of charging multiple shop retail prices is the best in peacetime, but it considers that this policy may have to be reviewed. There is certainly a danger that goods sold at a lower price may be bought for resale elsewhere. Control of NAAFI supplies, too, has been almost culpably lax, to judge from recent revelations. But it is a risk worth taking in the interests of the individual soldier whose available pay for personal purchases is so small, and the argument that local tradesmen must be protected from cut-price competition should be ignored.

*

Among the amenities purchased by the profits of NAAFI is entertainment, which is provided by ENSA, a voluntary organisation formed six months before the war. In March, 1941, the net cost to NAAFI of providing entertainment for the forces and for munition workers, after allowing for the Ministry of Labour contributions and charges made to the forces, was about £800,000 per annum. This was more than NAAFI could afford, and the Treasury has proposed that the total expenditure, exclusive of sums provided for munition workers, should be limited to £1 million per annum, of which £600,000 should be borne by NAAFI and the remainder by the Exchequer, which already bears all wartime losses made by the Corporation in excess of £350,000. Nobody will question the amount of the expenditure on entertainment, or that a large part of it should come out of public funds. But it may well be asked whether something could not be done to provide better value for the money ; it is frequently said that the forces themselves can provide, out of their own talent, better shows than those given by the average ENSA company.

Economist 1942

The Paper Market
1942

NEW FEMINIST MOVEMENT

THE DEMAND FOR EQUALITY

GIRLS TRAINING TO BE' M.P.s

Unnoticed by most people,. a strong movement has begun which is designed to secure equality between men and women when the war ends.

After much thinking, the women behind it have drawn up a plan of attack on all the vulnerable points in a man-monopolised world This is how their argument runs:—

War provides the golden opportunity for women to prove that they can be as valuable to the community as men. In the Crimea war, led by Florence Nightingale, middle-class women, for the first time, were allowed to work for the cause of their country. Then in the last war women acquitted themselves so well that they could no longer be refused the vote.

Now, in this war, the final moves must be made that will revolutionise the status of women and usher in the epoch of equality.

It is all being conducted constitutionally and in complete contrast to the old suffragette methods of firing pillar-boxes and knocking off policemen's helmets. Instead of chaining themselves to the railings the women are hitching their wagon to a much more hopeful star

Observer
1942

A CHALLENGE TO ANTI-SEMITISM

Council of Christians and Jews

The systematic persecution of Jews by the Nazis and their underlings in Europe has prompted the formation of a Council of Christians and Jews, of which the joint presidents are the Archbishop of Canterbury, Cardinal Hinsley, the Moderator of the General Assembly of the Church of Scotland, the Moderator of the Free Church Federal Council, and the Chief Rabbi of the United Hebrew Congregations of the British Empire.

The aims of the Council are: to check and combat religious and racial intolerance; to promote mutual understanding and good will between Christians and Jews, especially in connexion with problems arising from conditions created by the war; to promote fellowship between Christian and Jewish youth organizations in educational and cultural activities; and to foster co-operation of Christians and Jews in study and service directed to post-war reconstruction.

Inquiries should be addressed to the honorary secretaries, the Council of Christians and Jews, 21, Bloomsbury-street, London, W.C. 1..

Church Times
1942

WAITER!

Man Who Set A Dish Before The King

A FORMER Chester waiter has written home to his parents describing how he was chosen to wait upon the King during His Majesty's visit to Tripoli.

He is Driver Thomas S. Jones, R.A.S.C., eldest son of Mr. and Mrs. P. Jones. of Appleyard-lane, Handbridge, Chester, who, before joining the Army, was employed at the Grosvenor Hotel, Chester.

His letter reads: "They scoured the Eighth Army for experienced waiters and I was picked as one. I served the King on two occasions. I was his waiter. There was a party of 14, all 'big shots,' and, boy, was I thrilled to say 'Will you take soup, sir?' and hear him answer 'Yes.' or 'No thank you.'"

Aged twenty-five, Driver Jones was slightly wounded in the fighting in France, and his three brothers are all in the Services.

THE BEST AGE FOR RECRUITS.

What is the best age at which young people should be attracted to the belfry? This is a question which has often been asked, and in the coming times of reconstruction when some bands will have to be built up anew almost from the foundation, the answer to it will be of more than merely academic interest. There are people who say that if we can get recruits at all, it does not matter what age they are, provided they are of the right quality. None is too young though he be but a child, and none is too old though he hath reached middle age. And to do those people justice who talk like this, they are usually just as ready and willing to teach the one as the other. Certainly the problem which has always faced many leaders of bands is to get recruits at all, and they are almost compelled to take anything they can get and to try to make the best of it.

Ringing World 1942

People 1942

THE KING AT LATHE

Not a 'regular'

CANNON guns which the King helped to make at a war factory near London are in use on a number of R.A.F. planes.

But the story that the King is doing regular part time work at the factory on two nights a week is wrong. These are the true facts, writes a Sunday Express representative.

Nearly a year ago the King was paying a private visit to the factory when the manager suggested, half as a joke, that he should try his hand at one of the precision lathes.

The King said he would try to come along when he had time to spare. Four or five times since then the King has looked in at the factory and worked the lathe for short periods.

Sunday Express **1943**

FUEL ECONOMY IN GOVERNMENT DEPARTMENTS

ALL our readers will be fully seized with the necessity for the strictest economy in fuel both domestically and in their offices. An E.O.C. No. 602 dated August 10 has been issued to all Government departments enjoining the utmost care in the use of heat and light, the operative portion of which reads as follows :

Every member of the staff should be instructed on the following lines :

(i) a supplementary fire can never be allowed in a room which has effective central heating, except on production of a medical certificate ;

(ii) those who have fires are responsible for ensuring that there is no waste, that they are not lit unless it is really too cold to work without, and that fires are allowed to die by the time the occupants of the room leave ;

(iii) even in winter such fires should not be lit before the occupant of the room arrives ;

(iv) he should always turn out the light when leaving a room empty or when artificial lighting ceases to be absolutely necessary ;

(v) he should never use more than one light for working by. Where possible officers should share a light, and they should be invited, if lights are badly arranged for this purpose, to ask the Office Keeper or other appropriate official if he can have them altered.

Civil Service Opinion **1942**

A Quaker Girl's Two Months in Prison

❡ *The writer of the following, who has just passed her 20th birthday in Strangeways Prison, Manchester, is a member of Halifax Meeting. She is,* THE FRIEND *believes, the first woman member of the Society to be imprisoned for refusal, on conscientious grounds, to change her occupation at the direction of a National Service Officer.*

ON October 24 I was sentenced at Halifax Police Court to two months' imprisonment for refusing to obey a direction of the Ministry of Labour. After being four hours in the cells at the Police Court, I was taken by train to Manchester Prison. Upon arrival I was taken before the prison doctor and provided with prison clothes, hairbrush and a Bible. I was then taken to my cell and locked in.

The cells are equipped with an iron bedstead, table, washstand, chair, and a mat on the floor. At 9 o'clock the lights were switched off until 5.30 in the morning. At 6 o'clock the rising bell rang, when we cleaned and scrubbed our cells. Breakfast was brought to the cell at 7 o'clock, and I was again locked in until 8.30. The first morning I appeared before the Lady Governor after breakfast and was later given a reception letter to write. After dinner at 1.30 we had one hour's exercise, walking around the court in twos, and then along with four more new prisoners I was sent to the workroom. At 4.30 we returned to our cells, I was given tea and locked in for the night. Apart from the cell task, the work on an ordinary day in prison is from 8.30 to 12.15, and 2.30 to 4.15.

The work for women prisoners is mostly cleaning, laundry work or sewing. C.O.s are usually put in the workroom, where a certain amount of war work is done, but we were not asked to do this, and were kept on prison clothes the whole of the time. For cell work one is given each day either three mail bags to seam, or 12 to rope; these are collected each morning.

Each Sunday at 2.15 I was allowed to attend the Men's Meeting for Worship. I always left these Meetings strengthened and determined to continue the struggle for freedom of conscience.

I also owe a great deal, more than words can express, to the visits of the Quaker Visitor and Quaker 'Chaplain,' who are allowed to visit not only Friends, but all who register as Quakers. I received two books sent in by Friends, Parts One and Two of *Christian Discipline*, which were a great help to me. I was also allowed two books from the prison library each week.

I did not find prison life too hard, and soon learned to look forward to the solitude of the evenings when one

The Friend **1942**

The bucolic side of `Digging for Victory' in the Crown Film Unit's 1942 short *Summer on the Farm.*

Miners receive their extra meat coupons at Caroline Pit, Newcastle, 1946.

Pay-as-You-Earn

THE scheme for taxing weekly wage earners on a pay-as-you-earn basis, announced on Wednesday, is admirably designed to achieve its limited objectives. The system of income tax is left unaltered ; but its application to one section of taxpayers—the large majority, by numbers though not by payments—will be radically changed. In the words of the White Paper (Cmd. 6469), which sets out the details with great lucidity, " The tax deducted from earnings *in* any financial year will represent the liability *for* that year, measured by the actual earnings *of* that year, and the deduction of tax week by week will keep pace with the accruing liability." The prospect is removed of wage earners being saddled with heavy retrospective obligations when abnormal wartime earnings fall or if, as is likely in the case of many women, they go out of gainful employment when the war ends.

The new method of collecting income tax, which will come into force on April 6th next year, and will apply to all weekly wage earners whose tax is deducted at source (with the exception of civil servants and railway officials, to whom special arrangements already apply), is ingenious in construction and simple to operate. The weekly liabilities of wage earners, which will of course fluctuate week by week with earnings and employment, will be worked out according to a complicated formula ; but this will be calculated beforehand by the tax authorities to cover all cases and translated into a series of tax tables, which will serve as an automatic ready reckoner for employers in making deductions of tax from weekly wage payments.

At present the amount of one year's tax is assessed, for every taxpayer, on the basis of the preceding year's earnings. In the case of weekly wage earners, who are also weekly taxpayers, the lag between money earned and tax paid is ten months, which gives rise to misunderstanding and may cause definite hardship when earnings fluctuate, decline or cease. The new system provides that the weekly tax payment will be based on the same week's earnings, with allowance every week for a proportionate share of the exemptions and reliefs to which the taxpayer may be entitled. The amount of tax to be deducted each week will be the tax due on the total wages received in the tax year up to and including that week, *less* the tax already deducted in the previous weeks of the year. For example, the tax to be deducted in the first week will be the standard rate less one-fifty-second of the reliefs and allowances for the year ; the tax to be deducted at the end of the second week will be the standard rate on the earnings of both weeks, less the tax deducted in respect of the earnings

Economist 1943

Sunday Express 1943

AARON, 82, BEGINS A NEW LIFE

Sunday Express Reporter

AARON PICKLES, who has worked down the pit for 72 years, came up in the cage for the last time at Dewsbury (Yorks) yesterday, and handed in his lamp.

A week ago Mr. Pickles, with 10s. a week Old Age Pension, had nothing to look forward to at 82 but more work.

Mr. Wilfred Hill, Birmingham philanthropist, read his story in the Sunday Express and gave him a pension of £156 a year for life.

On Monday Aaron Pickles draws the first instalment of his pension—paid monthly in advance.

At 10, after three years' schooling, Aaron Pickles began work at 5d. a day.

Biggest pay

For 50 years he was a coal-getter, packing coal or pushing tubs. For the last 14 years he did lighter work at the first seam, 285 feet down.

"And the last job," he said yesterday, "earned me my biggest pay. As a coalgetter I rarely got more than 24s. a week."

His last pay note was for £3 18s. 11d., which, after deductions and tax, left him £3 1s. 2d. to take home to his daughter—one of his 14 children.

Aaron Pickles was 50 when he went to Scarborough for his first holiday. Years later he had another break—at Morecambe. To-day, thanks to Mr. Hill, he goes on holiday—for good.

'At Sotheby's, on November 10th, *A View in a Park, 1886–7*, with a figure in the foreground and a house in the distance on the right, by Vincent van Gogh, fetched £1,350; *The Holy Family* (on panel), ascribed to van Cleve, £145; *The Woodman returning Home: Evening*, by Francis Wheatley, £140; and *A Skating Scene in Holland* (on panel), by E. van der Poel, £105. On November 30th, nine plates (in colours) from Wheatley's *Cryes of London*, offered separately, brought a total of £487; and paintings, on December 15th, included a Ben Marshall representation of a brown hunter, with a dog, in a landscape, signed and dated.

The Connoisseur 1944

King and Queen visit the miners

Seventy Yorkshire miners lunched with the King and Queen in the Elsecar Colliery canteen yesterday.

Their meal of roast beef, brussels sprouts, roast and boiled potatoes, golden pudding and coffee was the ordinary 1s. lunch served daily to miners.

"It is a long time since we have had a better meal," the Queen told the men afterwards.

The King and Queen were making an all-day tour of the West and South Yorkshire coalfields.

News Chronicle 1944

SALFORD RECTOR COMMENDED

Salford Watch Committee yesterday decided to send a letter of thanks to the Rev. A. Wasey, rector of Stowell Memorial Church, Salford, for his part in persuading an angry crowd of over a thousand people who besieged a police-box last Friday week to disperse. Mr. Wasey's rectory adjoins the police-box, and going among the crowd at some personal risk he succeeded in persuading most of the people that they had been misled.

The committee also awarded £3 each to Sergeant A. Longden, Corporal L. Pemberton, and Private J. Gordon, of the Salford Home Guard, and to Able Seaman A. Heaton for assisting the police during the disturbance.

Manchester Guardian
1944

BALLOT WILL PICK
30,000 MEN FOR PITS

From GEORGE SINFIELD, Daily Worker Industrial Reporter

THE year 1944 is the year of the great impact on the enemy. Nothing must be left to chance to see that the great basic industries are supplied with coal. Coal is now the most vital commodity."

Mr. Ernest Bevin, Minister of Labour, told me this yesterday after announcing in the House of Commons the call-up to the mines of young men between 18 and 25.

The Minister declared that the coalmining industry must have 30,000 newcomers by April next year. A similar number is required in the following coal year to make up for wastage.

The ballot to decide the entrants will take place in Mr. Bevin's presence at the Ministry of Labour. "I will see that it is carried through fairly," he said. First draw will take place at mid-December for conscription early in January. Draws will then follow at monthly periods.

Training will be given as follows:

Stage "A"—eleven special colliery centres are being organised by the Ministry of Labour in consultation with the Ministry of Fuel and training will last four weeks. A longer training will be given to men who require it.

Stage "B"—this will be given by employers at the pits, following completion of Stage "A."

Trainees will be paid the National Service Workers' minimum of 44s. at the age of 18, rising to 78s. at the age of 21.

EXEMPTIONS

Exclusion from the ballot will be limited to three classes of men—those accepted for flying duties in the R.A.F. or Fleet Air Arm, those accepted as artificers in submarines, and those in a short list of highly skilled occupation who are called up only for certain Service trades and not even accepted as volunteers for coal mining.

Special medical examinations will be arranged for those who claim they are not fit for coal mining on medical grounds.

Commenting on the scheme last night, Mr. Ebby Edwards, secretary of the Mineworkers' Federation, said: "More men must be found from somewhere."

Mr. Arthur Horner, president of the South Wales Miners' Federation, said: "The scheme will work provided the men are not segregated, and there is no effort to make soldiers of them. The industry must have more workers."

Daily Worker **1943**

'If only **more** women would help'

Have you noticed those girls in A.T.S. uniform? Smiled a little, admired them perhaps, and thought 'Rather they, than me.' Those girls are helping to bring down the planes that come to bomb you. They are helping your menfolk to shorten the war. Cooking and catering for them, transmitting secret messages, working on secret devices. There's a good job waiting for you in the A.T.S. . . . a job that you will like.

Send for the full story of the A.T.S. and all the opportunities it offers you: to The AUXILIARY TERRITORIAL SERVICE A.G.18/b.3 Hobart House, Grosvenor Gdns., London, S.W.1 Or, have a friendly talk at any Employment Exchange, A.T.S. or Army recruiting centre.

30,000 GIRLS
are urgently needed in the **A.T.S.**

Daily Express 1945

CITY BEVIN BOY SAYS "I COULDN'T BEAR IT"

"**I** TRIED to do my best in the pit, but I couldn't bear it. I got giddy. I am not used to confined places," said James Charles Nutland (21), of 8, Princes Street, Portsmouth, who at Portsmouth on Tuesday was summoned under the National Service Act for leaving his work in the mines without permission.

It was stated that Nutland left work at a Stockton colliery on February 15, saying that he was getting more and more nervous and was worried about his father, who was ill. He had been a week in the colliery and had had a month's previous training.

Nutland told the magistrates that he was needed to help at home. He had been discharged from the Army as medically unfit, but would rather go back to the Army than to the mines, as he could not stick working underground.

A medical examination was stated to have shown that there was no reason why defendant should not work in the mines.

In adjourning the case a week to give Nutland a chance to go back to work, the Chairman (Mrs. M. Malcolm) told him: "You seem to take rather an obstinate view of things. You must conquer your fears and go back to work, or we shall have to deal with you in a very different way.

Nutland replied: "I'll go back to the pit, but I swear I won't go back underground."

Hampshire Telegraph and Post 1944

Backwards to success

"*Tea Boys from 16 to 60 are required to make tea for bomb-damage repair men.*"
(News item.)

AS Organising Secretary of the Tea Boys' Brigade it has been a long, bitter struggle for me to develop what used to be sneered at as a dead-end job into a worthwhile profession. All we tea boys need now is for some golden - hearted philanthropist (perhaps in early life one of us?) to endow a few dozen University Chairs, or even Stools, and there you are! If a knighthood would help, I think *perhaps* that could be wangled. Pardon me. Arranged.

News Chronicle 1944

One-vote defeat for Government

No harm meant, say M.P.s

By the Parliamentary Correspondent

LAST night's Commons vote was taken on an amendment to the Education Bill by Mrs. Cazalet Keir (Con., Islington) providing that in the fixing of salary scales for teachers there should be no differentiation between men and women solely on the ground of sex.

Mr. BUTLER RESIGNS BUT IS PRESSED TO STAY

By the Political Correspondent

AFTER the Government had been defeated for the first time in the House of Commons last night by 117 votes to 116 on the question of equal pay for men and women school teachers, Mr. R. A. Butler, Education Minister, tendered his resignation.

I understand that up to a late hour it had not been accepted and further efforts are to be made by Mr. Churchill and other Cabinet colleagues to persuade him to retain his post.

Mr. Butler regarded the adverse vote as a vote of censure on his personal conduct of educational affairs, despite repeated assurances from all parts of the House that this was not intended.

Closing Down

BUT CAN THE SAME be said of the blow which will fall on working mothers this weekend? From March 31 the Ministry of Health grant for day nurseries will be sharply reduced, and local councils are having to decide whether they can afford to keep the nurseries going. Many of them are having to give a regrettable no.

What then? Miss Helen Saville, matron of a Hampstead nursery which is closing down, reports that mothers of children who cannot find places in other nurseries say they will have to give up their jobs.

And this at a time when the Government is urging women to continue working and thus help the drive for greater production!

John Bull 1946

Conscription

The lamentable R.A.F. "strikes" have underlined the need, rightly stressed in Parliament last week, for early decisions on the permanent future organisation of our Armed Forces. A sense of impending break-up is invariably bad for morale and discipline. Our permanent Forces will have to be larger than our pre-war establishment, but it does not necessarily follow that they should be raised by conscription. One objection to a peace-time conscript army is that it tends inevitably to military conservatism. It has to act as a school, with relays of military apprentices trained by professional instructors, and the instructors are naturally inclined to keep on repeating the old lessons they already know. In the atomic age we shall need an Army (and equally, of course, an Air Force and a Navy) whose officers realise that they are in the midst of a tremendous military revolution. They must be keen military scientists, prepared to unlearn and relearn their craft from year to year, to experiment boldly, and to play the role of a pioneer force. Continental experience suggests that a professional Army is best fitted to fill this role.

Observer 1946

Homecare Without Tears 1946

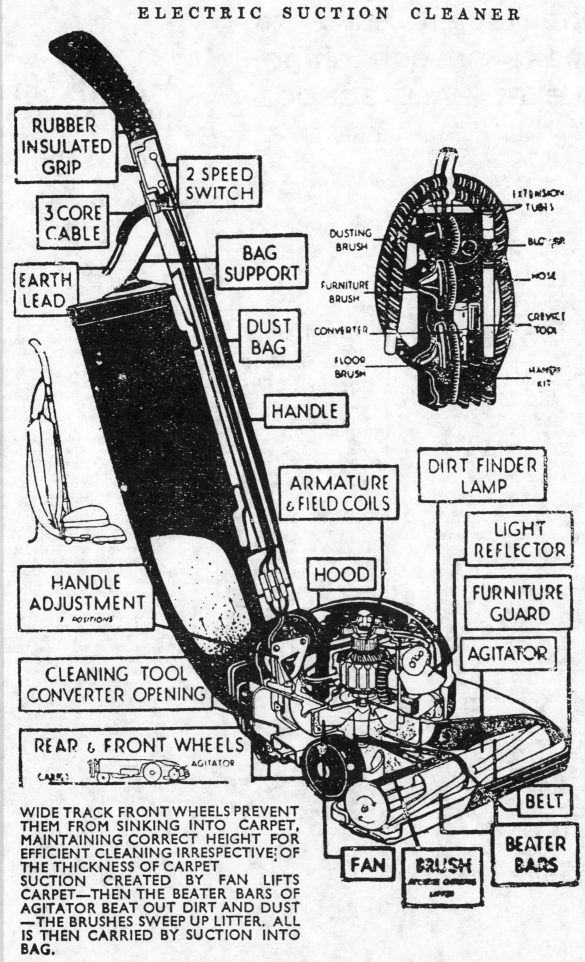

ELECTRIC SUCTION CLEANER

RUBBER INSULATED GRIP

3 CORE CABLE

EARTH LEAD

2 SPEED SWITCH

BAG SUPPORT

DUST BAG

HANDLE

HANDLE ADJUSTMENT
8 POSITIONS

CLEANING TOOL CONVERTER OPENING

REAR & FRONT WHEELS
AGITATOR

ARMATURE & FIELD COILS

HOOD

DIRT FINDER LAMP

LIGHT REFLECTOR

FURNITURE GUARD

AGITATOR

FAN   BRUSH

BELT

BEATER BARS

EXTENSION TUBES

DUSTING BRUSH

BLOWER

FURNITURE BRUSH

HOSE

CONVERTER

CREVICE TOOL

FLOOR BRUSH

HASTER KIT

WIDE TRACK FRONT WHEELS PREVENT THEM FROM SINKING INTO CARPET, MAINTAINING CORRECT HEIGHT FOR EFFICIENT CLEANING IRRESPECTIVE OF THE THICKNESS OF CARPET
SUCTION CREATED BY FAN LIFTS CARPET—THEN THE BEATER BARS OF AGITATOR BEAT OUT DIRT AND DUST —THE BRUSHES SWEEP UP LITTER. ALL IS THEN CARRIED BY SUCTION INTO BAG.

How it works : carriage-type vacuum cleaner.

[by courtesy of Electrical Association for Women.

She taught stars to make speech shine

ALBERT HALL SCHOOL

THE death of a woman but for whom such stars as John Gielgud, Sybil Thorndike, Laurence Olivier and Edith Evans might never have risen from obscurity was announced yesterday.

She was Elsie Fogerty, former principal of the Central School of Speech Training and Dramatic Art, London, who died at Leamington Spa, aged 79.

Scores of famous names owe their success to her teaching. They called her "The Godmother of Stars."

Every year aspiring young actors and actresses passed through the doors of the Royal Albert Hall to the famous "diction room," where they were taught to speak properly.

Miss Fogerty had dance rooms, a library, rest rooms, property rooms and a theatre hidden away in the vast and elusive passages of the Albert Hall.

It was her "school": it will remain as her memorial.

It was she who persuaded the London University to grant a diploma for dramatic art—the first time the stage had been raised to university status.

Famous names

In 1942, scores of famous names turned up at the New Theatre to honour the jubilee of the school which she founded.

Here are some of the things she had to say about:—

WOULD-BE ACTRESSES: A girl over 5ft. 7ins. has little chance in the dramatic world.

ENGLISH DIALECTS: The Shropshire dialect is the most beautiful in Britain. Cockney is one of our worst dialects. It is "thieves' slang"—largely the language of the underworld, having no variance or quality.

STANDARD ENGLISH: Many Americans speak beautiful English, better than many of our own triflers with their mother tongue. Our "refaned" English accent is now worse than the "Oh, yeah" of the films.

WOMEN AND THE B.B.C.: There is nothing in the construction of a woman's voice that makes it unsuitable for broadcasting. The reason women do not come up to the standard of the B.B.C. mike voice is because the B.B.C. do not take the trouble to tune their mechanical reproduction devices to bring out the individual qualities of a woman's voice.

Miss Fogerty also advanced the science of speech therapy; and was superintendent of the speech clinic at St. Thomas's Hospital, London

Sunday Express 1945

'Impossible' life of the doctor's wife

DR. PAUL R.E. KIRBY, of Dyke-road, Brighton, wants cheaper domestic help for doctors' wives, whose task today is, he says, "a physical impossibility unrewarded by Government remuneration.

"The doctor's wife," he says, "attends to her household duties, minds her children, and often has to answer the telephone for her husband from nine o'clock in the morning till late afternoon.

"Most of the calls are from panel patients and the National Health allowance of 10s. 6d. per year for each patient does not allow for the high wages asked by domestics just to answer the telephone.

"Domestics sent by the labour exchange ask three guineas a week for answering the telephone while the doctor is on his rounds. So the work usually falls on the already overworked wife."

Sunday Express 1945

90,000 Miners Idle: Nobody Knows Why

By OUR INDUSTRIAL CORRESPONDENT

BARNSLEY, April 1

THE Yorkshire miners' strike, which now affects over 90,000 men and boys in some seventy pits, is an unaccountable and confusing affair. Neither the Ministry of Fuel nor the owners, neither the union officials nor the miners themselves can explain how and why it happened.

Ninety-nine per cent of the men would like to be back at work, one collier told me to-day. He said that the aftermath of twenty years' history was responsible for the present situation.

The trouble is that the miners' suspicions of the owners are so deep-seated that they see a snag in everything. They do not understand the effects of the recent wage awards, and there is a sense of frustration throughout the coalfield. They are not happy about this strike but are acting out of a misplaced sense of loyalty to their colleagues.

A meeting of the Council of the Yorkshire Mineworkers' Association to-day unanimously condemned the strike, which is paralysing four-fifths of the coalfield.

A resolution expressed deep concern at the prolongation of "an unconstitutional stoppage which, if persisted in, can only result in injuring the future of the Association," and again instructed all members to resume work at once.

The immediate cause of the stoppage is the dispute over the deduction for home coal. The number affected by the deduction is actually less than two per cent of the total number employed underground.

Mr. J. A. Hall, the Yorkshire miners' president, described the strike as "sabotage on the eve of the Allied invasion," and said there had been deliberate provocation by irresponsible "Trotskyist" elements.

The Government should take firm action, he said, and, if necessary, issue call-up papers

Delegates representing 25,000 of the strikers at eleven collieries in the Doncaster area to-night decided to recommend their men to resume work.

Observer 1944

Exeter Express and Echo 1945

'NOT ENOUGH FOR THE JOB'

MR. BEVAN, in his new charter for the nursing profession, aims at more pay, better conditions and a home-like life.

The intentions are laudable—the Public and the Florence Nightingales will be pleased. So far, so good.

At the moment there is a deficiency of between 33,000 and 34,000 nurses, to say nothing of 12,000 domestic staff. What is far more serious is this (and it is Mr. Bevan's own warning): "If we are faced with an epidemic this winter the seriousness may degenerate into a tragedy."

• • •

Instinct

NONE can deny the aims of the new charter. But are more-pay and better-conditions the solution to the problem of British nursing? They may go some way towards alleviating the situation, but from what one hears from one who has given a "lifetime of service" to suffering humanity, they can never completely solve the problem. The plain fact is that "there are not enough people to do the job." It needs be remembered, too, that the nursing instinct is something which is born, not made, and having been born, develops in the hard school of experience.

• • •

Compulsion

MR. BEVAN'S "great national effort to recruit more women of the right type" to this grand profession is to include an offer to 2,000 girls in the Forces of immediate release under Class B provided they take up nursing. A calling which demands of those fitted for it the highest degree of sympathy, understanding, perseverance, patience and self-sacrifice, certainly needs not Direction but the Power to Attract. Make the training more interesting is one suggestion. In the latter it is hoped the new charter may find the success it urgently and richly deserves. The nation wants to see its nursing profession lifted from the old condition of "drudgery" to that plane where good service conditions are the essential part of any system dedicated to the care of mankind.

Engineer 1946

On December 20th the Coal Industry Nationalisation Bill prepared by the Government was made public. A detailed analysis of this most important and revolutionary measure would be too long for inclusion in this article, but the more striking of the proposals may be briefly referred to.

With regard to assessment of the amount of the global sum to be awarded by way of compensation to the owners of the mines, this is to be settled by a tribunal composed of two judges of the High Court (appointed by the Lord Chancellor) and an accountant, to be agreed between the two parties (*i.e.*, the Government and the Mining Association of Great Britain) or, in default of agreement, to be nominated by the President of the Institution of Chartered Accountants. The sum decided upon will be apportioned to each coalfield or district. The task of valuing the 850 separate undertakings will be carried out by District Valuation Boards, broadly in accord with the practice followed in the case of the transference of minerals to the Coal Commission. The apportionment of the global sum as between districts will be decided by a Central Valuation Board. The basis on which the valuation of the undertakings is to be made is that as between a willing buyer and a willing seller in the open market. Payment of compensation is to be made in Government stock and certain restrictions are imposed upon the disposal of the stock. It is estimated that it will take two years to assess the value of the mines.

A National Coal Board of nine persons is to be established for the management of the industry and to secure its efficient development. Appointment to this Board will be made by the Minister of Fuel and Power. It will work as a business corporation and be free from the Civil Service, but the Minister will have power to give it directions of a general character in regard to matters affecting the public interest. The capital requirements of the Board for the first five years are to be met by a sum up to £150 millions, to be advanced by the Minister, and subsequently as Parliament may determine. In addition, the Board is to have power to borrow temporarily up to £10 million.

The Dustman

TOM D—— is a dustman in charge of a block of flats not much smaller than a largish village. He has six deputy dustmen under him, and he is paid £4 a week. But Tom D—— isn't far off pulling down a four-figure income.

How does he do it? He is intelligent enough to realise that there is hardly such a thing as rubbish. When his deputies bring him their waste, he sorts out the old books, the newspapers, bottles and other odd lots from the 400 dustbins in the block. He knows his market and he finds a sale for almost everything.

"I'm better off than the manager here," says Tom D—— "and I don't have to dress up for it either."

Leader 1947

POWER-LESS DAYS TO SAVE FUEL
Some may work 4½ days
By Daily Mail Reporter

OFFICIAL watch will be kept this winter for industrial defaulters failing to co-operate in the national plan to spread the electricity load and cut peak demand by one-third.

Details of regional plans for Greater London and the Midlands were announced in London and in Birmingham yesterday.

In the area covered by the London and South-Eastern Regional Board for Industry, it is hoped to achieve the peak electricity saving by the introduction of double-shift working, night shifts where necessary, week-end work in lieu of normal hours, and the transfer of heavy processes to night operation.

Industry in the Midlands will work principally on the basis of a power-less day per week when firms will be allowed to use only emergency plant. This will mean a four-and-a-half-day week for many.

Taking into account the 47,000 kilowatts saving under the power-less day scheme, there still remains another 103,000 kilowatts to be saved in the Midlands.

Observer 1946

TO EASE COUNTRY WIFE'S BURDEN

While the agricultural worker's wife remains "a beast of burden carrying water," said Mr. Aneurin Bevan, Minister of Health, in Hull yesterday, "we shall not succeed in making our countryside socially wealthy."

Therefore, he said, "we are doing our best to end the situation in which a large proportion of Britain is not yet covered with a piped water supply."

Birmingham Gazette 1947

Here is John Everyman

The midwife gloved, gowned and masked has brought him into the world. With her skill and training she looks after both him and his young mother at this time. It's a job a thousand times worth while. That is why many nurses specialise in midwifery after taking their S.R.N.

I am interested in training to be a NURSE

Please send me details of training for State Registration and the 2-year course for the State Enrolled Assistant Nurse (W.J.14)

NAME... Age..........
(If under 21)

ADDRESS...

Post to Ministry of Labour (Dept. N.R.), 23 Portman Square, London, W.1

LABOUR REDUNDANCY

TRAIN has frequently drawn attention to the amount of concealed unemployment in British industry through the retention of redundant labour.

Last year firms were content to carry this uneconomic load, partly because they hoped the slowdown would be transitory and partly because they feared to lose workmen in case they could not be replaced later.

The New Year has opened a new chapter in this matter. Firms now realise that the slowdown is here for some time anyway, and they are paring their labour.

Rover Company workers have now struck twice over the dismissal of redundant workers. The Transport and General Workers' Union maintains that employers no longer have the right to dismiss staff without Union consultation, and claims that ability and length of service must be taken into account when redundancy occurs.

This problem is also cropping up in many metal works throughout the Midlands, where production tempo has recently slowed down.

And only the other day the National Union of Journalists challenged the *Daily Mirror* owners' right to dismiss redundant journalists.

There is now no doubt that this problem will have to be tackled on a national scale very soon; and the intervening indecision and difficulties will have an adverse effect on companies' wages payments.

Train 1949

Forbidden To Leave Job

SICK GIRL FIGHTS MINISTRY

'Daily Sketch' Correspondent

Here is a tale for to-day, March 9, 1946, exactly 305 days after Germany was defeated in the war that was to bring Freedom to the people that won it. It is the story of a Girl, a Firm and a Ministry.

THE GIRL

is Miss Sheila Strawn, aged 22, a shorthand typist, of Hailsham-avenue, Streatham Hill, London.

For five years she has been employed in the City, unable to leave under the Essential Works Order.

Now she has a doctor's certificate to say she must leave London for a job by the sea, and she has been offered a post at Scarborough.

Her application for release has been refused by the Moorgate National Service Officer, despite the fact that

THE FIRM,

Mortimer Gall and Co., Ltd., of Cannon-street, London, E.C., have re-employed a pre-war employee on his release from the Navy, and he has taken over the duties on which Miss Strawn was engaged during the war.

She is now engaged in typing invoices. They have informed.

THE MINISTRY.

of Labour that they will release Miss Strawn if a substitute is found for her. The Ministry have refused.

Miss Strawn has also told the Ministry she will move to Scarborough in any case, and they have told her she can't go.

Miss Strawn, whose case has been placed before her M.P., will appear at Hackney on Monday before an appeal board.

"I'll go in any case," says Miss Strawn. "The war's over. I've done my job. I've got to look after my health now."

Daily Sketch **1946**

For my own part I believe that at present the world wastes a vast amount of really valuable feminine ability and that the Partnership has gained heavily from the extent to which in making important appointments it has disregarded sex. At present (February 1948) the Partnership has one hundred and fifty posts that are already carrying four-figure incomes and of these thirty-nine carry £2,000 a year or more. Of the former thirty-four are held by women and of the latter ten.

Partnership for All, John (Spedan) Lewis **1948**

MINERS DON'T WANT 'SPIVS' AS RECRUITS

" There has been a lot of talk recently about directing ' spivs ' into the mining industry, but we do not want them. We have had a bitter enough experience of drones in the past without bringing them in at present. The type of men we want in the mines are those who are determined to work to meet our difficulties."

This statement was made by Mr William Pearson, secretary of the Scottish Area of the National Union of Mineworkers, when he spoke on " The Crisis in the Coal Industry " at the Summer School of the National Council of Labour Colleges in Edinburgh to-day.

The whole future of the coal industry in this country, he said, depended on the way the Government solved the present mining crisis, and in view of the fact that this industry was now nationalised the successful solution of the problem depended not only on the miner himself but on everyone. To fail in this meant failure in all other national problems.

Mr Pearson described our coal mines to-day as a " deplorable " legacy of private enterprise. They lagged far behind anything on the Continent, and in most other countries, and it was of paramount importance that conditions should be improved if the recruiting campaign was to be at all successful.

Despite all that was being done, recruitment to-day was still lower than the rate of man-power wastage. In spite of the improvements in working conditions which were being introduced under nationalisation, the number of men in the mines at the present time was 11,000 fewer than had been expected.

FIVE-DAY WEEK

Defending the introduction of the five-day week, Mr Pearson said critics of the scheme could easily be answered by the coal output figures. In April of this year the average weekly output was 3,488,900 tons, whereas in May, when the shorter working week was introduced, it had risen by 92,560 tons. In June it as 3,623,900 tons. This compared with an average in June 1946 of 3,394,300 tons—a magnificent effort on the part of the miners.

On July 5 of this year our national coal stocks, at 10,522,000 tons, were more than 2,000,000 tons greater than at the same period last year under private enterprise.

Edinburgh Evening News 1947

National Insurance and Teachers

SIR.—Our profession includes a high proportion of single persons, and it seems that the new Insurance will prove a bad proposition for our bachelors and spinsters.

A deduction will be made from our salaries of 4s. 7d. a week (4s. 9d. after the first five years). (£11 18s. 4d. and £12 7s. a year respectively.)

For this we shall get the following :—

(1) Unemployment benefit of 26s. a week for up to a year.

(2) Sickness benefit at the same rate (but if salary continues to be paid, this will be deducted from it).

(3) Retirement pension at the same rate. Not payable until the age of 65. During the period 60-65 contributions will be paid; if not employed these will amount to a total of £65.

(4) Health benefits (cost 10d. a week). It would seem that most teachers will have a job to get their money back, unless they require hospital treatment, and can last until their turn comes.

(5) The benefits under the headings Widows, Guardians, and Maternity will be especially appreciated by single teachers.

(6) If a £20 funeral will suffice, then you may safely spend this amount now, while you are able to enjoy it, for that is the amount of the death benefit.

BACHELOR.

Schoolmaster 1948

WOMEN MAY BE OFFERED JOBS AS DIPLOMATS

By 'Daily Sketch' Correspondent

GREAT BRITAIN may have women diplomats on a permanent basis for the first time—if the report of a special committee now being studied by Mr. Ernest Bevin, the Foreign Secretary, is approved by him.

This would open a fascinating new career abroad for British women, and give them an opportunity to apply the woman's touch in what has been regarded as a masculine sphere.

Women did such good work in temporary positions during the war that a committee, whose report has now been presented, was appointed to consider whether women should be given posts in the senior branch of the diplomatic service on a permanent basis.

This branch includes diplomatic secretaries, diplomats, consuls, and the staff from whom ambassadors and trade commissioners are eventually chosen.

At present we have only temporary women assistants in the highest branch of the diplomatic service.

Daily Sketch 1946

Four Big Appointments

Four women holding important jobs abroad are: Miss C. M. E. Hastings, aged 21, temporary vice-consul in New York; Mrs. Marjorie Spikes, aged 51, attaché for women's affairs, Washington; Miss Muriel Lamb, aged 21, temporary third secretary in Oslo; and Mrs. A. R. Burn, temporary third secretary at Athens.

In London there are about 25 women in the Foreign Office in the top grade, and they are classed as temporary administrative assistants.

An official of the National Council of Women said: "It is high time that more scope was provided for intelligent women in international relations.

"Women's ability should not be wasted. They have a good deal to contribute to the management of world affairs."

Our Women–By The Queen

THE Queen yesterday thanked the women of Britain for "a difficult job magnificently done."

She was addressing at the County Hall, Westminster, a big gathering of women Civil Defence workers, police, and members of the W.V.S. from all parts of the country.

"I believe strongly," said the Queen, "that when future generations look back on this most terrible war, they will recognise as one of its chief features the degree to which women were actively concerned in it.

"I do not think it is any exaggeration to say that in this country at any rate the war could not have been won without their help.

"British women have won laurels in many fields, but nowhere have they played a more distinguished and courageous part than in the many spheres of activity that go to make up Civil Defence here at home."

Mr. Herbert Morrison, Minister of Home Security, said the parade of women was a symbol of five years' courageous effort.

Daily Herald 1944

Misery Loves Company

CRICKET has been reprieved. Last week, when Mr Chuter Ede announced that a ban would be placed on mid-week sport, on football, greyhound racing and some horse-racing fixtures, it was feared that, in the name of equality, cricket, too, would have to go. The Home Secretary has, however, listened to the arguments that the attendances at first-class cricket matches are so small that they do not interfere seriously with production, and has exercised his prerogative of mercy.

Economist 1947

Preparing the fields for potatoes with both horse-drawn and tractor-drawn ploughs at Hextable, Kent, 1947.

The Ministry of Works' 1948 film *Watch Your Step* urged workers and bosses to take first aid seriously.

Scientific Manpower Committee Report

THE report of the Committee on Scientific Manpower, which was appointed by the Lord President of the Council, on December 9th, 1945, to consider the policies which should govern the use and development of our scientific manpower and resources during the next ten years, has been published, as a White Paper—Cmd. 6824—by the Stationery Office, price 6d. The committee is of the opinion that the procedure for expediting the return of scientists to civil life is adequate to present needs, and no improvements are recommended. The fullest use, it states, should be made of the facilities offered by the Appointments Department of the Ministry of Labour, and applications for the release of experienced assistants under Class B should be considered sympathetically, where it can be shown that if release is not granted, the work of a scientist will be held up. Everything possible should be done to meet the immediate needs of Universities for accommodation. Dealing with the longer term problem, the report states that there were 45,000 scientists registered on the Ministry of Labour's Central (Technical and Scientific) Register at the end of 1945, and our existing capital must be, therefore, somewhere between 45,000 and 60,000. It is unlikely, the report states, that the nation has at its disposal to-day a force of more than 55,000 qualified scientists. Figures for 1950 and 1955, are assessed as a minimum requirement of 70,000 and 90,000 fully qualified scientists, respectively. It is essential, the report goes on to say, that the output of scientific graduates should be increased very much above the level of expansion at present envisaged by the Universities. The immediate aim, it states, should be to double the present output, giving approximately 5000 new scientists every year, at the earliest possible moment. The recommendation of the Percy Committee on Higher Technological Education is endorsed, that full-time technological sources of University Degree standard should be developed at a selected and limited number of Technical Colleges. The problems of individual universities are discussed, the quality of science teaching, and the effect and implementation of the committee's proposals.

Engineer 1946

A MORAL PROBLEM

SIR,—Your annotation last week raised several interesting points. Personally I hope that a serious effort will be made to collect together the results of all the experiments carried out on prisoners in German camps, and that anything of value will be published. The reasons given against such publication seem to me to be simply pernicious sentimentality. If I myself had been a victim, and some results of value or of interest had been obtained from my death, I am sure that I should have preferred to know that this knowledge would have been used and that I had not died entirely for nothing.

At times I have felt a good deal of sympathy for some of those who were responsible for carrying out the experiments. Accounts of the trials leave little doubt that many of the so-called scientists were men of no academic standing, with no idea how to carry out an experiment, and some were no more than irresponsible sadists: all these deserve the appropriate treatment at the hands of the courts. But others were serious research-workers. If one were given the chance of using prisoners for experiments which one believed to be of great importance and value to mankind, what would one do, particularly if government propaganda had convinced one that the victims were dangerous criminals who were anyhow condemned to death, and likely to die in some particularly abominable manner? This is indeed a moral issue, and I am not at all sure what I should myself have done. I have always been most fortunate, in that I have been able to obtain willing and coöperative volunteers when I have wished to carry out experiments on man, but there are many types of investigation for which one must hesitate to use such subjects. I believe that while capital punishment is retained, condemned murderers should be given the opportunity of volunteering to serve as subjects for experiments. The question is rather different when the victims are innocent prisoners, though to a keen research-worker with little contact with the world outside his laboratory and who believes what his government tells him the answer may be simpler.

The method in which these results should be published requires careful consideration. At all costs sensationalism must be avoided, and it might perhaps be as well to grade them as " confidential " and make them available only to bona-fide investigators. Otherwise the press should be taken into the confidence of those responsible for the editing of the reports before publication ; the average journalist is a responsible person, and in this way accurate and unobjectionable reporting would be ensured.

KENNETH MELLANBY.

Department of Entomology, London School of Hygiene and Tropical Medicine.

The Lancet 1946

PITSIDE HEROISM

Bro. S. Llewellyn, 2nd hand melter of Malleable No. 4 Branch, owes his life to the courage and resourcefulness of three of his mates. He slipped from the staging on which he was standing, into the pit and finally came to rest between four ingot moulds each of which had been filled, some half an hour earlier, with seven tons of molten steel.

He was seen to fall by Bro. S. Bell who hastily summoned Bros. F. Simpson and F. Pearce. Bro. Simpson, quickly followed by the others, stepped down from the pitside and, precariously balancing themselves on the six-inch rims of the ingot moulds, hauled Bro. Llewellyn up from his dangerous position and got him safely onto the pitside.

Bro. Llewellyn weighs 14 stone, and the task of hoisting him to safety whilst standing balanced, in intense heat, on the narrow rims of open topped ingot moulds, each of which contained hot steel, required calmness and courage of the highest order. One false step could have brought disaster to them all.

We are pleased to learn that Bro. Llewellyn, though in hospital suffering from severe burns, is reported to be comfortable. But for the prompt and courageous action of his mates he would undoubtedly have been slowly burned to death.

Man and Metal
1949

An Office Conference

A GOOD MODEL can model anything—even a maternity skirt—and frequently Gina is called upon to consult with the people concerned on details of presentation, colour and so on. Here she makes suggestions and discusses the launching of a maternity skirt with Anna Newton and Donald Gardiner, both on the staff of a well-known London advertising agency.

Interior of a kiln

The Saturday Book 1947

HIGHER STIPENDS FOR CLERGY?

"WORST-HIT CLASS."

DIOCESAN SCHEME FOR IMPROVEMENT.

At Friday's meeting of the Oxford Diocesan Board of Finance, held at the County Hall, Oxford, under the chairmanship of the Bishop of Oxford, (Dr. K. E. Kirk), it was stated that, as a result of a resolution passed at the recent Oxford Diocesan Conference, a meeting of the Chamber of Laity of the diocese would be held in Oxford on 24 September to consider the question of raising clerical stipends.

The Bishop, commenting on the storm-damage appeal, said that more than 100 applications for assistance had been made, and in some cases the cost was as high as £330.

New cases were continually coming in, and they had reason to suppose they would need at least £3,000. The total raised so far was £1,834.

£500 Income Needed.

The Maintenance of the Ministry Committee reported that, in connection with assistant curates' and lay workers' grants, under the Ecclesiastical Commissioners' new scheme for assistance by means of block grants to diocesan boards of finance the amount of the block grant to the Oxford diocese for 1947-48 was £3,730.

With regard to clergy stipends, the administration of the central fund would be carried out by Queen Anne's Bounty.

The total amount provided by the Ecclesiastical Commissioners and Queen Anne's Bounty would be £480,000, to be allocated on a graduated scale over a period of six years

The sum made available to the diocese for 1947 was £6,900, to be applied, as the Board of Finance might decide, to benefices with incomes under £500.

A memorandum, issued with the committee's report, stated that it was generally agreed that every priest with a charge ought to have a gross income of at least £500 a year.

North Berkshire Herald 1947

BIAS AGAINST DIDCOT ALLEGED.

REFUSAL OF CATERING LICENCE.

Bias against Didcot in the refusal of catering licences was alleged by Mr. S. Freeman at yesterday's meeting of Wallingford Joint Food Control Committee.

With only Mr. Freeman and Mr. R. G. Andrews dissenting, the committee had refused a catering licence for the Oxford Co-operative Society's premises, 126, Broadway, Didcot, on the ground that there was no consumer need.

"Wallingford has three times as many licences as Didcot," said Mr. Freeman.

"There is need for another half-dozen in Didcot," declared Mr. Andrews.

The committee then proceeded to approve a licence for sandwiches and snacks for the "Travellers' Welcome," East Hagbourne.

Mr. Freeman said the committee's attitude was inconsistent, for if there was no need for an extra licence at Didcot, there was no need for one at East Hagbourne, which was virtually part of Didcot.

"This committee has got an unnatural bias against Didcot," he said.

North Berkshire Herald 1947

COUPON TRAFFIC

Leader 1947

JOANNA HALL is paid four pounds twelve a week for standing behind the perfume counter in a West End shop, and looking smart. She has had the job six weeks, and likes it.

Last week the shopwalker drew her aside.

"That dress, Miss Hall," he began, shaking his head. "It won't do, you know. Not in the West End, it won't. It's too well-worn. And those shoes—just a little down at heel, I'm afraid. If the personnel manager were to see you . . ." He wagged his finger solemnly.

"A word to the wise, you know. A word to the wise!" He moved off.

Was it a coincidence that a friendly little man approached Joanna in the A.B.C. at lunchtime and offered her a sheet of coupons at two bob each?

She thanked him and spent the rest of the lunch hour queueing at the Post Office to draw two pounds to pay for them.

That evening Joanna attached the sheet of brown coupons to her clothing book, and the following lunch hour she dashed off to buy a pair of shoes.

With the new shoes wrapped up, she handed her coupon book to the assistant, who began clipping, then stopped to hold the page up to the light. She gave Joanna a hard look, and tossed down the book.

"These are forgeries!"

"But they can't be," said Joanna, "I just bought them."

"More fool you," said the assistant. "Next time look for the watermark. These are fake."

Blushing hotly, Joanna left the shop and went back to the perfume counter.

That is Joanna Hall's first acquaintance with the black market in clothing coupons. It won't be her last.

"What can I do?" she asks. "If I'm not smartly dressed I'll lose my job, and I simply cannot manage on four coupons a month."

Remember?

. . . AND YOU'RE WANTED BACK BECAUSE THE R.A.F. REMEMBERS TOO

The R.A.F. still needs your help; invites you to come back and share the old comradeship, the big new opportunities.

Attractive terms of the **W.A.A.F.** EXTENDED SERVICE SCHEME

PROVIDED you served at least a year and are still physically fit, you can rejoin for two, three or four years. There is no upperage limit. (If married you must guarantee you would not be neglecting home commitments.) You get a gratuity of £20 *tax free* for each year, payable at the end of engagement, provided you serve a minimum of two years. You get also an extra 28 days' leave. You come back in your old temporary rank and, if it is possible, to your former trade. The W.A.A.F. is now being re-formed on a permanent basis and, by rejoining now, you will have the best possible chance of a peacetime career in the Service. Meantime, living conditions are already being improved. New, smarter uniforms are on the way. Take the first step now. Fill in and post the coupon. (Ex-W.A.A.F. officers should write to Air Ministry, S.11. Serving W.A.A.F. should ask their officer for particulars.)

Open only to released and serving W.A.A.F.

- -

I am interested in rejoining. Please send details without obligation.

NAME (Mrs./Miss) .... No. ....

ADDRESS ....

To : AIR MINISTRY (DEPT. W.J 2) VICTORY HOUSE, KINGSWAY, LONDON, W.C.2

Daily Worker 1947

10,000 PROTEST AGAINST MASS SACKING

From SAM RUSSELL

MANCHESTER, Friday.

NEARLY 10,000 workers at a mass meeting at the great Metro - Vickers works here today denounced the issuing of mass-dismissal notices to almost all of the 17,000 workers employed.

Mr. Hugh Scanlon, convener of shop stewards and chairman of the works committee, told them that the shop stewards had been in almost continuous session for a week.

"There is nothing in the guaranteed week agreement signed between the engineering workers and the employers in April, 1946," said Mr. Scanlon, "which absolves the employer from his responsibility to pay a guaranteed week during the crisis."

He roundly accused the employers of trying to turn feeling against the Government.

How far this move has succeeded can be judged from the fact that there was unanimous approval from the meeting for a resolution expressing support for the Government.

In all, 25,000 employees of the Vickers group of companies have received a week's notice.

Guy's Diary

NOVEMBER—DECEMBER

Guy's Hospital Gazette 1948

ACADEMIC

Nov.

Exhibition. "Tuberculosis of Bone and Genito-Urinary System." Gordon Museum.

Exhibition. "Dysphagia." Surgical Dept.

22nd. 1.00. Dr. P. R. Evans. Clinical Lecture. "The Hazards of being born."

3.30. Dr. Barber and Dr. Forman. Demonstration of Skin Diseases. Preclinical Classroom.

4.45. Dr. R. C. MacKeith. Postgraduate Lecture in Pædiatrics. "Primary Staphylococcal Infections in the Respiratory Tract of Adults and Children." Preclinical Classroom.

23rd. 5.00. Dr. P. M. F. Bishop. Clinical Lecture. "Cushing's Syndrome and Adrenal Cortical Over-Activity." (M.R.C.P. Candidates and Senior Students).

24th. 2.00. Dr. Marston. Postgraduate Revision Lecture in Anæsthesia. Clinical Theatre. (Surgical Block).

25th. 1.00. Mr. Grant Massie. Clinical Lecture. "Subphrenic Abscess."

4.30. X-Ray Meeting. Gordon Museum.

26th. 1.00. Dr. Hardwick. Clinical Lecture. "Ascites."

2.15. Dr. Bishop. Combined Round. Endocrine Diseases. Preclinical Classroom.

27th. 10.00. Surgical Dept. Clinico-Pathological Meeting. Anatomy Theatre.

Maj.-Gen. Sir Alexander Biggam. Demonstration of Tropical Diseases, R.A.M.C. Hospital, Milbank.

29th. 1.00. Dr. Forman. Clinical Lecture. "Skin Changes with Malignant Diseases."

3.30. Dr. Barber and Dr. Forman. Demonstration of Skin Diseases. Preclinical Classroom.

The Development of "Prepared" Trimmings
by D. Attwood

Director, W. Attwood Ltd., Bias Binding Manufacturers, London.

Apparel Production
1950

WHEN OUR forefathers started to make clothes their problems were very different from those that our modern factories have to face. Even when the first Wholesale Clothing Factories were started they made a straightforward garment with no " fancy bits "—quite a different proposition from that which our manufacturers face to-day, with increased competition and the " choosiness " of the public.

In the old days the garment and all the trimmings were made in the factory, but now-a-days " ready processed " trimmings are produced by specialists and are supplied to the factory ready for use, thus saving processes in the factory which formerly took up a key man's time, and they are produced in a form which saves time for the machinists. Overhead costs are thereby reduced ; the rate of production is stepped up, and the general efficiency of the factory is improved.

The use of ready-made trimmings is now almost universal in the clothing and allied trades. Bias bindings for women's clothing, trouser waist banding, bias collar canvas and cuff canvases, cut edge tapes for bridles, pocket stays, etc. for men's clothing, have become a necessity and an esential part of the garment from the point of view of the clothing manufacturer.

Like all innovations, these new ideas were looked on with suspicion by most factory managers, who could not at first see any advantage in the new method, and it was not until 1930–31 that these ideas gradually came into general use by the more progressive manufacturers.

Joint Stock Company Journal 1950

Leadership in Industry.

Let us not underrate the importance of leadership in industry, as in so many other spheres of life. Vision and daring, knowledge and experience, mature judgment allied to the capacity to take risks—these are the qualities which enabled those at the head of our affairs to lead us to victory in the war. They are no less necessary in the arduous tasks of peace.

A " do as you have done before " policy in industry will not lift us out of our economic difficulties. We cannot afford to rest on our industrial laurels—they are somewhat faded. We must intensify research and development, scrap old machinery, adopt new methods, introduce new products, capture new markets. To achieve this we need the utmost exertions on the part of our industrial leaders; we should encourage to the greatest degree those qualities of imaginative daring and originality which are so vital. —Mr. Charles Colston (Hoover).

MATRON OF 21 " TOO YOUNG "

PROTEST ON NURSERY APPOINTMENT

DAILY TELEGRAPH REPORTER

A protest against the recent appointment of 21-year-old Miss Marjorie Julia Evans as matron of a day nursery in West Thurrock, Essex, is being made by the National Association of Nursery Matrons. Miss Evans, who was 21 last April, gained her diploma in 1945.

Mrs. Mace, secretary of the association, which is recognised by the Royal College of Nursing, said yesterday that she had written to Dr. W. T. G. Boul, medical officer for Thurrock, on the matter. She had not yet received a reply.

" I believe her appointment was made by the public health committee of the local authority," said Mrs. Mace. " I have heard that the matter is now being considered by the Ministries of Health and Education. " Miss Evans's appointment is contrary to guidance given in a joint circular issued by the Ministries. This states that matrons should be not less than 25 years old and deputy matrons not less than 23.

"EMOTIONAL MATURITY" NEED

" A degree of emotional maturity is necessary in a nursery matron. The job carries a large responsibility in arranging meals and other details as well as just looking after the children.

" We believe the appointment of one so young is morally wrong. There is no quarrel over Miss Evans's academic qualifications.

Daily Telegraph 1950

OFFICIAL NOTICES
Appointments by the Chairman

To be, from the date of this *Gazette*, Deputy Director of Financial Operations—Mr. S. A. Weatherfield. (Acting rank confirmed.)

J. S. L.

*   *   *

To act, from such date as the Director of Maintenance and Expansion, who is at present holding this post, may arrange with her, as Managing Director of John Lewis—Miss M. J. Ahern.

J. S. L.

Note: Miss Ahern will retain for the present the Managership of the Intelligence Department but in due course she will specialise upon one or other of these two posts.

This Managing Directorship is the second of a number of experiments that the Partnership will be making of the same kind. A notice upon the broad idea will appear in *The Gazette* as soon as possible.

Gazette of the John Lewis Partnership 1951

1d. an hour more if they don't get on knees to job

Daily Mirror 1951

By JOYCE CHESTERTON

TO try to persuade older workers to abandon cleaning methods they have used all their lives, domestic hospital workers are being paid an extra penny an hour if they will use electric scrubbing machines to clean floors, instead of getting down on their hands and knees.

Miss F. R. Brown, Ministry of Health adviser on hospital domestic management, disclosed this at a London conference yesterday.

She told me afterwards:

"The older type of woman in the hospitals has never been brought up to use electrical machinery and is suspicious of it."

The solution, she suggested to a conference of electrical housecraft advisers, was to pick a team of suitable workers, particularly the younger type of non-resident hospital domestic, who might have electrical equipment in her own prefab.

They would use each type of equipment and be trained so that they had an interest in keeping the machine in order.

Miss Brown told me that she looked forward to proper training schemes for domestic workers which would lead to a better status in the hospitals

"There's always a certain difference of opinion as to how much time machines can save," Miss Brown said.

They Wanted to Show

"I've heard of a scrubbing machine being demonstrated and the staff promptly replying: 'We can do better than that.'

"They go down on their knees to prove it.

"But that's probably because the demonstrator didn't know his job.

"There's no doubt that machines can do a better cleaning job in many cases—they can get the dust out from between the cracks, where hands can't!

"We have a number of the 'old faithfuls' who like to scrub and clean and polish their own bit of the hospital. I don't know what we'd do without them.

Didn't Like Change

"One woman was disgusted when she was transferred from a staircase which she had cleaned for years to another staircase, exactly the same.

"'It's a rotten staircase,' she told people, 'not nearly as good as my own one.'

"And that kind of worker would much rather go on getting down on her knees."

The men ask for more women barbers

WOMEN are taking up jobs as men's hairdressers—and both barbers and customers welcome them. It was stated at the National Hairdressers' Federation conference at Whitley Bay, Northumberland.

Mr. W. I. C. George, president, said: "I am all in favour of a 'silk stocking' influence in our shops."

Later he told the *Daily Mirror*: "Those already working in gents' saloons—and there are far too few of them—are doing a good job.

"They are ideally suited to hairdressing. What's more, wherever there are women working you notice the feminine touch in the cleanliness and decoration of the place."

Mr. David Bingham, of Hamilton, Scotland, whose sister Peggy, 26, helps run his shop, said: "Men like Peggy to do their hair, and the way she suggests new hair styles for them.

"They come back to her time after time."

Daily Mirror 1951

Petula Clark sounds rather like Helen Kane, the "Betty Boop" girl, in *Teasin'*, and like Nellie Lutcher at times in *Black Note Serenade* (Polygon P1005). On the same label (P1006) we find **Jimmy Young** reviving two old ones, *Don't Worry 'Bout Me* and *Life's Desire*. He has clear diction and an easy style, which are definite assets in these days of striving for novelty at the expense of everything else;

Gramophone 1951

Cost of a cup

The building industry is behaving abominably. If only we could abolish tea-drinking in Britain it would reduce the price of a house by about £300.— *Sir Herbert Williams, Tory M.P. for East Croydon, last night.*

Daily Express 1952

Packing tins at Crosse and Blackwell's factory in Bermondsey, London, in 1950.

Spring planting on a hill farm in Wales, 1951.

Daily Mirror 1951

They tucked away for a title

FOR lunch yesterday, Ron Lilley, 17, electrician's mate, got through: One raspberry jam-coated doughnut, three glasses of water and TWENTY HOT-CROSS BUNS.

And 300 of his work-mates in an Oldbury (Staffs) steel tube works, watched him eat it.

Ron ploughed through his traditional Good Friday lunch in thirty minutes.

Alongside him, Doug Round, 16, polished off sixteen buns, Brian Jackson, 13, a baker's dozen. Red-haired John Rutherford, 15, could manage only ten.

The winner —with his mouth full of bun.

So Ron was crowned Bun King of the works.

But Walter Lovett, 36, list. organiser of this year's contest—the bun feeds have been held in the works annually for nearly a century—shook his head.

"These chaps seemed to have lost their appetites. When I won in 1939 I had to eat my full dinner first. Even then I got through thirty-six buns."

Ron apologised: "I had six cheese sandwiches for breakfast."

Gamekeeper and Countryside 1950

Daily Express 1952

QUOTE

—By Mr W. S Wood at yesterday's meeting of Denbighshire Standing Joint Committee, which is paying two police cadets £3 for a 38-hour week :—

IF boys of 16 are to be trained to believe that 38 hours is a week's work, then it is a public scandal. If a boy starts out on that foundation, people who will have to employ him later are going to have great difficulty.

Daily Mirror 1951

MINERS WEAR WIVES' UNDIES AT WORK

IN BRIEF

MORE and more of Britain's miners are wearing their wives' undies because they cannot get the special type of underpants they need, said the Coal Board yesterday.

The type of underpants the miners normally wear are of a twill material, which gives them greater freedom of movement when working in cramped spaces.

But these special drawers are becoming difficult to get, explained Mr. John Burke, Manchester area welfare officer of the N.C.B.

And women's underwear is the next best thing, he said.

So now many men are going to work wearing panties beneath their overalls.

Daily Express 1951

Catch of the season

News Chronicle Reporter

NINE Scottish fishermen—after working continuously for 50 hours—finished unloading at Great Yarmouth last night the largest catch of herring landed in East Anglia since, it is believed, 1913—and, possibly, the largest single night's catch in East Anglian history.

In their 74-ton 86ft. drifter Star of Bethlehem (Peterhead) they had caught 302 crans—more than 360,000 fish—with an estimated value of nearly £910.

Five pits refuse to take Italians

From Our Doncaster Staff

STRONG opposition to a move by their area headquarters to introduce Italian miners into the pits is evident among the Doncaster district miners.

Of the pits in the area which were asked yesterday to discuss and accept the recommendation, five refused to accept a quota of Italians. Bullcroft pit are to accept 30 and Yorkshire Main are to discuss the matter at a later date.

Askern, who were asked to take 100, refused to do so. Mr. M. Thompson, the secretary, told "The Yorkshire Post" that the men's reasons were that they felt that the money spent on training Italians could have been used for attracting British men into the pits, and that Italians often left the pits after they had been trained.

' Thrust on management '

At Hatfield Main, Mr. R. Kelley, secretary, said his branch refused 40 Italians because men who had left the pit for other collieries and who wished to return had been refused jobs. He alleged that the colliery agent said recently that it was unlikely that any Italians would be taken to Hatfield as there was no need for them. "It is not a policy which has been dictated by the needs of the pit. It looks as though it has been thrust upon the management from above," said Mr. Kelley.

Brodsworth, who have refused 100 Italians, yesterday mandated branch officials to see that under no consideration should any efforts be made to induce the men to change their minds.

Mr. W. Kellner, delegate to Thorne branch, said: "Thorne, which has consistently refused to accept foreign workers of any kind, is to continue to do so and will not take the 20 Italians which the Union at area level, recommends."

Mr. R. E. Hughes, branch president, said the Rossington men had refused to accept 100 Italians as they considered there was insufficient face room at the colliery.

Union support for the introduction of Italian miners was a condition of a wages increase for lower paid men negotiated between the National Union of Mineworkers and the National Coal Board in January.

Yorkshire Post
1951

BBC PLAN 20 NEW STATIONS FOR BETTER LISTENING

By CLIFFORD DAVIS

THE B.B.C. are to seek Parliamentary approval for a new system of broadcasting calling for the setting up of twenty new radio stations, costing £15,000 each, that will cover the whole country.

The switch-over means a new deal for millions of listeners. By using the V.H.F. method of transmission interference from cars, trams, vacuum sweepers and other electrical equipment will be cut out.

So will interference from foreign stations in Britain's black spot radio areas, which include the South Coast and North Norfolk.

Present transmissions will continue, but existing sets can be adapted, at a cost of under £5, to pick up the new wavelengths as well. The radio industry is already making self-contained sets for both methods.

The new plan was disclosed last night by Sir Noel Ashbridge, the B.B.C.'s chief engineer, at the House of Commons when he faced 100 M.P.s and Peers at a special demonstration of the V.H.F. (Very High Frequency) system, on which the new stations will operate.

The B.B.C. propose to broadcast from the new stations the Home, Light and Third programmes on V.H.F. Frequency Modulation, using super short waves, which ensure complete freedom from interference.

Already B.B.C. engineers have been experimenting on V.H.F. broadcasts from their Wrotham, Kent, transmitter. The B.B.C. report to the Government is based on these tests.

Sir Noel told the M.P.s that the change-over was inevitable. Present medium wavelengths were congested and reception throughout Britain would get steadily worse, he said.

Daily Mirror
1951

Daily Mirror 1951

Girls go on strike—for music

GIRL workers in a large gown factory yesterday burst into song—by way of protest.

The management had switched off the B.B.C. "Housewives' Choice" programme, which was being relayed.

"No music, no work," said the girls.

The leader of the "singing strike" was promptly ordered to leave the factory. In sympathy, the rest of the factory's 200 girls walked out too.

The management appealed to the girls to return. They even switched on the music again. And after a ten-minute delay, the girls went back to work.

One girl at the factory, the Athena Works, Maesteg (Glam), said later: "We were warned that the manager felt 9-10 a.m. was too early for music.

"But we have always had 'Housewives' Choice' on—it's much nicer to have music while you work."

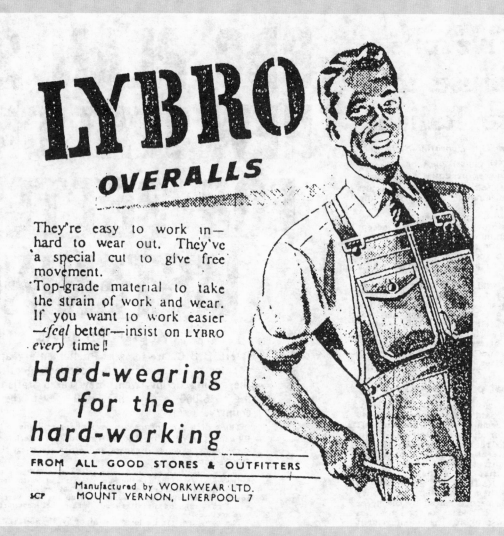

LYBRO
OVERALLS

They're easy to work in—hard to wear out. They've a special cut to give free movement.
Top-grade material to take the strain of work and wear. If you want to work easier—*feel* better—insist on LYBRO *every* time!

Hard-wearing for the hard-working

FROM ALL GOOD STORES & OUTFITTERS

SCP Manufactured by WORKWEAR LTD.
MOUNT VERNON, LIVERPOOL 7

'ONE TUBE LASTS ME MORE THAN HALF-WAY ROUND THE WORLD!"

SAYS CHARTER-PILOT HOPKINS
of Silver City Airways, Ltd.

"Whether my cargo is a load of private cars, pedal cycles and their owners or an International football team there's one piece of personal freight I always carry," adds Capt. Hopkins, "that's my tube of Rowntree's Fruit Gums. Over sea, Alps or desert they never fail to soothe and refresh me."

LONG LASTING
ROWNTREE'S FRUIT GUMS
soothe and refresh

RE-UPHOLSTERY, LOOK!

Dining chairs recovered from 8s. 9d. each, fireside chairs 70s., armchairs 5 gns., 3-piece suites 15 gns. Let Charlie Brown, your personal upholsterer call with his inexhaustible range of cloths. Antiques and deep buttoned upholstery a speciality.

HIGH FORCE UPHOLSTERY,
22/24 Westbourne Terrace, Reading.
Tel. 54798/74198.

5,000 TONS FIRST-CLASS SOIL FOR SALE

Suitable for gardeners, nurserymen, etc. Delivery to all parts in 6-ton loads.

THE CROFT GRANITE, BRICK & CONCRETE CO. LTD.
CROFT.
NEAR LEICESTER
Phone Narborough 2261-4

CLINTON RESTAURANT

WEYMOUTH   Tel. 467

famous for

WEDDING RECEPTIONS

MASS OBSERVATION, the group which records British public opinion and behaviour, has been probing what the average man and woman think of their day, and now says . . .

How You HATE Monday
The Things You Like—And Dislike—In Your Daily Round

Black Monday

MONDAY means work again, tiredness and irritability after the week-end, cold food, washing orgies and the next week-end too far away even to be imagined. In the office, employers "bustling with efficiency and economy schemes" face unresponsive staffs, at home there is, according to one housewife:—

"A soapy smell all over the house, awful household tasks like cleaning the flues and scrubbing out the gas stove. No cigarettes left No sweet ration left Just the same old weekly grind ahead." (Housewife - typist, aged 30).

Here is one of the more violent of the Monday haters with, it would seem, good reason:—

"The day I like least is Monday. This is the hardest day of the whole week and lasts the whole day. There is always a large clothes basket piled high with dirty clothes. I start working about 8 a.m., but have to leave off many times to see to various breakfasts, washing-up, bed-making, preparing lunch, &c. Usually Monday lunch doesn't suit everybody. The result is that we end by having a hotch-potch meal. During this meal the copper (which has been very slow in boiling all the morning) nearly always boils over, making another mess to clear up. The washing completed by about 4 p.m., I now have a large brick floor to scrub, which I hate doing, and by the time it's done I'm almost exhausted. The weather is wet, indoors drying goes on by degrees until bedtime! (Housewife; aged 50).

Liverpool Echo 1952

Off to the 'Z' men

Mr. Antony Head, Secretary for War, took off in an helicopter from the heart of Chelsea to-day to visit anti-aircraft units in Norfolk.

Mr. Head said: "I want to see the 'Z' chaps and it is an immense asset going this way."

Brighton Evening Argus 1952

New job for Bruce

Bruce Woodcock, former British heavy-weight boxing champion, took over yesterday as landlord of the Angel public house in Bolsover, Derbyshire.

Daily Express 1952

Beecham's burden

Mr. Thomas Beecham, of Hove Park-way, Hove, told the Brighton and Hove Post Office Advisory Committee to-day that people were still ringing him up in mistake for Sir Thomas Beecham.

"When I complained before," he said, "the telephone manager had the word 'Mr.' inserted before my name in the telephone directory, but it has disappeared from the current issue. People are getting me out of bed at midnight to ask for opera tickets."

Mr. Beecham said he had been asked by a Hove businessman, Mr. Thomas Farr, to say that people rang him up to talk about boxing although he was no relation to Tommy Farr, the boxer, who also lives in Hove.

Brighton Evening Argus 1952

Opinion

The Cabinet changes

MR. CHURCHILL'S decision to give the Health Ministry to Mr. Iain Macleod is both daring and imaginative.

Daring because Mr. Macleod is untried and inexperienced in office.

Imaginative because he has all the other qualities that command success. He has youth and eloquence and faith in his cause. He is brilliant in debate. He has fire and courage. And his technical knowledge of the Health Service is unsurpassed.

It is always good to see youth being given a chance.

The nation—young and old—will join in the hope that 38-year-old Iain Macleod grasps the chance that Mr. Churchill has given him. And remains for many more years at the glittering top.

Daily Express 1952

A publican without a pint

AS from last night Mr. H. Dixon Clark became licensee of the British Queen, in Islington, for the seventh successive year. And Mr. Clark has never had a customer; has never drawn a pint of beer.

In fact, the doors have never opened since Mr. Clark took over, at a Brewsters' Session, in 1945.

Stranger still, Mr. Clark, the licensee, is also town clerk of the borough. He explained:—

"The council took over the British Queen and its surrounding site for development in 1938. The British Queen was pulled down in 1945, and I have been granted the licence ever since, though I had never been inside the place for a drink.

"The licence will be sold back to the brewers for £1,000 plus costs if they can find a suitable site elsewhere.

"Meantime, I'm a publican with not a drop to serve."

Daily Express 1952

So bored . . .

A policeman arrested R.A.S.C. Private Charles Frederick Bailey and asked him why he was away from his unit without leave. Bailey replied: "I got bored with nothing to do all day long." Torquay magistrates remanded him in custody yesterday to await escort back to his camp at Bordon.

. . . So useful

Men home helps make extremely good workers about the house, Mrs. M. L. Richey, chairman of the National Association of Home Help Organisers, told the association's first international conference at Westminster yesterday.

Daily Express 1952

Miss Squeaker stirs up trouble

Express Staff Reporter

THE SQUEAKER has raven hair, wide blue eyes, a scarlet dress. She is attractive—and sinister.

Already she has helped to put 50 workers out of a job. Because of her thousands of pounds in sterling has gone behind the Iron Curtain.

The Squeaker is just eight inches tall, a rubber squeaking doll made in Czechoslovakia.

Price in Britain's stores is 2s. 9d. "And that," said Mr. Albert Berry, 43-year-old director of a Chichester firm of toymakers last night, " indicates a clear case of dumping."

Staff cut

Mr. Berry has cut his staff from 130 to 80 in the last 18 months because of the Squeaker and similar under-priced foreign toys.

The Squeaker has a boy friend, about her own height. In bright green bathing helmet and blue swimsuit, he has that same butter-won't-melt-in-my-mouth expression.

" These dolls must be landing here for as little as a shilling each," he said. " We could not make a similar grade doll for less than 3s. 4d.—to sell at 7s. in the stores.

" If the Squeaker stays—more of my men will have to go. And not only my firm is affected."

Dumping?

How do the Czechs do it? The Federation of British Rubber Manufacturers' Associations believes that the Prague Government, anxious to get sterling at all costs, is subsidising toy makers.

The federation complained to the Board of Trade. The official reply : If you can get evidence of dumping we will take it up under the General Agreement on Tariffs and Trade—GATT.

Under a trade pact signed in 1949 Czechoslovakia may send us £155,000 worth of rubber toys this year.

" But how can we get evidence of what is going on between manufacturers and Government behind the Iron Curtain ? " asked a federation official.

And while the wrangle goes on little Miss Blandishment, the Squeaker, lands in her thousands and is selling like hot cakes.

Daily Express 1952

Feminine Achievement

THE RIDING SCHOOL INSTRUCTRESS

—one of the many careers today in which women's poise and athletic grace have won success. In their choice of cigarettes, more and more women of achievement prefer GOLD FLAKE, famous for quality since 1883.

WILLS'S Gold Flake CIGARETTES

HIS MAJESTY THE TENOR
By AIDA FAVIA-ARTSAY

He is the *divo* of the opera, the capricious ruler whose idiosyncrasies are indulgently looked upon as manifestations of artisitc temperament (until a level-headed impresario puts his foot down) and whose frequently mediocre performances are forgiven for the sake of a soul-melting C in *Che a me riveli la fanciulla*, or a stentorian one in *o teco almeno corro a morir*.

We collectors also love our tenors, but how do we listen to their records ? Do we just wait enraptured for some awesome vocal gymnastics to particularly tickle our ears, or do we use our critical faculties to analyse every phrase, absorbing the good and turning up our noses at the bad until, bit by bit, a complete picture of the performance is formed in our minds ? A little discriminating understanding will allow the records to give infinitely more pleasure, and to accomplish this one need not be a finished singer or musician : a fairly good ear and some knowledge of the fundamentals of music and singing is all that's necessary.

Gramophone 1951

Golden teeth

The value of gold supplied for essential dental requirements in 1951 was about £200,000. — Sir Arthur Salter, Minister for Economic Affairs.

Daily Express 1952

IGNORANCE IS NO EXCUSE

BRITAIN HAS 12,300 LAWS—SO DO BE CAREFUL

A NEW and up-to-date edition of Halsbury's Laws of England is soon to be published. Though it costs £175 the set—or £30 to hire—this is good news to Merseyside lawyers, to your family solicitor and to anybody liable to be hauled into court. For ignorance of the law is no excuse and Halsbury's Laws is a reasonably quick index to the amazingly complex legislation that governs our lives.

A legal best seller, " Halsbury " has been the standard work ever since a former Lord Chancellor earned £10,000 by compiling it

By MARK PRIESTLY

back in 1907. Since then, of course, it has been revised by several editors. Yet the task of clarifying and keeping pace with the law is tougher than hacking a path through the jungle.

Britain already has more laws than any other country on earth. And as a whole our laws are in such an untidy muddle that a special Parliamentary Committee has been sitting these last 15 years in an attempt to prune them . . and it expects to be sitting for 15 years more.

Daily Quote

The first law on the Statute Book—that great constitutional roll call of what you may or may not do—dates back to the year 1235. For over 700 years our legislators have been discussing, amending, passing and repealing laws by the thousand, and they have forgotten to keep the signposts painted along the way.

One ancient law, passed in 1361, is quoted almost daily in Liverpool to cover the process known as "binding over." A Statute of 1275 still justifies the Liverpool Assizes. Far from being archaic, a law of 1360 is used to prosecute "Peeping Toms."

Yet High Court judges of long experience cannot incisively say how namy laws are still in force. To-day not even the highest authorities really know how many laws rule us from cradle to grave.

As originally written the full laws of the land run to 173 volumes or a bulk of fully 160,000 pages. Attempts at compression have admittedly reduced this. At the start of the century British official law occupied 118 volumes.

Liverpool Echo 1952

SIR JOHN DISLIKES SECURITY

Daily Herald 1953

THE HAGUE, Thursday.—Sir John Fisher, chairman of a Barrow-in-Furness firm which once owned 100 deep-sea sailing ships, today told the Baltic and International Maritime Conference what he thought of the Welfare State and social security.

"Security is against all natural laws," he said. "Whether we like it or not the principle of the survival of the fittest has operated since the world began. This most certainly applies to shipping.

"High wages and food subsidies may have to give way to lower earnings and market prices. Then it will be realised in those countries which have been living beyond their means that their cost of living standards have been purely artificial."—Exchange.

Tobacco workers to claim more

Wage increases and shorter hours were yesterday claimed as being vital to the future of tobacco industry workers.

The speaker was Mr. D. G. Bowry, London, in his presidential address to the Tobacco Workers' Union conference which opened at Weston-super-Mare, Somerset.

A resolution claiming a 10s. a week increase on basic rates was passed.

Daily Herald 1953

COLLEGE-TRAINED Nannie for boy nearly 3; living in Chelsea at present; moving to delightful new home Hampstead (close Finchley Road) mid-July; central heating; day and night nursery; own bedroom and bathroom; other staff kept; mother well-known novelist who requires someone kind and capable; every amenity and consideration; high salary to right person. Box NWM2456.

COLLEGE-TRAINED Nannie; girl 13 months; Birmingham now, moving August country house near Worcester; references essential; own bed-sitting room; other staff. Cogill, 33 Augustus Road, Edgbaston 3147. (NW6897)

COOK-HOUSEKEEPER required to take entire charge for professional couple with boy aged 7 (at day school); on 'bus routes; daily help; own sitting room and wireless. Write: Balfe, Beeches, Eton Road, Datchet, Bucks. (NW6902)

DOMESTICATED Resident Help wanted, able take full charge two children, aged 2 and 4, or turn hand to other work; £3/10/-; ample time off; own room, but live as family. Write 9 Chelwood Gardens, Kew, Surrey, or ring Greenwood, RIChmond 1612. (NWM2504)

DOMESTIC HELP to assist with cooking and light household duties; £4 per week; good time off; own bedroom; other help kept. Mrs. Mann, Greenacre, Cannon Hill, London, N.14. (NWM2554)

FITE AGENST ILITERUSY . . .
   *fonetick speling reers its ugli hed
   agane, it seems; and let it heer be sed
   there may be sumthing in the skeem, of cors,
   of teeching skolers how to spel a " hors "
   without the " e " that is its egstrer tale,
   or so to speek; but i konfes i fale
   to see wot gud kan kum of this wile we
   hav radio and pikchers and TV
   as daly clames upon the yungsters' time,
   and, tharefor, just bekos ive rit this rime
   fonetikaly, dont think for a minit
   that ime in faver of it—ime agin it!*

Truth 1953

Nursery World 1953

Workers march against a reduction in their cost of living allowance, 1952.

Helping to launch a lifeboat at Dungeness, 1957.

Daily Mail 1952

NIGHT WORKER

A hen owned by Mr. P. D. Wilson, of Ashover, Derbyshire, laid eight eggs overnight. Last month Jenny the Hen at Minworth, Warwickshire, laid ten eggs in 45 minutes. She died.

Big Fish strikers win support

FULL support for 800 of its members on strike at Clydeside was pledged by the United Society of Boilermakers yesterday.

Two hundred boilermakers came out at John Brown's shipyard over a fortnight ago because of a demarcation dispute with the shipwrights. They were joined by 600 more on Wednesday.

And an emergency resolution passed unanimously at the Society's Eastbourne conference yesterday said that all other members at the yard are likely to be on the street. This will bring the total in the dispute up to 1,000.

Proposing the resolution, Mr. J. Chalmers, of Clydeside, said: " We are the big fish in John Brown's, and if we are gobbled up the smaller fish in other parts of the country would be gobbled up with no trouble at all."

There was a shortage of boilermakers on the Clyde, he said, and because of this shipwrights were being employed to do boilermakers' work.

Daily Herald 1953

'SING LOW' SO THEY WALK OUT

NEARLY 200 men and women workers at a factory in Wales staged a walk-out yesterday because they had been told to sing softly.

When the Welsh get together they sing automatically. And Welsh airs were seldom meant to be crooned dreamily, as are the modern dance tunes.

The mainly - English management of the Avon Rubber Company at Bridgend, Glam, had told its workers: " Sing if you must as you work, but softly, softly."

The management reckoned that in the midst of full-throated singing there might be accidents because of lack of concentration.

Machines in different parts of the factory are worked at varying tempos, so there is no Music While You Work from loudspeakers because the management thinks that a uniform rhythm would put the workers off their stride.

So, when the workers sang at the tops of their voices, a lot of " shush - shushing" came from above. Yesterday, long-standing complaints about this " shushing" came to a head.

Mr. Elfed Rowlands, branch secretary of the Transport and General Workers' Union, approached the management. He was ordered off the premises. Others on the day shift walked out in protest.

But they came back in the afternoon so that discussions could go on. There was a 10-minute talk at six o'clock.

Afterwards, Mr. Bryn Rees, district organiser of the T & G W U, said: " The position is stalemate. We have had no discussions about grievances and I don't know if the workers will be on duty tomorrow."

The management says Mr. Rowlands has not been sacked.

There was some singing during the afternoon. It was ever so soft. But in the buses on the way home the workers—especially the girls—sang their heads off.

Daily Herald
1953

News Chronicle
1953

Tenor Swallows a Fly

Mr. Kenneth Neate, the Australian tenor, who was to have sung in "Rigoletto" at the Royal Opera House, Covent Garden, tonight, will not appear. He swallowed a fly two days ago : coughing followed, and he has been ordered to rest his throat. His deputy will be Mr. Anthony Marlowe.

Daily Mail 1952

Nice to get up in the morning..

WAKING up in the morning is never difficult for 38-year-old Ted Mahon, furnace man at an Irlam steel works. The clothes are off his bed a few seconds after the ring of his alarm clock ends his slumbers.

In the bedroom of his home in Bradburn Road, Irlam, near Warrington, Ted has his own provisionally-patented invention to ensure his early rising.

It is an electric motor, encased in a home-made box, with special attachments from the motor to his bedclothes. When his alarm clock rings it sets off the motor.

In one whirring second the motor has drawn in the string attached to his bedclothes, pulling them off the bed.

" You are awake then and there is nothing you can do about it," Ted said last night. " You might as well get up."

He has used his invention for 12 months. He reckons that it has saved him £50. " It's the complete answer to absenteeism," he says.

" I used to lose a pound a week by being late for work or missing a shift because I could not get up in the morning," he said. " Now I can always get up."

Has Ted Mahon's patent alarm any commercial future ? " It could be mass produced at less than £5 for each one," he says.

Millions will see a demonstration of the Mahon method of waking up on September 7. Its inventor has been invited to take part in television's Inventors' Club that evening.

Pals from work who persuaded him to write to the B.B.C. about his invention will be watching the demonstration in an Irlam social club where ex-Arnhem paratrooper Ted spends his evenings.

Daily Mail 1953

Britain making stronger tea

People are making their tea stronger, especially in the North of England. Consumption of tea is 2,000,000lb a week more than when rationing ended last year.

Daily Mail 1954

Jack Pick watched a fortune drive by

INVENTOR MADE ONE MISTAKE

By Daily Mail Correspondent

JACK PICK made one mistake in his life. But for that he would have been a multi-millionaire, a second Henry Ford. His trouble? He could not master finance, though as an inventor he was a genius.

That mistake was made before World War I., when he was building one of Britain's first cars, "The Pick."

He had about 250 workers at Stamford, Lincolnshire. The cars he had designed were being sent all over the world, and he was on his way to fame and fortune.

One day he had a letter from a young man asking him to concentrate on making his four-cylinder engine. The writer wanted to use them in cars he planned to make. A partnership was in the offing. But Jack Pick said "No."

The other man went on alone. Today he is known as Lord Nuffield.

Growing vegetables

After the war Jack Pick found himself hard up: his money had gone on patents. So he sold his business and decided to grow vegetables.

But he still went on inventing. He devised a push-pull hoe and a back-pedal cycle brake. He missed a second fortune by not keeping up payments on his double-cam expanding car brake.

He grew his produce and sold it from a little shop on the Great North Road until he was 85. And daily he saw the famous fortune he had missed as a constant stream of Morris and Nuffield cars passed by.

Now the man who missed fortunes but was happy growing vegetables has died, aged 87, at his daughter's home at Harlaxton, near Grantham, Lincolnshire.

Daily Mail 1953

Millions more earn £5 to £10 a week

Daily Mail City Reporter PATRICK SERGEANT

ABOUT 9,600,000 people earn between £5 and £10 a week today. In 1938 only 2,700,000 had incomes above £5 a week.

The more-money-for-more-people story is told today in a Treasury Blue Book on national income and expenditure since the war.

The under £5 a week earners today total 9,090,000; about 5,800,000 earn between £10 and £20; 740,000 between £20 and £40; 254,000 between £40 and £200; and 11,000 people had incomes last year of more than £10,000 a year.

The Blue Book also examines how we spent our money. In 1952 personal incomes rose by 6½ per cent., or £800,000,000 over 1951. Last year we spent £530,000,000 more in the shops and on entertainment, travel, and so forth, than in 1951. Part of this was due to lower taxes.

Our main spending was the £3,315,000,000 we spent on food in 1952, compared with the £2,965,000,000 in 1951, and £1,820,000,000 in 1946.

Apart from food last year, we spent £850,000,000 on alcohol, £821,000,000 on tobacco, £736,000,000 on rent, rates, and water; £438,000,000 on fuel and light, and £581,000,000 on durable household goods, and £1,017,000,000 on clothing.

RISE FOR PCs

Now they start at £8 10s a week

CONSTABLES will get an increase of £45 a year under new pay scales agreed to by the Police Council yesterday. Their new minimum salary will be £445—about £8 10s. a week.

Other increases are: sergeants £50 (£590); inspectors £55 (£700); chief inspectors £55 (£790).

The new agreement now goes to the Home Secretary for approval.

Daily Mail 1954

Miss Taylor's men go back to work

By Daily Mail Reporter

MISS KAY TAYLOR, the 48-year-old head of a Preston contracting firm, decided on action when she found her six skilled electricians missing yesterday morning.

She sent each a telegram: "Men at some other firms are working. Why have my men let me down?"

By the afternoon four of the men were back at work.

Said Miss Taylor: "I knew they did not really want to strike. Only one sent back a flat refusal, but I expect he will come back with apologies."

Daily Mail 1954

News Chronicle 1953

'Cut our pay' plea refused

A town has refused "with regret" to accept an offer from some of its building workers to cut their bonus pay by 20 per cent.

The offer was made to Jarrow housing committee by men in the National Union of General and Municipal Workers, who are "perturbed at the high cost of houses." Alderman J. B. Symonds said that all employees were not members of the same union and it would not be possible for some to receive more than others.

Achievement

MRS. Margaret Thatcher (above), one of the new women counsel who will be "called" to Lincoln's Inn early next month, sat for her final Bar examination only three months after her twins were born.

She looked after them herself for two months, then got a nannie so that she could swot for the last month.

She is 28, and in the last General Election was the youngest Conservative candidate, unsuccessfully contesting Dartford, Kent.

Mrs. Thatcher is the daughter of a grocer and a former mayor of Grantham, and won a scholarship to Oxford. At the Bar she will specialise in income-tax problems.

Daily Mail 1954

Treasure hunters reach galleon

The Tobermory treasure-seekers believe that their frogmen have found the Spanish galleon.

Commander "Buster" Crabbe, who is directing diving operations, said last night: "We have struck what seems to be timber with our probes." They are now driving a shaft to where the galleon may lie.

The "timber" discovery was made by frogmen, using 20ft. pressure hoses which "probe" through the silt.

Daily Herald 1954

A Message from the New Managing Director of B.I.F. Ltd.

The following message from Mr. Kenneth Horne is addressed to the British toy trade:

On July 1st I became Managing Director of British Industries Fair Limited, and, at the start of my new job, the decision of the B.T.M.A. to join the B.I.F. at Earls Court is a most heartening one.

We at the B.I.F. will go all out to make the 1956 British Toy Fair an even more outstanding success than it has been in the past. You are our customers, and, although the customer is not *always* right, we intend to fit in with your plans wherever possible.

British Toys 1955

Daily Herald 1954

Words and music

Dear Sir—With reference to yours of the . . .

THAT was what Mr. John Poole, clerk of Uxbridge, Middlesex Council, said into his dictaphone.

But when a typist turned on the machine to type out his letter there was someone in the background singing a French cabaret song.

Another time it was the "Sabre Dance." And then the news in French.

Officials called in the manufacturers to explain. They found that the machine, fitted with valves, was picking up a French radio station.

"The music and the speaking did not completely drown Mr. Poole's voice," a council spokesman said yesterday. "But it was disconcerting for the typist."

60 girls go on strike for one girl's song

'KNOCK-KNEED HEN' STOPS THE TOFFEE

Express Staff Reporter

SIXTY girls, all under 20, went on strike last night—all for a song.

THE SONG: "I'm a bow-legged chicken. I'm a knock-kneed hen."

THE SINGER: Pretty, fair-haired Jean Stewart, aged 16.

Jean was breaking up slabs of toffee ready for wrapping when she started to sing.

But the boss heard the song. And, said Jean last night at her parents' home at Bramwirth Lock, Stainforth, near Doncaster :—

"He marched out of his office and asked me if I was singing. When I said I was, he gave me a week's notice. The other girls were furious. They said they wouldn't stand for it."

It was a week ago that Jean was given notice. Yesterday she did not turn up for work, and when the others saw she was missing from her place at Doncaster's Radiance sweet factory, all but 27 marched out, leaving the toffee boiling in the cauldrons.

THE SINGER
Jean—16

The girl strikers went to see officials of their union— the Transport and General Workers. Last night a packed meeting arranged by the union was held.

The girls were told that the firm refused even to discuss the sacking of Jean, although approached by the Ministry of Labour at the union's request.

'We'll stay out years'

So the girls decided to stay on strike. Said one of them : "Why shouldn't we sing at work? We will stay out for years if the firm does not give Jean her job back."

Jean earned £2 9s. 9d. at the factory. And the other girls made her their shop steward. For it was she who persuaded most of them to join the union.

Last night Mr. Albert Armitage, the union district secretary, said.

"We cannot understand why the girls should not be allowed to sing at work, since most of the factories round here have 'Music While You Work' programmes on the amplifiers."

Mr. Philip Jackson, boss and founder of the firm, said : "Of course, the girls cannot sing at work. They have a job to do. I don't care if the strike goes on for three months.

"The unions are as big a curse to this country as Hitler was to Germany."

Daily Herald 1954

TESS IS EXPERT IN FTMHFSS*

By Philip Phillips

THE official of a big cinema circuit looked at me steadily in London yesterday and said: "There is no doubt that *Four-Track Magnetic High Fidelity Stereophonic Sound* is the answer to the challenge of T V."

I looked at her lovely blue eyes and sighed: "How right you are."

The official continued: "Moreover, the optical and magnetic tracks have so improved that audience participation is being made much easier."

I whispered: "You're right . . . dead right."

"If," said the official, briskly shaking hands with me, "you wish to have any other technical problems explained to you, you know where to find me."

"Absolutely," I replied.

HER TITLE

She is Miss Tessa Fenton, B.Sc. She is 21 and blonde and was appointed by the chief of the circuit (Sidney Bernstein, chairman of Granada Cinemas) to explain how Stereophonic Sound works.

She was selected from scores of applicants for the job because of her specialised knowledge. Technical adviser is her official title.

Miss Stereophonic Sound, 1954, is the unofficial one—on which she frowns.

Tomorrow she will address experts on her subject.

I am certain that the new technical adviser's office is going to be full of seekers after knowledge about Stereophonic Sound in the future.

MAN STRIPPED BY HARVESTER

A 54-YEAR-OLD Ash farm labourer had a narrow escape from serious injury and possible death last week, when he was caught in the works of a combine harvester.

The man, Mr. Harry Marsh, of Goss Hall-cottages, was adjusting the harvester when a spinning cog caught the backstrap of his waistcoat and lifted him from the ground. He was stripped of all his clothing, except a Wellington boot.

Hearing his shout, Mr. C. Chittenden, the machine minder, snatched Marsh away as he was being drawn towards a bed of sharp spikes on the combine table.

Mr. Marsh escaped with abrasions and a twisted knee. He has been ordered to rest.

Broadstairs and St Peter's Mail 1954

MADAM!
ARE YOU THE WOMAN

you would like to be?—could or would you stand up, perhaps on a platform, before a room or hall full of strangers, and make a speech? Can you stand, sit or curtsy correctly? If not, I can teach you by post, in eight lessons, NOT what to say, but the self-confidence to say it. Golden opportunities of pleasure and profit come the way of women who

STAND UP AND TALK

Free prospectus from

MISS ANN HOWARD
Platform and Poise
Correspondence Course.

46A The Hall, Centurion Road, Brighton, Sussex.

Townswoman 1954

If you want to get ahead...

GET A HAT!

YES DEAR, YOU DO NEED A NEW HAT TO GO WITH THAT NEW SUIT

Daily Express 1954

Studio 44

Compact and complete, the Studio 44 is designed for the small office and the busy professional man. It is a sturdy, all-purpose typewriter with the distinctive characteristics of flawless Olivetti design.

86 character keyboard
Full-length platen
Carriage on roller bearings
Key-set tabulator
Personal touch-tuning
Standard size ribbon spools
Half spacing

British Olivetti Ltd.
10 Berkeley Square - London W. 1

Area Distributors

TYPEWRITER TECHNICIANS LTD.

17, Eastgate, Exeter—Tel.: Exeter 54564

Authorized dealers throughout the country   A1

Boom in records is earning singers £1,000 a week

By MICHAEL GILBERDALE

A POP singer's* paradise—that is what Britain's gramophone record manufacturers are calling 1954. It has been a record year for records sold both at home and overseas.

Top marks, said company spokesmen yesterday go to "the disc jockeys' darlings," the singers of *popular love songs and ballads.

In Britain we have bought £12 million worth of records of all kinds, a £2 million increase on last year's sales. Import bans restrict sales to Commonwealth countries, but the demand for British artists and British compositions grows with each month in America.

Money spinners

Which are the biggest money spinners?

In little more than six months more than one million records of "O Mein Papa" were sold. This "pop plus" was made by Britain's Eddie Calvert, the trumpet player.

Queen of the keyboard, Britain's Winifred Atwell, recorded a catchy number called

News Chronicle 1954

"Let's Have Another Party." It was released by Philips towards the end of last month, but already nearly 400,000 people in Britain alone have bought the recording, for 5s. 6½d. a time, including tax.

To pop singers, one hit number can mean stardom overnight—and a small fortune. An income of about £1,000 a week is not unusual.

Rosemary Clooney jumped to fame with one song : "Come on-a My House."

One of our best record exports at present—a refreshing change from "pops"—is the voice of the late Kathleen Ferrier. In Denmark and Holland, where she was so popular towards the end of her life, they order her records 2,000 at a time.

Vera Lynn built up a big reputation in America, and lately Germany has been clamouring for her. One of our best ambassadors of song in America now is David Whitfield, and his recordings of "I Believe" and "Cara Mia" have sold especially well.

Demand grows

Spokesmen of the big firms, such as Electric and Musical Industries Limited (comprising H.M.V., Columbia, Parlophone, Regal-Zonophone and M.G.M.), and Decca, all agree:

1—Business will continue to boom, and would be even better now, if radiogram manufacturers could meet the demand for their products. Record players, often minus radio, and priced from about 9 gns., are increasingly in demand.

2—Microgroove records — the L.P. (long playing) and E.P. (extended play) are growing in popularity, especially for orchestral music.

3—Commonwealth import bans are not completely effective. Countries like Australia and New Zealand are allowed to order the "positive" of a record made in Britain. This they process and press, then pay royalties to the manufacturer.

Matter of choice

One leading question : Why this boom ? Record manufacturers say they do not know the full answer. "But it could be that radio, TV and films only half fulfil the need for entertainment. Turn those knobs and you must accept the fare they offer. Spin a disc, and you know—'this is my own choice.'"

NO FRILLS

Medical officers attending the seminar of the Central Council for Health Education were confronted by a pictorial guide in personal hygiene.

Listed as "essential" were: a towel, a weekly bath, soap, detergent, clothes on a line, disinfectant, a tooth brush.

As "helpful": a brush, tooth paste, deodorant, hot water, hand cream, a face cloth, shampoo, mouth-wash, and a nailbrush.

And as "unnecessary": Bath salts, suntan lotion, laxatives, face powder, lipstick, eye lotion, hair cream, nail varnish, and face cream.

Exeter Express and Echo 1955

NEW WOMEN'S COLLEGE
From Our Special Correspondent

Cambridge began the Michaelmas term this week with a new collegiate foundation, the first since Selwyn College 72 years age. New Hall with 16 undergraduates and two dons is not yet a college but a "recognized institution for women." It is confidently expected that it will achieve full status beside Girton and Newnham before long.

The society occupies a former private house, more recently a guest house, in Silver Street, its garden backing on the river. There are bed-sitting rooms for 15 undergraduates. Only in their first year will the girls live in. In this it differs from the other women's colleges which are wholly residential. The house in Silver Street is only temporary quarters, for the society has been presented with another house in Huntingdon Road which has two or three acres of ground for extension. The lease of the present occupiers of this house does not expire before 1960, so after its third year when the numbers of New Hall will have reached 45, the most the dining hall will seat, there may be a pause in its expansion.

The Society has been financed by private benefaction. Neither the university nor the Treasury has contributed to its funds. Grants have come from other Cambridge colleges, from the old students' societies of Girton and Newnham, and from many girls' schools, whose interest in any scheme for more places for girls at Cambridge is keen. The tutor of New Hall, Miss A. R. Murray, has said that a public appeal for funds will soon be launched, probably next year.

The first 16 undergraduates were chosen from those who had entered this year for Girton and Newnham. In future New Hall will run its own competition for entry. This will not be a full-scale examination as in the other women's colleges, but will consist of one general paper, headmistresses' recommendations and interviews. Selection will be made just before the other colleges make their's. Already there have been 400 applications for next year's 15 places.

The first students are reading a variety of subjects. Dr. Murray will tutor the chemists and Dr. Hope Hammond, the other member of the high table, those reading English. The rest will, as is common practice, be farmed out among other colleges. The girls seem alive to the distinction of being founder members of the society—a distinction that will not diminish as time goes on. One girl even abandoned an Oxford scholarship in order to be one of the first generation, though she adds that English is taught more to her liking at Cambridge than at Oxford.

Times Educational Supplement 1954

HOME GUARD 'DOING THEIR STUFF': STUDY EVENINGS

The 6th Devon Home Guard Battalion have had another of its "study evenings" at Bn. H.Q., Newton Abbot.

Like all Home Guard battalions in this part of the country, the 6th Devons is only at "cadre strength" in peace time; that is to say a total of about 100 company, platoon and section commanders, etc., who would expand in an emergency to a battalion many times this size. The evening was an extremely valuable one; and the battalion is making real progress in its preparations for an emergency which we hope will never arise.

The Staff Officer who deals with Home Guard matters at H.Q. Southern Command came from Salisbury for the conference, which was attended by over 50 members of the battalion cadre. There are still some vacancies in the cadre; and anybody interested can get full information from any of the following:—

Battalion Headquarters, T.A. Centre, The Avenue, Newton Abbot; O.C. "A" company (Newton Abbot area)—Lt.-Col. D. G. M. Shewen, Torview, Ipplepen; O.C. "B" company (Bovey - Chudleigh - Morton - Chagford area)—Col. G. A. Wadham, of Neadon Cottage, Manaton; O.C. "C" company (Ashburton-Buckfastleigh-Widecombe area)—Brig. W. H. Langran, of The Glen, Poundsgate; O.C. "D" company (Totnes-Totnes Rural District)—Lt.-Col. E. J. Baly, Higher Week, Dartington; O.C. "E" company (Torquay-Paignton-Brixham-Dartmouth)—Lt.-Col. F. A. Cocksedge, of Fairmeadow, Cadewell Park Road, Torquay.

The Home Guard really is doing its stuff, and men who join the cadre do a valuable job of work; they certainly do not waste their time.

Exeter Ladies' Choir

Members of the St. Sidwell's Methodist Church Wesley Guild were entertained by the Exeter Ladies' Choir who presented a concert at St. Sidwell's school-room in aid of Church Jubilee Funds. A varied programme included madrigals, vocal duets trios, and solos and piano solos and duets. Conductor was Laura Coote and the accompanist Phyllis Phillips. Cecil Cope (baritone) was accompanied by Nellie Cope. Other artistes included Emma Boddy and Joan Pickford (piano duets), Olive Eastmond and Irene Harris, Carol Howe, Rosina Madge, and Iris Tippett.

Exeter Express and Echo 1955

'ROBOT LAYS 60,000 BRICKS AN HOUR'

Machine Made in Poland

Interest is being expressed in Britain in a brick-laying machine invented in Poland, said to be capable of laying 60,000 bricks an hour. If imported here it would give a big fillip to house-building, and would probably put thousands of unskilled bricklayers out of work.

Enquiries about the machine are being made in a private capacity by Mr. A. A. Maxwell, vice-chairman of the West Midland Industrial Development Association and Surveyor to Bromyard Urban Council.

The Polish Ambassador in London has promised to send him soon full details of the robot bricklayer, and Mr. Maxwell has already been in touch with one British civil engineering company which, he says, is interested in the machine.

Spreads the Mortar

Electrically operated by one man, the machine took its inventors less than three months to design and was recently demonstrated in Warsaw. The inventors, a team of Polish workers and engineers, claim that as well as laying bricks it also spreads the mortar and spaces the openings for windows and doors at very little cost; it can build walls of any height and thickness; it can build three houses a day; and it would cut about £100 off the cost of every new house.

Mr. Maxwell said at his home at Worcester: "There are workers in this country who call themselves bricklayers but are not proper tradesmen. They have not served any apprenticeship and their work is slipshod. They just pray for the plasterer to come along and cover up their bad work. Therefore I have no compunction about what I am trying to do. The bricklayers have asked for it in a big way."

Birmingham Post 1956

Vacuum Variety

MEN AT WORK

If your men folk have to eat 'on the job' don't forget to include a drink in a vacuum flask. Filled with comforting hot soup, tea, coffee or cocoa in cold weather, and with some refreshing iced drink in the summer months, a vacuum flask is a necessity for every man whether he lunches in factory, field, workshop or office.

Keeps Hot - Keeps Cold in a VACUUM FLASK

❋ *One of a series issued by the Vacuum Flask Manufacturers of Great Britain*

Townswoman 1955

PREPARATIONS FOR NEXT WINTER'S FEED

Exeter Express and Echo 1955

"**W**OULD you advise me to modify my fodder conservation programme for 1955?" is a question being asked by farmers, many of whom are still suffering from the effects of 1954.

Although the answer is generally "yes," the nature of the problem varies from farm to farm. For example, although well made silage or tripod hay of not more than 12 per cent crude protein in the dry matter may be an entirely satisfactory food for store cattle. It will almost certainly be more profitable to aim at a silage of 15 per cent to 16 per cent crude protein for milk production.

Greatest yield

The greatest yield of hay in terms of bulk per acre of dry matter and crude protein is obtained when grass is cut near the full bloom stage. For lowland swards this means about mid-June.

But although the yield per acre of crude protein and dry matter falls off rapidly towards the end of June, weather conditions at this time are more likely to suit rapid drying. The herbage then has a much lower moisture content and is more easily cured in the swath. It is only natural, therefore, that on at least part of the mown area on many farms bulk and quality should be sacrificed to ease of making.

But the stock farmer can no longer afford to convert the whole of his surplus summer grass into a roughage of indifferent quality.

HER FIRST JOB

I have recently left school and, after taking a secretarial course, have found a post as junior in a large office.

I have been told that I may have to do some work for one of the partners while his secretary is away ill, and I would like your advice on correct office etiquette.

Do I rise from my seat whenever this gentleman comes into the room ? Do I call him " Sir " ? And should I knock, on the door before entering any other room in the office ?

IT will be wise to find out the usage prevailing in this office, for etiquette in the business world varies according to the firm and what is generally done there.

But it is usually accepted that, as a member of the staff however newly joined, you have the right to go into the general offices without knocking, taking care, of course, to depart if you find a conference going on, or think that your presence is inopportune. But you may be told to knock discreetly before entering the office of a senior on the staff.

When you work for one of the partners, rise when he comes in the first time of a morning and acknowledge his " Good morning," but do not rise every time he enters the room afterwards.

He should be called " Mr —— " and not Sir, unless he definitely prefers it otherwise.

I wish you success in your first job.

Woman and Home 1957

SIX YEARS OF STANDING ABOUT, *lie behind Francis Bradley* (left) *It has been broken by one short period of employment· in England.*

by WOODROW WYATT

Picture Post 1955

BEFORE the war, I went to Merthyr Tydfil, a desolate centre of the mass South Wales unemployment of the 30's. It was a town of the hopeless dead. Dead, not physically, but in spirit. No laughter, no quick movement, nothing but grey apathy.

With the war came employment and it has stayed ever since. If you talk about unemployment now, people do not know what you mean. They have either forgotten it or they are too young to have seen it. Sixteen years of full employment have made us think that full employment is permanent—and is enjoyed by every place in the United Kingdom.

But in Northern Ireland I found myself suddenly shot back into the past. There are nearly 30,000 people unemployed in Northern Ireland. The population of Northern Ireland is just over a million and a quarter. That is the equivalent of having at least a million and a half unemployed in England, Wales and Scotland.

Standards boss: We are not spending £4m to employ the same number

FIRST AUTOMATION STRUGGLE IS ON

The fear of 12,000 strikers

By BRYAN THOMPSON and GEOFFREY GOODMAN

THE first automation struggle has begun. The managing director of Standards, where 12,000 men are on strike against redundancy sackings, declared yesterday: "We are not spending £4 million on new tractor plant in order to employ the same number of men."

The fear of unemployment, of men being replaced by machines, brought about the strike. And after the declaration by the Standard chief, 39-year-old Mr. Alick Dick, Britain's great unions are almost certain to swing into line behind the strikers.

On May 18 Standards plan to sack 1,900 workers and begin work on a completely new production line for a Massey-Harris-Ferguson tractor — made by Standards — involving automation. Eventually some 3,500 workers are likely to be laid off.

MEN'S COUNTER-PLAN

Shop stewards and local union officials put up a counter-plan to the sackings. They proposed spreading out short time working and saving the jobs.

The firm said it was impracticable. So the workers struck last week.

The Standards chief made his statement at a Press conference last night in his cream-painted board room at the Standard Banner Lane works.

The new tractor, he explained, was revolutionary in design.

It would involve virtually a complete changeover in production methods, and a shut-down of the existing tractor plant.

He listed: 1,400 machines to be shifted; 950,000 feet of factory space replanned; £4,000,000 of new equipment brought in. The aim: 2,000 tractors a week, a third more than in the old plant.

And he added: "We are not installing £4,000,000 worth of equipment in order to employ the same number of men. We can't carry people for fun. The number to be taken back will depend on car production at the time."

News Chronicle
1956

Birmingham Post
1956

Smaller Bakers Fix Prices

10½d.-1s. Loaf in Midlands

The Midland Federation of Master Bakers Associations, which covers Warwickshire, Worcestershire, Leicestershire, Nottinghamshire, Herefordshire, Staffordshire, Shropshire and Derbyshire, recommended its members yesterday to charge between 10½d. and 1s. for the 28-oz. loaf (standard) and between 6d. and 7d. for the 14-oz. loaf when the subsidy ends next Sunday.

The federation, which met in Birmingham, recommended that the price should vary according to the type of bread and the district in which it was sold. The federation is a body of smaller bakers.

Other Costs

The prices recommended for the Midlands by the Federation of Wholesale and Multiple Bakers are 10½d. for the household tin loaf and 11½d. if wrapped and sliced. The recommended price for the 14oz. tin loaf is 6d. unwrapped and 7d. wrapped and sliced.

Mr. Douglas Broadhead reminded bakers at yesterday's meeting that their national association had advised a charge of at least 11d.

Mr. N. Owen (Bromsgrove), said that the end of the subsidy was not the only thing that bakers had to consider. There had been increased costs in all directions and these should be taken into consideration.

Mr. G. Roberts, chairman of the federation, said that he felt there should be a higher price for hand-made bread of high quality

Birmingham Post
1956

British Firm to Make German Scooter

The West German Bayerische Motoren Werke (B.M.W.) disclosed at Munich yesterday that an unidentified British company plans to build the B.M.W. four-wheeled, enclosed-cabin motor scooter in Britain.

Exeter Express and Echo 1955

Two fire calls in hour

Exmouth Fire Brigade dealt with two fires in an hour yesterday. They extinguished a fire in a lean-to shed next to a private garage at 47, Hulham Road, Exmouth, belonging to Mr. W. G. Morris. A few minutes after the crew returned to the station they were called to deal with a chimney fire at 62, Shelley Road

Avoiding 'Oppression' of Coloured Workers

Enquiry Report and Fair Employment Legislation

An increase in the proportion of coloured workers in Britain might cause a worsening of discrimination against them, and widening unemployment might lead to their becoming an oppressed minority. These are conclusions of the report of an enquiry into the employment of coloured area published yesterday by the Institute of Personnel Management*.

The enquiry was initiated by the Birmingham Christian Social Council and undertaken by the Race Relations Group of Fircroft College, Birmingham. The report has been written by the warden of the college, Mr. Leslie Stephens.

The report recommends the examination of proposals for fair employment legislation by an independent body such as the Haldane Society, and suggests that the T.U.C. and leading trade unions might work out their own code of fair employment.

Welfare and Work

It urges that to increase the effectiveness and raise the level of the work of local authorities and voluntary bodies, a Government Department—perhaps the Home Office or the Colonial Office—should be given an over-all responsibility for the welfare of coloured people and other immigrants.

It also recommends the establishment in Birmingham of an advisory committee on the employment of coloured people, suggesting that it might consist of a small group of interested employers, personnel managers, trade unionists and representatives of the city council, together with some independent members, especially the leaders of coloured communities.

"Although the conditions revealed by this enquiry do not give grounds for very grave concern and contain many hopeful elements," the report states, "it is true to say that there is some discrimination in the relations of employers and workers to the coloured people.

Birmingham Post 1956

British Girls Pass Charm Test

Ten girls out of 120 interviewed have passed psychological and charm tests for jobs as transatlantic stewardesses with Pan-American Airways. An official said: "We employed 11 British girls as stewardesses for the first time in May this year. They were such a great success with passengers, who love their English accents, that we decided to engage some more."

Birmingham Post 1956

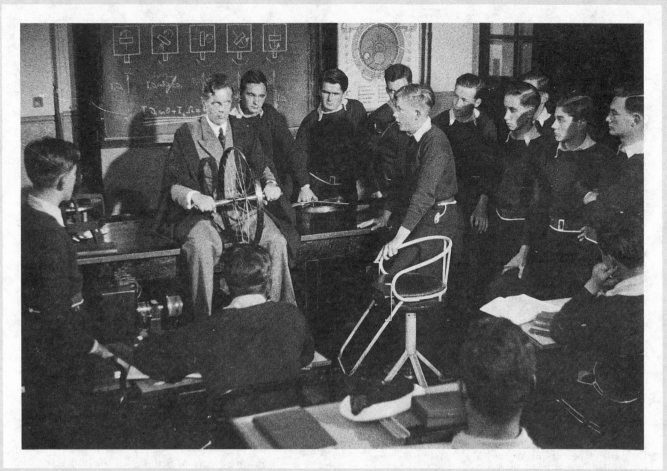

Trainees at Dartmouth Naval College are inducted into the mysteries of the gyroscopic compass, 1957.

The world's first translatlantic submarine telephone cable is hauled to the terminal station at Oban, 1956.

BRITAIN'S FIRST ATOMIC POWER STATION

Electricity Released into National Grid by Her Majesty The Queen

HARNESSING NUCLEAR POWER ON CUMBERLAND'S COAST

WHEN Her Majesty The Queen visited Calder Hall in West Cumberland on Wednesday she saw a project as futuristic in design as anything which has been dreamed up in science fiction—but this is not fiction but fact.

For Calder Hall is Britain's first atomic power station and when Her Majesty turned a switch on Wednesday morning, electricity generated by nuclear power began flowing into the national grid system. Eventually this plant will have an output of 65,000 kilowatts and beside it is growing up a second reactor which will have an output of 85,000 kilowatts.

The first of twelve nuclear power stations to be built in Britain by 1965, Calder Hall works have been a familiar feature to West Cumberland people for the past four years, the site being marked by the huge concrete cooling towers which rear up above the other buildings.

The site is a few miles south of Egremont and the high barbed wire fence includes not only the power station at Calder Hall but the nearby works at Windscales where plutonium is produced in two atomic piles.

Once inside the fence, The Queen was in another world—a world where everything is so strange to the layman that the experts find it difficult to find common words in which to describe what is happening. For the Calder Hall station, in supplying power on a commercial scale from nuclear reaction, is doing something that has never been done before anywhere in the world. Calder Hall is an experiment in the use of nuclear energy for peaceful purposes and lessons learned there will be used to make future stations more efficient and more economical.

Cumberland and Westmorland Herald 1956

THE 'STANDARD' DISMISSALS

by W. J. BROWN

THE announcement by the Standard Motor Car Company that some 2,600 workers are to be laid off permanently will add considerably to the heat of the controversy about automation. But it is clear that automation is responsible for only part of the dismissals; the other part is to be explained by the falling off of demand—abroad and at home—for the cars which the Company produces. This is not peculiar to the Standard Company's products and other motor-car producers are facing, or will shortly have to face, a similar problem.

The truth is that for years now the production of motor-cars has been in effect a sheltered industry. There was the immense backlog of the war years to be made good and in the foreign markets Germany had been knocked out as a competitor. But the backlog has been wiped off and Germany has emerged as the biggest European exporter of cars, largely at the expense of Britain, for the long series of wage increases have forced British car-producers to raise their prices. Automation or no automation, the British industry would have had to adjust itself to a new situation in which it would no longer find itself in a sheltered position.

Time and Tide 1956

Electronic 'brain' joins staff of Milk Marketing Board

"Belfast Telegraph" Reporter.

WHAT IS BELIEVED to be one of the largest punch electronic card installations in Ulster is now streamlining the work of the Milk Marketing Board, which pays out 23,000 cheques each month to producers.

Everyone knows that farmers leave milk cans at the side of the road every day to be picked up by transporters, but how many stop to consider the amount of clerical work undertaken before the postman delivers the cheques the following month.

To find out what happens in the interval, I visited the headquarters of the Board at Castlehill Road, Belfast.

Before the introduction of this new installation, a large office staff, under the chief accountant, Mr. J. Magee, dealt with more than a million different entries and thousands of calculations each month.

Now the new electronic "brain" has transformed the work of the Board in this department into a quicker operation.

Belfast Telegraph 1958

OUR CAREERS SERIES

"What Shall I Be?"

*

If you would like advice on your own particular career problem, you can write to our Careers Expert, c/o WOMAN AND HOME, The Fleetway House, Farringdon Street, London, E.C.4, enclosing a stamped, self-addressed envelope for a personal reply.

SHORTHAND IN A FOREIGN LANGUAGE

My daughter will be leaving school shortly and is planning to take a secretarial course in London. She has always done extremely well in languages at school, especially French, and it occurred to us that if she were to learn how to write French shorthand as well as English she might afterwards find a really interesting post and make use of her gift of languages. Is this possible?

YES, the ability to take shorthand dictation in a foreign language such as French or German can lead to highly interesting posts—usually in business firms. A girl may find herself working for a foreign executive who likes to dictate his letters in his own language, which she may then have to translate into English. Or she may work for an Englishman who has to send letters abroad. If he is unable to dictate in the foreign language it will probably be left to his secretary to translate from English, so her knowledge of the language must be good.

A student can learn to take shorthand in a foreign language as an optional part of the course at a good secretarial college—it is not usually taught as a single subject on its own. The important thing to remember is that an English shorthand system must be learnt first, which can then be adapted without difficulty to the foreign language.

French and German are the most useful languages—at least for finding openings in London at present.

THE DRESS TRADE

My daughter is hoping to obtain a junior vacancy in a dress firm in order to learn dressmaking. We are a little muddled, however, as there seem to be so many different types of firms in the dress trade. Can you tell us anything about the difference between them?

FIRST of all, there is *haute couture.* This is a French term now accepted as meaning the perfection of the art of making lovely clothes. It is exemplified by such famous names as Christian Dior, Norman Hartnell, Digby Morton, and other designers who have become the accepted leaders of fashion, and whose houses make exclusive models. There are also many less well-known firms which undertake dressmaking for the private customer.

Secondly, there is the vast field of dress manufacture, ranging from *whole-sale couture*—good ready-to-wear clothes which go out to the shops under a label which is itself a guarantee of excellence—to *mass production*—garments made by the hundred on the assembly line.

Applications for junior vacancies can be made direct to any dress firm. Addresses will be found in the " Trades " section of the Post Office Directories for London and other large towns.

WITH A VETERINARY SURGEON

I am seventeen and would like to train as a receptionist to a veterinary surgeon and help to look after the animals. How do I set about finding a vacancy?

YOUR best plan would be to seek the advice of your local Youth Employment Officer, as she may be able to help you find a first post with a veterinary surgeon in your district.

Church Times 1958

Mothers at Work

The Mother of the Son of God is hailed by all Christians as a pattern of motherhood. That unique and lovely human relationship is now suffering grave damage in England, as the Bishop of Woolwich has pointed out this week, in a Mothering Sunday sermon in St. Paul's which has attracted useful publicity. Referring to the fact that half the enormous number of women now employed in British industry are married, he suggested that the consequent loss of home life was far too high a price to pay for economic prosperity. A mockery is made of the very idea of home, when young children habitually return from school to an empty house. Many mothers are even content to leave infants to the impersonal care of day nurseries, simply in order that they can work full-time in factories. We hope that the Bishop's appeal to industry not to offer young mothers more than part-time employment will be widely heeded. Many business houses are already following this rule. It used to be argued that the employment of so many married women was absolutely essential to the working of the country's economic system. With the possibility of unemployment growing, this argument is likely to have less force. Even if it were true, that would be a reason for changing the economic system, not for an indefinite continuance of a practice which is bad.

The new department of experimental surgery at Hammersmith, perched on the top floors of a shimmering nine-floor block, is a research-worker's dream: a string of wonderfully spacious laboratories; experimental operating-theatres (equipped with changing, washing, recording, and sterilising rooms that many a non-experimental hospital might envy); animal-houses; a library; a conference room; and, fittingly from the roof, a gorgeous view stretching from the dome of St. Paul's into rural Berkshire. The whole proclaims the generosity of the Wellcome Trust and the enterprise of the University of London, the Medical Research Council, and no doubt many individual patrons of research; the details reflect the careful planning of dedicated teams of research-workers. They have already given ample proof of their capabilities; and the projects now in hand have the right flavour of realism and scientific imagination. One need not be much of a prophet today to predict that organ transplantation and tissue banks will change the face of surgery as completely as did antisepsis and antibiotics in the past (blood-transfusion gives but a foretaste of what is to come); but to embark on this work a few years ago was a bold venture. It has already yielded impressive results: and the new unit promises a brilliant future not only by providing materal facilities but also by bringing home and together the now scattered teams and thus ensuring the intellectual stimulus of discussion and argument.

The Lancet 1959

JEAN'S TOPS

A FEW years ago I gave an audition to a young singer who was then part of a girls' vocal trio. She sang very well and I promised to try to do something for her if ever the occasion arose.

A few weeks later Pearl Carr, who was my singer at that time, announced her intention of leaving my band in two weeks. I was away on tour, and engagements did not permit me to get back to London to find a new singer. Suddenly I remembered that audition.

I sent the girl a telegram, and asked her if she could join my band at Cardiff the following week.

She did and, what's more, she stayed with us for more than three years.

She has now become one of the most versatile singers in our business. Her engagement book is so full she finds it difficult to find time to eat.

Her latest solo recording is on Polydor BM.6042. Her name is Jean Campbell, and the song she sings so well is Cole Porter's newest hit from "High Society." "True Love."

Daily Express 1956

Danger to farmers of "free-for-all" market

"UNLESS we get a two thirds majority, the new Egg Marketing Board, legalised by Parliament in January, will be cancelled, and the egg market will become a free-for-all with no guaranteed prices, no guranteed market, and no organisation at all," said Mr. S. F. Jones, County secretary, at a meeting of the Northallerton branch, N.F.U., on Monday.

It was wrong, he stressed, to think that the National Egg Marketing Organisation, which was set up as a temporary measure during the war, would continue if the Egg Marketing Board failed to get the required two-thirds majority. The packing stations to-day handled about 16,000,000 cases of eggs a year, and it could well be imagined what conditions would be if they were thrown on the open market.

Mr. Jones went on to explain the full working of the new board, and later answered questions from a very well attended meeting.

Mr. H. T. Shaw, Hambleton district Advisory Officer to the National Agricultural Advisory Service, gave a talk on "Solids-not-fat" in milk.

The falling off in the "solids-not-fat" percentage in milk, he said, was an old problem that could not be solved except by long term measures. No-one really knew the causes, but from his 20-odd years' experience, he had noticed that, after mild wet autumns and winters, when cows were allowed out far later in the year on wet lush grass the "solids-not-fat" percentage began to fall in the following spring.

He considered this was due to the lack of dry fibrous material in the lush grasses, leading to a deficiency in starch. He advocated the feeding of extra starchy foods, which could be done by including ground or rolled oats, or barley, in the feeding ration. Cows must have roughage containing starch.

Thirsk, Bedale and Northallerton Times 1957

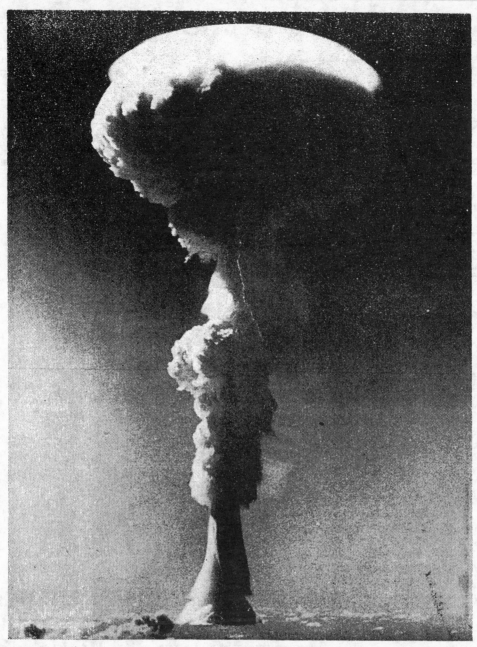

A photograph, released last weekend, of the first British nuclear explosion which took place over the Pacific, near Christmas Island, on May 15. A second and bigger hydrogen bomb was tested off Malden Island on May 31

Punch
1959

"Down tools!"

100,000 BUSMEN ON STRIKE

MONEY REFUNDED TO THOUSANDS OF HOLIDAY-MAKERS

From Our Labour Correspondent

The strike of some 100,000 busmen employed by private companies in all parts of England, Wales, and Scotland, started at midnight. No official efforts were made to avert it at the last minute. Union leaders, Ministry of Labour officials, and employers were equally silent.

On Thursday, Mr F. Coyle, of the Transport and General Workers' Union, had said that the unions would ask for a meeting with the Minister of Labour and would suggest that he should withdraw the dispute from the Industrial Disputes Tribunal and appoint a court of inquiry instead, but late last night no word had reached the Ministry. Mr. Coyle himself had "no statement to make."

London Transport and municipal buses should be running as usual, but they will not be able, because of union policy, to operate any extra services. Nor will the railways. A few private buses will be operated by companies not in the Conférence of Omnibus Companies.

The unions have called the strike in support of a claim for an increase of £1 a week, which would reduce the difference between their rates and those of London busmen. The employers offered an increase of 3s., which was rejected. The Minister has referred the dispute to the Industrial Disputes Tribunal, which will hear the case on Wednesday, though Mr. Coyle has stated that the unions will not give evidence.

The Times
1957

QUESTIONNAIRE THAT BROUGHT 561,000 REPLIES

At a meeting of advertising executives in London last month, BASIL THORNTON, O.B.E., head of B.B.C. Advertisement Department, referred to the questionnaire issued in December "on a matter of purely editorial arrangement" which brought the astonishing result of 561,000 replies.

For this number of people to be interviewed—say twenty interviewers making twenty calls a day—it would take nearly four years to complete the interviews, and if each interviewer were paid £10 a week, the cost of interviewing such a vast number of people would be approximately £40,000.

In Roman times, said Mr Thornton, they used to take the omens or auspices before any important course of action. But now, instead of having a priest watching the vultures or eagles flying in from east or west, or counting the strokes of lightning, or studying the entrails of animals, we go to the research boys who examine a "properly constituted sample", multiply by the appropriate number, and the answer, more often than not, is a lemon.

So successful a response on the part of the readers of the *Radio Times* is a testimonial to the close interest which this paper, with its circulation of well over 8 million a week, enjoys.

Incidentally, this number of copies eats up more than 50,000 tons of paper in a year. And when it is remembered that the paper used to cost £11 a ton and now costs £60 it is not greatly surprising that from May 2 the *Radio Times* is going to cost 4d. instead of 3d. a copy.

The *Radio Times*, said Mr Thornton, has a readership of 22 million out of a national total of 37 million adults.

Marketing
1958

Birmingham Post
1956

British Books in Moscow

A LARGE exhibition of British books and periodicals sponsored by the British Council and the Soviet Ministry of Culture opens in Moscow this week-end and will be on show for a fortnight. The President of the Publishers Association, Mr. R. W. David, and Sir Stanley Unwin are going to Moscow as the official delegates from this country, and they will be the guests of the Ministry of Culture. A reciprocal exhibition of Russian books and periodicals will be shown at the Festival Hall in London next February.

This is the largest exhibition of British books to have been shown in Russia at any time, so far as is known. Between 3,000 and 4,000 books are being exhibited, together with 600 periodicals, a display of posters and large photographs. The exhibition is being shown in the main lecture hall of the Lenin Library.

The books selected by the British Council have been provided free of charge by British publishers through the co-operation of the Publishers Association. The main emphasis lies on science and technology although there are important sections dealing with the arts and the humanities. Under the terms of the agreement made with the Soviet Ministry of Culture there are no sections on religion, politics or economics.

Bookseller 1959

TEACHERS WIN SCHOOL MEALS CASE

No Obligation to Collect Money

Mr. Justice Barry, in the High Court yesterday, held that school teachers were under no obligation to collect and record money paid by pupils for school meals. It was, he said, purely voluntary work.

He gave judgment in a test action in favour of six Sunderland school teachers against the Sunderland Borough Council. The teachers claimed a declaration that a resolution passed by Sunderland Borough Council on April 11—that teachers in their employ who were members of the Sunderland and district Association of Schoolmasters, and refused to collect money for school meals in school hours, should be given notice to terminate their engagement on August 31, 1956—was *ultra vires*.

Record and Show Mirror 1960

Watch This Decca Youngster

Will he emulate the success of Tommy Steele or Cliff Richard? Don't be surprised if he does. This is PAUL RAVEN (see next column). He could achieve the same success we predicted for the first couple named here and who had their first "write-ups" in this paper.

—R&SM Picture

Daily Telegraph 1960

UNION CLEARS MAN SENT TO COVENTRY

3½ YRS. DUES PAID

DAILY TELEGRAPH REPORTER

RATHER than rejoin the Boilermakers' Society, Thomas Dobson, 37, arc-welder, who was " sent to Coventry " by his fellow workers, paid the union £15. He is employed at the Birlec engineering works, near Walsall, Staffs.

Dobson objects to the union because of " the many petty strikes in which it is involved." As he would not accede to their demand to join either the Boilermakers' Society or the Sheet Metal Workers' Society, the 140 craftsmen at the firm stopped talking to Dobson.

All the men belong to one or other of these two unions. Dobson offered, however, to join the Amalgamated Engineering Union, in his view " run by responsible leaders who opposed strike action."

He recently applied for membership of the A.E.U. But a decision could not be reached until he had first been " cleared " by the Boilermakers' Society, to which he last belonged.

BREAK WITH UNION

Last night Dobson said: " Because of the position regarding the A.E.U., I attended a meeting of the Bilston branch of the Boilermakers' Society to settle with that union once and for all. They made it as difficult as they could for me not to rejoin.

" Mr. George Cooper, the secretary, said if I wanted to clear myself of the union I should have to pay nearly 3½ years' arrears of contributions amounting to £15. But he said I could rejoin the union on payment of only £2 13s 6d; this included a £2 fine, 10s readmission fee and two weeks' contributions.

" It was pretty obvious the Boilermakers' Society thought I would jump at the chance of getting off as lightly as £2 13s 6d. But I flatly refused to rejoin the union. I paid up the £15, though I could ill afford it

" I seriously question the legality of the Boilermakers' charge. Most unions automatically exclude members when they are 26 weeks in arrears. They are re-admitted on payment of a nominal fine and a small readmission fee."

Tatler 1960

HIGH SEASON NOTES

In the no-man's-land of fertilizer bags behind the buffet I met Miss **Victoria Feilden** (the success of her dance in Hampshire the previous week was a talking point) and Mr. **Auberon Waugh** whose first novel is to be published in the autumn. "I'm hoping for a great future as a novelist," he told me. "My father says the book is much better than anything he wrote at my age."

RANK PLAN FOR RADIO STATION IN LEICESTER

ANOTHER group of companies has been formed by the Rank Organisation to establish and operate Leicester and other commercial radio stations. Rank has now registered 29 companies.

There are about 100 registered in connection with local radio stations throughout Britain. All the Rank companies have £100 capital, and Leicester's is called Rank Radio, Leicester.

Twenty-one others registered—for both radio and television broadcasting — are associated with newspapers.

They will not know until 1962 or 1963 whether local radio stations will be permitted

B.B.C's Intention

Four Midlands companies, including one for Leicester were initiated less than six months ago by Mr. Norman Collins, of Associated Television, for the purpose of establishing local commercial radio stations.

Since Mr. Hugh Carleton Greene became director general he has said a good deal about the B.B.C.'s intention to develop the city radio station idea.

In Birmingham last month he said he thought this should be done by the corporation and would be a job they could do better than commercial concerns.

He ruled out the possibility of television developing on the same pattern because of high capital and operating costs.

Leicester Advertiser 1960

'MEET THE FAMILY' AT GORSE HILL

Difficulties Overcome

There was a rather poor attendance for the Gorse Hill (Swindon) Community Centre Theatrical section's presentation of Meet the Family last Wednesday, but those people who did attend seemed to enjoy themselves.

The two-act comedy by John J. Melluish was handled quite well on the extremely small stage.

Prompting, however, was needed a little too often and in many cases spoiled the continuity of the humour. Mrs. Dorothy Woods put up a brave show, reading the part of Cook, as stand-in for Joan Ruggles who had been taken ill.

Mervyn Batchelor lived the part of Jarvis, the butler. He managed to keep a deadpan face through the funniest of lines. Geoffrey Peace's handling of Major Singleton was also worthy of mention.

The production (Les Wood) was good and the stage management (Jack Badnell) was excellent. In some cases the make-up was rather overdone.

Wiltshire Gazette 1960

NO MORE MEN TO BE CALLED UP

END OF NATIONAL SERVICE

The last National Service men to be called up joined their units on Thursday and no more enlistment notices will be issued, Mr. Hare, the Minister of Labour, announced yesterday.

Mr. Hare said that it had already been announced that there would be no further call-up after the end of the year. " In fact," he said, " it has been found convenient to complete the arrangements during November."

Mr. Hare made the announcement in a written reply to Sir Spencer Summers, the Conservative member for Aylesbury, who had asked for information on progress with call-up to the forces.

The Ministry of Labour said that the enlistment notices for this final group had been sent out about two weeks ago. The group included 2,000 men for the Army, 50 for the R.A.F., and none for the Navy. Most of these were men who had been deferred as students or apprentices and their average age was 21½.

Since the end of the war 2,300,000 men had been called up to do National Service. Since 1939, when the scheme began, 5,300,000 men had been called up—3,800,000 for the Army, 500,000 for the Navy, and one million for the R.A.F.

The Times 1960

The evidence for the Law – if it is regarded only as a general tendency between widely different social levels – is a matter of common observation. The Divorce Court, it has been said, is the only seat of British justice where invariably the parties to a case are better shod than the witnesses, and where chauffeur-driven limousines outside are less likely to be waiting for the judge than for the people appearing before him. (In the recent £30,000 Boyd-Gibbons case, for example, the Husband, the Wife and the Other Man had a Rolls-Royce each. The judge took a cab.)

Town 1962

National Service 'Dodgers' Abandoning Farm Work

Crediton Gazette 1960

KNITTING FINISHES DEMONSTRATED

After the business session at the May meeting of Tiverton Townswomen's Guild, with Mrs. C. Bending in the chair, Mrs. Hutchings gave a demonstration of knitting finishes. Mrs. Cullum won the competition for the best article knitted from an ounce of wool, and Mrs. MacLeash won the draw for guild funds.

At the April meeting, eggs were collected from members, and Post Hill and Belmont Hospitals were each sent 9¾ dozen. Letters of thanks have been received.

THE ENDING of the National Service call-up means that at least 200 Leicestershire farmworkers will leave the land for better paid jobs in industry.

At the other end of the scale a drastic drop in the number of school leavers entering the agricultural industry has also been noticed since the ending of conscription was announced.

Leicester Advertiser 1960

Sir Richard Yeabsley, C.B.E., J.P., F.C.A., chairman of The Ruberoid Co. Ltd., has announced that agreement has been reached with Bitroid Ltd., of Johannesburg, a subsidiary company of Anglo-Transvaal Industries Ltd., to manufacture Ruberoid bituminous building materials in South Africa. Mr. G. D. L. Goslett, O.B.E., joint managing director of Ruberoid, will be appointed to the board of Bitroid Ltd.

Arrangements have been made for modifications to the Bitroid plant at Boksburg to be carried out in co-operation with Ruberoid technicians. These modifications will enable the existing plant to be utilised for the manufacture of a wide range of products to the Ruberoid specifications, meeting the requirements of the South African Bureau of Standards where applicable. The existing range of Bitroid products will continue to be marketed.

Through the Republic of South Africa, South West Africa, Swaziland, Basutoland and Bechuanaland, a complete technical roofing and waterproofing service will be made available to architects, engineers and specifying authorities. The builder, farmer, estate manager and householder will be able to purchase South African-made Ruberoid products through retail outlets.

Factory Manager 1962

SECURITY BAN ON COMMUNISTS

Union risks stressed in Radcliffe report

CLOSING GAPS AFTER BLAKE SPY CASE

By. H. B. BOYNE,
Daily Telegraph Political Correspondent

A MAJOR recommendation in the report on security by the Radcliffe committee, set up after the imprisonment for 42 years of the spy George Blake last year, amounts to a new ban on trade union officials suspected of Communist associations.

The report, published in part yesterday [Details—P24] was submitted to the Government 4½ months ago. Since then " positive vetting " of civil servants with access to secrets has been carried out more intensively than ever.

Recommendations from the report include:

Telling senior civil servants more frankly of the scale of Communist penetration of Civil Service unions;

Sustained effort to overcome a general lack of conviction that any substantial threat to security exists;

A man held captive or interned by Communists should only in exceptional circumstances be employed;

The security element of diplomats marrying foreign wives should always be borne in mind.

Daily Telegraph 1962

Lighthouse Keeper at Beachy Head

After eight years on the storm-bound Wolf Rock, Fred Burgess has settled in, or on, the comparatively soft number of Beachy Head lighthouse. With two assistants he keeps constant watch on the light, winding up the clockwork motor, filling the paraffin tank, polishing the immense lens of prisms and, in fog, firing an explosive signal that shakes the tower every five minutes.

The rest of the time—people are always asking Mr Burgess what lighthouse keepers do all the time—is taken in cleaning operations which keep the whole tower brighter than white.

The tower itself is beautifully made —enormous pieces of granite polished and dove-tailed together so closely that only a hair-line shows where they meet.

Within the tower everything is curved: the stove, the bunks, the doors. The staircase is a ladder, the garden a balcony (wind-swept) and a rock (tide-lashed, but marvellous for shrimps).

The Trinity House vessel *Siren* calls regularly with stores. All water, kept in a tank in the bottom of the tower, comes from Cowes. Milk, on the other hand, comes from tins.

Mr Burgess and his merry men spend one month in every three ashore, but find their sea-legs quickly enough once they get aboard again. Little wonder. The Burgess family have been keeping lighthouses for over 150 years.

DR RAMSEY WILL BE NEW PRIMATE

Bishop of Bradford to succeed him at York

The Scotsman 1961

THE 100th APPOINTMENT

The Archbishop of York, Dr Arthur Michael Ramsey, is to be the 100th Archbishop of Canterbury and Primate of All England, it was announced yesterday. He is 56. He will be succeeded as Archbishop of York by the Bishop of Bradford, Dr Frederick Donald Coggan, who is 51.

The nominations by the Queen of Dr Ramsey and Dr Coggan were announced yesterday afternoon in a statement from the Prime Minister's office. The announcement came only two days after Dr Geoffrey Fisher had told the Convocation of Canterbury in London of his resignation from May 31.

The salary of the Archbishop of Canterbury is £7500 and that of the Archbishop of York £5000.

Dr Ramsey is the ninth Archbishop of York to become Archbishop of Canterbury.

OUTSPOKEN

Dr Ramsey, Archbishop of York since January 1956, has been described as one of the most learned of present-day English churchmen. A dominating thick-set figure with sparse grey hair, he has a reputation for outspoken and challenging pronouncements on many of the controversial issues of the day.

His appointment to York was a break with tradition, for most Archbishops of Canterbury and York in recent times have come from Oxford, while Dr Ramsey graduated at Cambridge, where he gained a reputation, as president of the Union, for his forceful and witty speeches.

Born at Cambridge, where his father was a distinguished mathematician, Dr Ramsey was educated at Repton when Dr Fisher was head master, and Magdalene College.

He was ordained in 1928 and rose very rapidly in Church affairs. He was curate of Liverpool Parish Church from 1928 to 1930, and later lecturer of Boston Parish Church and vicar of St Benedict's, Cambridge.

From 1940 to 1950 he was Canon of Durham Cathedral and Professor of Theology in the University of Durham. He then became Regius Professor of Divinity at Cambridge University. During 1951-1952 he was also Canon and Prebendary at Lincoln Cathedral.

VISIT TO MOSCOW

He became Bishop of Durham in 1952. Approachable and friendly, he became very popular with the miners and their families with whom he mixed freely and talked frankly.

As Bishop of Durham he was one of the Queen's supporters at the Coronation, standing at her right hand during the service in Westminster Abbey.

The Times 1960

WESTMINSTER ABBEY SEEKS GARDENER

A woman may soon be tending the oldest garden in London—College Garden, attached to Westminster Abbey, which has been under constant cultivation since 1065. Applications for the post of head gardener—man or woman—are invited in *The Times* personal column this morning.

"The garden is quite large and rather beautiful", said Dr. E. S. Abbott, Dean of Westminster, last night. "It is difficult to find the right person, and we should be delighted to have a woman gardener." Though the Abbey had never had a woman gardener before they had decided to throw their net a little wider, especially as there was a shortage of men gardeners in central London.

People's Friend 1962

A Wife Speaks Out!

LIKE a lot of young wives these days, I kept on my job after my marriage. So now I have to work a five-day week and look after a house and husband as well.

This doesn't bother me too much, but what does annoy me is my husband's attitude. Whenever he helps me in any way, such as by washing the dishes, he thinks I should be most grateful for his consideration in doing one of "my" jobs.

But surely if I am out working all day it's only right he should help a little in the house. And so it's not "my" job he's doing but his own!

Considering I do all the cleaning, washing, ironing, baking and most of the cooking, I think he gets off lightly!—Mrs I. G., Edinburgh.

Do other working wives agree with Mrs I. G.? We'd be interested to hear their views.

Protestant Witness
1961

CORSICA IN THE NEWS

The Trinitarian Bible Society has, for some years now, been most generously assisting the Union with supplies of free Bibles for distribution in those countries where the Bible is a prohibited Book. It has, therefore, been a tremendous contrast to have been able to assist in distributing some of their so generously donated supplies of Scriptures in countries like France and Corsica where it is easier.

On April 7th Mr. Potton and I, with ten helpers, set out on a most memorable and eventful journey. Owing to the urgency of getting quickly on the job we set out with hardly adequate time, for a minimum of three weeks seemed hardly adequate for such a large and needy field. We had to do nearly 750 miles in the first leg of the journey to co-ordinate with ferry services from Marseilles to Bastia—the capital of that Island.

After having had a much needed night's rest at Garvi, where Mr. and Mrs. Hodson of the Glyn Vivian International Miners' Mission gave us wonderful hospitality and a delightful glimpse of their very prosperous work in that area, Mr. Potton and the party were able to guarantee six years rent for a new house to be taken over by the Mission for extending the work. Although the French Government gives full liberty for the distribution of the Scriptures and they were sent in advance, openly, to the Island, priests everywhere found means to hinder God's work, so it was only after three days' hard struggle and much prayer, then finally, having to advance in cash quite a fabulous amount for the exaggerated Custom's requirement, that we finally got our large supplies of Gospels released and commenced the arduous climb, with the overloaded minibus, over the precipitous mountains to the scattered villages in the mountains and valleys of that country. Sometimes we climbed to 7,000 feet with snow-capped peaks dotting the horizon even in summer time.

Everywhere we found a tremendous willingness to receive the Gospel and, before long, we were using printed French cards, prepared by Pastor Brooks, to enable them to sing with us the beautiful hymns and choruses available in the French language.

Carpet Review
1963

International Carpet Trade Fair

OPENING at Earls Court on 25th February next, *The International Carpet, Linoleum and Floor Coverings Fair*, now in its seventh year, will be held for five days, i.e. to 1st March incl. The Fair is now firmly established as the outstanding annual event in the carpet trade and the ideal meeting-place for everyone engaged in this field. Regular increase in popularity over the years since its inception has made continual expansion necessary and in response to demand the 1963 presentation will be open to the public for the first time for a limited period—on Wednesday and Thursday 27th and 28th February from 5 p.m. to 8 p.m.

Floorcovering is not only a flourishing industry in the United Kingdom—it is "big business"—contributing heavily to national export figures and providing constant employment for thousands of designers, technicians, weavers, machinists and numerous other occupations. Sales of carpets and rugs alone amounted to nearly one hundred million pounds last year and impending changes in international trading conditions, while presenting a stimulating challenge to everyone in the industry, offer, at the same time, the glittering prospect of a rich new market for British products in Europe.

Special arrangements have been made for the reception of overseas visitors to "Carpex 63", as the Fair is called, and European buyers in particular, have shown an increasing interest in the Fair over recent years. Enquiries concerning the 1963 Fair indicate that there will be a large influx of trade visitors from the Continent.

INDECENT LETTERS SENT TO POLICE

Lydiard Dealer is Fined £60

A travelling oil and hardware dealer, Harold Fisher, of Lydiard, Purton, was fined £60 by Swindon Borough magistrates on Friday after pleading "Guilty" to six charges of sending indecent letters through the post.

Most of the letters were sent to the Swindon Income - Tax inspector, said Chief Insp. E. J. Howard. "But since the summons was served he has been sending them to me instead," added the Chief Inspector.

Wiltshire Gazette and Herald
1960

Many Happy Returns!

Leading manufacturers of the British toy industry gathered at the Café Royal in London on March 8 to do honour to Mr. Walter Lines, the Chairman of the Lines Brothers Group of Companies. Mr. Lines celebrated his 80th birthday on March 10, and his colleagues in the industry, for which he has done so much, made this the occasion to pay tribute to him.

British Toys 1962

Woman's Realm 1964

The two faces of Sylvia

WE didn't realize how completely anyone's appearance could be altered until we visited the BBC's make-up training school in London recently. There, under the guidance of experienced instructors, students learn how to transform a thirty-year-old into an octogenarian and a young man into a balding middle-aged one. They are taught to simulate wounds and black eyes for punch-up scenes, and even to alter the shape of a nose with special flesh-coloured wax. Not, of course, that all actors need such elaborate attentions. Indeed, many TV performers do not wear make-up at all.

The course of study at the school lasts three months and culminates in a stiff examination. High standards of work are needed to deceive the searching eye of the camera. Students, who must be over 20½ years old, are paid while they train, and new recruits are welcome, since trained girls are constantly leaving to get married.

Our first picture shows trainee Sylvia Halliday with a glamorous "junior lead" make-up; next you can see how it is done, and last she appears as an oriental beauty. This transformation took well over an hour to complete.

When she saw the result, Sylvia thought the disguise so good, she reckoned even her own mother wouldn't recognize her!

New Daily 1963

The New Prime Minister Works On His Cabinet

ALL REVOLT CRUMBLES

Mr. Macmillan's Future Still Uncertain

LORD HOME, the Foreign Secretary, yesterday was invited by the Queen to form a Government, following the resignation of Mr. Harold Macmillan.

All the indications last night were that he will have little difficulty in doing so, and that many Ministers who served under Mr. Macmillan will remain in the Cabinet.

But the position of Mr. R. A. Butler, Mr. Macmillan's deputy, is still undetermined.

Last night the Prime Minister-designate was conducting hurried consultations with Ministers, and, it is believed, he asked most of them to stay at their posts.

Throughout the afternoon, they paid brisk calls at No. 10, Downing-street — beginning with the three defeated candidates: Mr. Butler, Mr. Reginald Maudling, and Lord Hailsham.

KEY FIGURES

Mr. Butler stayed with Lord Home twice as long as the others. He was there for 30 minutes, the two others being content with 15 minutes of his time.

Daily Mail 1963

No to Keeler

Equity, the actors' union, yesterday turned down an application for membership by Miss Christine Keeler.

8/9 rise

About 7,000 engineering craftsmen employed by local authorities are to get a wage rise of 2½d an hour, backdated to April 1. It means an increase of 8s. 9d. a week.

Daily Mail 1963

AIR CUSHION ON THE FARM

Hovertruck shows its paces

By W. D. THOMAS,
Daily Telegraph Agricultural Correspondent

THREE air cushion vehicles skimming over a 23-acre field of winter wheat near Ely yesterday appear to have solved the problem of how to work land too soft to take a tractor. The machines have been developed from the Hovercraft.

The demonstration of the vehicles was given at Woodhouse Farm, Chettisham, Cambs. It was staged by the developers, Vickers-Armstrongs, and the first agricultural firm to buy them, Soil Fertility.

The vehicles, which were being used to spray the wheat with liquid fertiliser, travelled lightly over the soft ground at a speed of from 12 to 14 m.p.h., with negligible damage to the crop. Only light wheel marks were left in the soil.

The Hovertruck, as the vehicle is called, is basically a Land-Rover fitted with two engines and a nylon rubber skirt. With the skirt fully down the air cushion can support 75 per cent. of the weight of the loaded vehicle.

SWAMP TESTS
3ft ditch crossed

During trials the Hovertruck was driven over crops in both wet and dry conditions. Some tests were successfully carried out in swampy areas which would have been impassable to other wheeled vehicles. The Hovertruck was able to cross a 3ft ditch with running water.

Britain is the first country to show the practical use of this type of vehicle and there should be good export possibilities for it. In this country several farmers have already expressed interest.

Mr. H. Hubbard, sales supervisor of Soil Fertility, said the machines could work a hundred acres a day. They were intended for seed bed work and for top dressings on land where a tractor would "make rather a mess."

Daily Telegraph 1963

GERMANS THINK BRITISH SKILL IS 'FANTASTIC'

Praise for the efficiency of an all-British patented machine and the skill of a British hosiery supervisor by Germans at the International Textile Exhibition in Hanover, West Germany, can serve as some consolation to the 'dismal Jimmies' who think that Britain falls behind some of her European counterparts in the textile industry.

The machine was the 'Wizard' hose examining machine of B. P. Hall (Textiles) Ltd., and the operator was Mrs. Lettie Jones, of A. Booth and Sons, Ilkeston.

'Fantastic' was the comment of one German buyer who watched Mrs. Jones turn a dozen pairs of stockings in 45 seconds. Mrs. Jones was stop-watched by many visitors, and in one case the figures quoted were challenged by a German buyer.

After he had been told that 12 pairs could be turned in 50 seconds, he refused to believe it. But Mrs. Jones proved him wrong by completing the job in 45 seconds flat.

Knitwear and Stockings 1963

SACK THREAT OVER 250

Drama of bid to save Rolls Razor firm

Willesden and Brent Chronicle 1964

by DAVE BAXTER

MASS sacking threatens 250 shocked workers at Rolls Razor, Cricklewood, today (Friday) after a company statement that the payroll is to be slashed to a minimum.

The statement, unsigned, came on Wednesday after a morning of tension during which reports that the firm was to shut down were repeatedly denied by spokesmen.

At noon, workers said they had been told at a pre-lunch meeting that they were to be fired with one week's wages and three days pay "in hand."

At 2 p.m. the report was hotly denied by Mr. Harvey Langer, personal assistant to washing machine tycoon John Bloom, who said. "The workers have been told nothing at all."

University news

Industry's hold too great, say students

By a Yorkshire Post Reporter

THE view was expressed at a conference of students from universities and training colleges in the North and Midlands, at Sheffield on Saturday, that industry was exercising too great a control on university work.

The conference, attended by students from Leeds, Hull, Bradford, Ilkley, Loughborough, Birmingham and Belfast, was convened to discuss topics for the Robbins Committee, which will meet next month to discuss higher education in general.

Also attending were Mr. Gwyn Morgan, of Aberystwyth, president of the NUS, and Mr. Eric Schumacher, of Leeds, the vice-president.

Delegates felt that industry, in founding departments and chairs, was also directing university policy and thought, particularly in the field of research.

Instead of industry taking such a direct share of control, it was felt it would be better to establish a central research award body to channel all such gifts. A danger could arise if industry had too big a personal stake.

Yorkshire Post 1961

Leylands for Cuba

THE Leyland Motor Corporation is to be commended for securing an order for the supply of 400 buses to the Cuban government in the face of intense foreign competition. The bus concerned in the order is the well-tried Leyland-M.C.W. Olympic—an integral design specially built for the overseas market. The order, including spare parts, is worth nearly £4m., and so represents a valuable addition to Britain's export trade. The buses—36ft. long and seating 45 passengers—will be used for urban passenger transport in the city of Havana and are part of the Cuban government's plan to standardise on Leyland buses throughout the country. This is the third bus order which Leyland has received from Cuba since the war—the first was in 1949 for 620 buses, and the second in 1959 for 200 buses.

Not surprisingly, in view of its strained relations with the Castro regime, the United States government does not view the contract with favour, but Mr. Hodges, the U.S. Secretary of Commerce, has admitted there is not much they can do about it. The United States maintains a stringent economic embargo on trade with Cuba, which Britain recognises only so far as it concerns "strategic" goods. It would be difficult for even the most patriotic American to suggest that buses are in this category. In any case, the protest against the Leyland contract—presumably because it involves a country with communist sympathies—comes very strangely from a government that has approved the sale of American wheat to Iron Curtain countries.

Passenger Transport **1964**

DOUGHNUT making in this country, although mostly in the hands of the smaller manufacturers, is nevertheless also carried out on a large scale by several plant bakers. While current consumption, comparatively speaking, is small compared with the per capita U.S. consumption, the demand might well increase under the stimulus of the recent American equipment exhibition in London, where doughnuts were the highlight.

Increased demand would depend on many factors, not least being the production of a quality product. Very little has appeared in the bakery trade press during the last 20 years concerning doughnuts, and these articles may, therefore, repair the omission.

Whichever spelling is adopted, it cannot detract from the enjoyment of this succulent, sweet flavoured cellular confection. When the author was a child, like others of his generation he delightedly anticipated a wait in the queue outside the local baker's shop to buy a pennyworth of doughnuts — all two of them. Two or three bits of the spongy sweetness was enhanced by the discovery of the jam in the middle.

When and where did the doughnut start? One theory is that the great-grandfather of the present doughnut was the French Cruller. There are some who, with perhaps more justification, confer the honour on the unknown baker who accidentally dropped a piece of bun dough into some hot fat. Whatever may have been its origin, the modern mass produced doughnut is held in high esteem in many parts of the bakery world — particularly so in the U.S.A.

Biscuit Maker and Plant Baker **1965**

INQUIRY INTO CORONERS' WORK

ENSURING HOMICIDE IS DETECTED

There is to be an inquiry into the working of coroners and their courts and death certification, taking into account criticisms that the law at present makes it too easy for homicide to go undetected.

Mr. Brooke, Home Secretary, announced yesterday that he is to set up an interdepartmental committee on the law and practice relating to death certification, disposal of dead bodies, coroners and coroners' courts and some related subjects. The medical certification necessary before a body can be cremated will be one of the matters considered.

MAIN TASKS

The committee will have the primary tasks of :—

1. Examining the arrangements for issuing medical certificates of the cause of death and for ensuring that further investigation is carried out in appropriate cases.
2. Considering whether the existing law and practice relating to coroners and coroners' courts provides the best basis for modern conditions for determining the cause of death. This will involve consideration of the procedures of the coroner, his jurisdiction, appointment, terms of service, &c.

It will also be part of the committee's task to consider such related matters as the organization of the forensic pathology service. The names of the chairman and members of the committee will be announced shortly.

The most recent major legislation affecting coroners was in 1926 (Coroners (Amendment) Act 1926). The office of coroner has not been subject to a general review for about 30 years.

THREE CERTIFICATES

At present if cremation is desired instead of burial, as well as the ordinary death certificate, two further medical certificates, giving much further information, are normally required. One of these must be given by the medical practitioner who attended the deceased during his last illness and the other must be given by an independent medical practitioner who must be of not less than five years' standing.

These certificates, together with the application for cremation, must be submitted to the medical referee of the crematorium who is responsible for deciding whether or not to authorize cremation.

If the death may have been a violent or unnatural one or if there are any suspicious circumstances the medical referee must report the death to the coroner. In 1963 a little over 40 per cent of all deaths were followed by cremation.

The Times **1964**

DENISE ROBINS

confidante of thousands, author of 143 romantic novels, answers your personal problems

CAREER FIRST?

"I DON'T want a baby . . ." This, I am sure, is a cry from the brain rather than from the heart of a reader. She is a young married woman who has a first-class, well-paid job. She says:

"My husband wants a family now, but this would mean such strict economy that it is not, in my opinion, worth sacrificing my job for. Has my husband a right to insist?"

I asked one of the most beautiful actresses whom we have ever had on the British stage—GLADYS COOPER—her opinion about this problem. Gladys is a woman of great experience; she had children early on, despite her active life on the stage. Her answer was brief and somewhat bitter. She obviously had no sympathy with the girl in question.

She said:

"He should get rid of her and try to find the right kind of woman who likes children."

It's plain to see that Gladys looks at the problem only from the husband's point of view. But I find just a little sympathy for the girl who may be very young and anxious not to be involved with motherhood too soon. Also it is only human for her to like getting out and doing things apart from household chores. But in the main issue my sympathies are with the husband and not with her. She must put a strict time-limit on her preference, especially if her husband wants the baby soon. After all, marriages are made for the procreation of children. I feel strongly about family life. I consider the morality of a nation depends to a large extent upon it.

To some, the blessing of parenthood is denied. They nearly always adopt a child when they cannot have one of their own. It seems a little unnatural for a young healthy girl to want to earn more money for more luxuries, rather than produce a child. First of all, she should not deny her husband the paternity which is his absolute right. I presume his pay-packet is sufficient to support a family. Secondly, her preference for keeping her job and her own money suggests that she is selfish and greedy and has little love for anyone but herself. She must think very seriously about what she is doing. Not only is she risking the loss of her husband's love, but possibly storing up a lonely and loveless future. She should not forget that no woman can go on crying *"I'll have children later—not now."* It's a dangerous policy because, as the years go by, she may find she grows less, rather than more, ready for motherhood. The day could even come when it would be too late.

She
1966

BAND STILL WEARING KILTS OF 1906

Dundee Corporation police committee last night recommended payment of £650 for new kilts and plaids "and renovation of feather bonnets and sporrans" of Dundee City Police Pipe Band, who played before the Queen at Braemar Games last week.

At the committee meeting Mr. Ian Borthwick, the convener, said the band felt they could not accept any more public engagements because of the poor state of their present kit. They were wearing the original 1906 kilts, sporrans and plaids.

Since then the corporation had never paid anything towards the band's upkeep, the convener said.

The Times 1964

Your money or your life!

Few visible signs still exist in Britain today of the bad old days when highwaymen roamed our lonely roads, terrorising travellers and robbing the mail-coaches.

These brigands, not infrequently, were captured and made to answer for their crimes, and were usually hanged. In the open country, the gallows were often set up at cross-roads, and a reminder of these times may be seen at the junction of the Cambridge and Huntingdon roads in a Cambridgeshire locality which, even today is known as 'Caxton Gibbet' owing to its proximity to the village of Caxton and the presence of its sinister gallows. These stand by the side of the road, on a slight bluff, where they would have been clearly seen (and still are) in what must have been a flat, windswept and desolate landscape —a grim warning of retribution to the wrongdoers.

R. S. Riddell, Totteridge.

Meccano
Magazine
1966

Town
1965

RICE, Michael, Public Relations Consultant; *b.* 21 May 1928; son of Arthur Vincent Rice, of Pembroke, West Wales, and Dora Kathleen (née Blacklock), of Bristol. *Education:* Challoner School. *Recreations:* racing, travel, poker, opera and serious music, study of ancient art and societies. *Publications:* occasional political pieces. *Clubs:* Crockfords, *Address:* flat in Hyde Park Place.

'I believe that the intelligent thing to do is to make a start in whatever you intend to do before you are 30. People are much kinder then, and tend to give you work and a sporting chance which they might not afford to an older man. And, if you make a go of it, you have those extra years in credit.' Michael Rice is, at 36, the head of the largest firm of public relations consultants in the country. It may not, he says, be the largest numerically – he employs between forty and fifty people – but it certainly is in terms of the size of the companies which it advises and in the fees which it can command. Rice is immediately impressive. He speaks in a cool, cerebral fashion, and confidently – as though from a prepared text full of highly articulated sentences thick with parentheses and dependent clauses. He is fond of slightly pedantic phrases like 'where appropriate' and given to curious initial remarks such as 'As things are – or as they seem to be. . .'

Plymouth Independent
1966

'Wilson must be tough'—M.P.

THE time has come for Prime Minister Harold Wilson to tell the trade unions who is boss.

And the time to do this, said Dr. David Owen, Labour M.P. for Plymouth (Sutton), is at the Trade Union Congress.

He was talking to a women's meeting at the Sutton division Labour headquarters about the Prices and Incomes Act when he was asked for his opinion about the unco-operative attitude of some unions towards what the Government was trying to do.

Dr. Owen commented: "I have a very great respect for the trade union movement, but this is the time for the Government to govern. It is time for the Prime Minister to go and say 'This is our policy—I stand or fall by it.'"

Universe
1965

Nun becomes a nurse at 50

Sr. Maria Amabilis, a 50-year-old member of the Cross and Passion community at St. Peter's convent, Bradford, has successfully completed a two-year period of training in nursing at the Leeds Road, Hospital, Bradford.

She was presented with her certificate in the presence of the Lord Mayor and Lady Mayoress of Bradford.

Her intention, she said, was to be of greater service in the convent.

Doughty Campaigner

JUDGING from the difficulty of reaching Mrs. Mary Whitehouse on the telephone her recruitment for the National Viewers and Listeners Association is proceeding briskly. She has no London office and operates from her home Postman's Piece, the Wold, Claverley, near Wolverhampton.

When, after four attempts, I got through she reported that her campaign is going well. Among the thousand subscribers are about 100 representing churches, branches of women's organisations and other small bodies. She needs £250 a month to run the association and denied most emphatically that she had received any large sums towards it from any one organisation. "We have been working on a shoestring. The money has come in small contributions."

This movement, which started as a protest against pornography, now aims at securing a voice in the councils of broadcasting for the people who pay the licence money.

If National VALA merely seeks to ventilate grievances I cannot see much future in it. I cannot see why the BBC should continue to countenance offensive programme intrusions that cause widespread annoyance. The tactless refusal of Sir Hugh Greene, the Director-General, and Lord Normanbrook, the chairman, to see Mrs. Whitehouse has added fuel to her fire and justice to her cause.

Law Times 1965

General Intelligence

THE NEW JUDGES

For the second time Judge Lane has made legal history. Those acquainted with her work on the county court bench will welcome her forthcoming appointment (we write on the day of its announcement) as a puisne judge, and the profession will congratulate her on her double achievement in being the first woman to attain judicial office both in the county court and the High Court. The six new appointments will raise the judicial strength of the High Court to the unprecedented total of 61.

Daily Telegraph 1965

Grimsby Evening Telegraph 1966

STRIKE OFF–BY 29 VOTES TO 16

But seamen give hostile reception to news

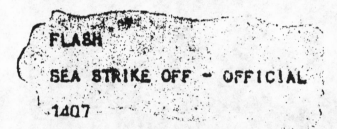

FLASH

SEA STRIKE OFF - OFFICIAL

1407

This is how the news was received by wire in the Evening Telegraph creed room this afternoon.

PEACE HAS COME AT LAST IN THE SEAMEN'S STRIKE — AFTER 45 DAYS. THE EXECUTIVE OF THE NATIONAL UNION OF SEAMEN DECIDED THIS AT THEIR VITAL MEETING BEHIND CLOSED DOORS TODAY.

They carried this resolution: "This executive council, being aware of the hardship caused to the citizens of the United Kingdom, accept the shipowners' improved offer of 28th June.

DON'T GET YOUR HAIR CUT, PLEA TO BROWN

By FRANK HOWITT

AN appeal has gone to Foreign Secretary Mr. George Brown asking: Don't cross a strike picket line to get your hair cut this morning.

The plea was sent yesterday by four maintenance electricians at a firm of men's outfitters which has hairdressing salons at some branches—including one in Piccadilly which Mr. Brown has used for many years.

A spokesman for the firm, Meakers, said last night: "Mr. Brown does not have an appointment at our salon tomorrow, but he could walk in at any time —as he usually does."

The electricians stopped work last Monday over a sacking. Their plea to Mr. Brown was addressed: "Dear Sir and Brother."

They said the Foreign Secretary calls in every other Wednesday morning for a trim.

Will Mr. Brown cross the line today?

His spokesman said: "He will be too busy—especially with the Common Market debate—to take time off for a haircut."

Shepherd's Bush Gazette 1966

Daily Express 1967

Industrial fire contest cancelled

Acton's industrial fire brigade competition, which was to be held at the C.A.V. factory on Saturday, was cancelled because of reorganization in local firms.

Mr. Peter Clay, secretary of the Acton Chamber of Commerce, said that fire brigade systems at Acton factories were being reviewed and the competition would probably be held in the spring.

"We hope to throw it open to the whole of West London, instead of chamber members only," said Mr. Clay.

Today it's Pen and ...

PARKER Quink

PERMANENT BLUE BLACK

'If I was in a tight corner, I'd hit first and ask questions afterwards.' Policemen talk freely about their work and the problems it creates, as Don Haworth who made the film explains

1

9.5

THE aim of tonight's programme is to give a true picture of the everyday work of a large police force. It was not scripted, there were no actors, and events were shot as they happened.

The Bobby's Way of Life

If it is excitement you want it is best to stick to police fiction. In life there are few calmer places than police stations. 'You've got to pace it,' a detective constable said, 'or you'd kill yourself.' He was pacing it by warming his back at the fire. But his normal working day was twelve hours and might easily run to twenty.

The police have no reserve of men (generally they are under strength) but they do through long habit maintain a calm reserve of energy which in other organisations might be frittered away in excitement over details.

Nobody we met shied away from the much-publicised question of violence. 'Since the Metro murders,' one constable said, 'if I was in a tight corner I'd hit first and ask questions afterwards.'

A detective put it in a different way. 'In the C.I.D. we give as good as we get. We call it a draw, sort of thing.'

Policemen in fact prefer those areas where regular Saturday night punch-ups leave no ill feelings on Monday to quieter districts where the bobby is merely—but continually—disliked.

A country sergeant speaks of the time when his own young children despised him because he was a policeman. A young policewoman says that boy friends drift away when they learn what her job is. 'They just take you out from idle curiosity.' And a constable's wife asks him: 'Why don't you give up the police force and became a normal human being again?'

The police always used to be regarded as the instrument of the ruling class, and still most policemen, although themselves working-class in origin, education, and income, identify criminals with the working class, particularly the worst-off section of it, the itinerants and the unemployed.

One police force (not the West Riding where all tonight's film was shot) trains its dogs on a chap dressed like a 'hunger marcher' from the 'thirties; if the poor animal had to wait for *that* kind of victim these days its jaws would seize up for want of an exercising snap.

'Thieves live in bloody awful places themselves,' a detective sergeant says, and in passing asks his subordinate to go to the labour exchange 'and see who's in circulation.' This springs from the fact that, as the police are keen to point out, the high crime statistics contain a vast number of crimes of extreme pettiness.

The West Riding Constabulary agreed to our interviewing in private whomever we wished and photographing whatever happened, subject only to the restrictions of law and decency.

Police, tonight's documentary, is not drama but it does, I hope, give a fair picture of the everyday work, and the attitude towards it, of a body of men and women who are familiar to everybody and intimately known to few.

Radio Times 1967

Spectator 1968

"A BIT HOT," SAID ALF

Police Horse Ate His Saveloys

Although hot-dog salesman Alfred Corper, aged 46, described as a street trader of Willesden-lane, N.W.6, pleaded guilty at North London Magistrates' Court to wilfully obstructing the free passage of the footway in Gillespie-road, Highbury, N.5, outside the Arsenal Ground last Wednesday, he pointed out to the magistrate, Mr. Evelyn Russell, that at the time of his arrest he was standing on private property.

Insp. Tanner said that at 6.50 p.m. at the entrance to Highbury Football Stadium, Corper was selling hot-dogs and as a result of the crowd that was around him an obstruction was caused.

He was asked to move, on four separate occasions and declined to do so and was arrested.

Asked by the magistrate if he wanted to ask Insp. Tanner any questions, Corper said: "What the officer says is quite true, but I was actually standing on private property at the time."

The magistrate said: "But I'm afraid your customers were not and they caused an obstruction."

Fined £5, Corper told the magistrate that the maximum fine for the offence of causing an obstruction was £2, but the magistrate told him that the maximum was, in fact, £10.

Interviewed later at his premises in Elgin-mews, Randolph-avenue, Mr. Corper said that he intended to write to the Commissioner of Police, Sir Joseph Simpson, pointing out that nothing was said in court about the fact that at the time of his arrest a police horse ate some of the hot dogs and saveloys on his handcart.

"I think a £5 fine is a bit hot, seeing that I lost part of my stock, and I think that if the magistrate had realized this he would not have imposed such a heavy fine."

Mr. Corper added: "Mind you, I've nothing against the horse — it just shows how good my hot dogs are!"

Westminster Chronicle 1968

'. . . and you see, well, I sort of promised this economic miracle, and I was wondering if, well you know. . .'

My cup of tea

Listener 1969

Lady Summerskill, on Radio-4, recalled the 1945 Labour government. 'It never occurred to me that I should be so fortunate as to be in that Labour government—the first Labour government with real power. I was in the dining room when Willie Whiteley, the Chief Whip, tapped me on the shoulder. He said, "Clem wants you at Number 10," and I'd been so accustomed to the men saying, "I've got a pain, Edith, what should I take?" that I thought: "Oh heavens, something's happened to Clem." I went over to Number 10 and as I strolled down I thought: "Good heavens, maybe he's offering me something." Then in I went to the Cabinet Room, and there he was with a pipe. He said: "I think you'd do pretty well as Parliamentary Secretary to the Ministry of Food—it'd be rather your cup of tea, wouldn't it?" I said: "Oh, absolutely my cup of tea. I've been longing to prescribe food for years and years." And he said: "Good. I think you'll get on with old Ben. Goodbye, Edith." My goodness me, I was in and out within a minute and a half—but then he was always like that.'

Landing on his feet

DEMOLITION worker Raymond Stiles fell four floors down a lift shaft in Golden Square, Soho, yesterday and escaped with cuts and bruises. It was his second escape. A few months ago Mr Stiles, 21, of Lampton Road, Hounslow, Middlesex, got off with burns when he sawed through a live electric cable.

Daily Mail 1968

"STUDENT POWER IN – PATERNALISM OUT!"

This was the cry raised by a large number of left-wing demonstrators from the Free University at the Inauguration Ceremony for the new University Chancellor, Lord Adrian, on Thursday morning.

Members of the Free University distributed manifestos to all the dons and guests queueing outside the Senate House before the ceremony.

Then, as the procession began, headed by the Vice-Chancellor, the University Marshal and the Proctors, laughter recorded earlier at the Free University poured out of a window in Caius to greet it. The cry was taken up by left-wing students chanting student power slogans, and singing the "Internationale".

A few minutes later Lord Adrian arrived, escorted by Lord Butler, and the ceremony started.

Sir Eric Ashby greeted Lord Adrian, speaking of the dignity and significance of the position of Chancellor; this was followed by the presentation of the Statutes and a long speech in Latin by the Orator, in which he spoke of present "alienation of the young from the old."

The point was forcibly brought home to the Congregation a few minutes later when an ex-Christ's undergraduate, Daryll Barker, stood up in the gallery and began to make a speech of his own on behalf of the Free University.

He had barely gone beyond "I have an announcement to make . . ." when he was seized by Stewards and hustled, protesting, from the Senate House.

Varsity 1968

TV ELECTRICIANS BAN OVERTIME

By Our TV Staff

An overtime ban by electricians at A TV's Elstree Studios yesterday caused "The Golden Shot" to backfire. The show was cancelled because members of the Electrical Trades Union refused to work on it as a protest against four staff electricians receiving their notice.

An episode from an old series, "Sentimental Agent," was shown instead. An A TV spokesman said: "Several months ago four additional electricians were employed on a temporary basis on the understanding that they would be relieved of their jobs when our present contract ended. This is a local dispute and does not have the backing of the E T U."

Daily Telegraph
1968

The Ceremonial procession

Punch
1968

"Elevenses Mrs. Purdy! What will it be?"

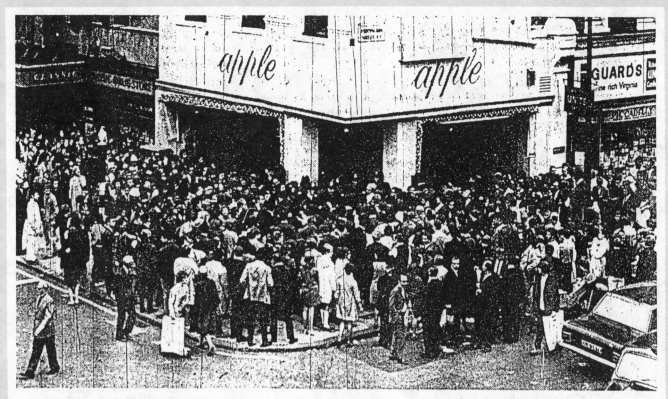

A crowd again gathered outside the Beatles' boutique, Apple, in Baker Street, yesterday when the give-away of stock continued. The Beatles are closing the shop eight months after it was opened, because they want to give up shopkeeping.

The Times 1968

Ban on work permits for immigrants rejected

The Home Secretary, Mr. James Callaghan, turned down demands by some Conservatives in the Commons this afternoon to stop the issue of all further work permits for immigrants.

Mr. Callaghan said the number of employment vouchers had since April been strictly related to the country's economic and social needs.

Mr. R. Gresham Cooke (Con., Twickenham) said it was best to stop any further work permits until the situation was under control. "If we do not we shall have an explosion in this country."

Mr. Callaghan said there was no question of the matter being out of control.

Distress

Mr. John Hall (Con., Wycombe) suggested a temporary halt to immigration, but Mr. Callaghan said: "That would cause a disproportionate amount of distress." An urgent examination was being made of the problem.

Mr. Emanuel Shinwell (Soc., Easington) asked if it had not been alleged, that immigration officers had behaved irregularly. "What was the irregularity?" Mr. Callaghan said that certain disciplinary charges were being investigated.

Cries of "disgraceful" came from one or two Labour backbenchers when Sir David Renton (Con., Huntingdon) asked: "As no State secrets were involved will you undertake that no-one will be punished for blurting out the truth?"

Mr. Callaghan: "You are asking me to do what I have already declined to do."

Cambridge News 1968

WOMEN GET VOICE IN WHITEHALL

By ELIZABETH CHOWEN

WOMEN are to have a bigger voice in Whitehall. The Prime Minister has set up an organisation which will have access to government departments and Ministers.

The Women's National Commission, announced yesterday, is to have as co-chairmen Mrs Judith Hart, MP, the Paymaster General, and Mrs John Tilney, president of the National Council of Women of Great Britain, and will have its government-paid secretariat in the Cabinet office.

Its brief is to make sure that the opinion of women 'is given its due weight in the deliberation of Government and in public debate on matters of public interest.'

Thirty major national women's organisations are being invited to join the Commission,

Daily Mail 1969

Daily Telegraph 1968

9,000 BACK AS FORD WOMEN WAIT

By BLAKE BAKER, Industrial Correspondent

MORE than 9,000 Ford workers in London and Liverpool, will be back at work today as a result of yesterday's decision by 382 women sewing machinists to end a three-week-old strike for "equal pay."

The decision came as a result of "heart-to-heart" talks on Friday between eight of the women and Mrs Barbara Castle, Secretary for Employment.

But the dispute, which cost more than £9 million in cancelled exports, is not over yet. The strike was called off pending a meeting today of the Ford national joint negotiating committee and pending also the court of inquiry under Sir Jack Scamp. This will resume its hearings in public on Wednesday.

Mrs. Rose Boland, leader at Dagenham, said yesterday: "This is a great victory for us. We have every confidence that the court of inquiry will be on our side." She emphasised that they expected an offer in today's talks.

The women complained that they were paid 1s 4½d an hour less than men for the same work, and also less than sewing machinists employed by other motor firms.

'ALL OUT RAIL STRIKE' FEAR BY GREENE

RAIL MILITANTS' DEMAND

By ROBERT BEDLOW
Industrial Staff

A GRIM warning that the railway go-slow may become a total stoppage was given in Penzance yesterday by Mr. Sidney Greene, general secretary of the National Union of Railwaymen.

As delegates arrived for the annual conference the traditionally militant Manchester and London district demanded strike action. Mr. Greene said: " A strike is always possible. Some people see it as a cure for all ills."

There are no "strike" motions on the agenda which was drawn up several months ago. But the possibility of emergency action cannot be ruled out.

The danger will come in mid-week if British Railways carry out their threat to suspend the guaranteed week. This will mean about 40,000 men left without any work by the go-slow; being sent home without pay.

Suspending the guaranteed week would give conference the opportunity for an emergency motion and there is little doubt it would match the Board in severity of action.

" Peace " hope

The Railways Board, is conscious of what the effects would be and is hoping for some " peace " move from the conference which is traditionally less militant than the executive.

The Board feels that it has made all the running and is not prepared to make any more suggestions. Mr. Leonard Neal, industrial relations member, is hoping that he might be invited to address conference to explain the latest offers which would give lower-paid men the chance of their pay being raised by up to 30s a week.

Mr. Greene said that he did not think the dispute would be drawn out. " I can't imagine this going on for a fortnight."

Daily Telegraph 1968

Mrs Castle defends strike deal

By ALAN LAW

MRS Barbara Castle denied in the Commons yesterday that the 11th-hour pay deal agreement which averted a national engineering strike was outside the Government's incomes criteria.

Mr Robert Carr (Con., Mitcham) said: 'It would appear that proposals, as reported in the Press, are very different indeed both in scale and in scope from the recommendations of the Prices and Incomes Board report last December.'

Mrs Castle, Minister of Productivity, replied that the proposals were 'broadly in line' with official prices and incomes policy because they contained important productivity features.

Because they would be spread over the next three years they would be seen to be 'within the ceiling.'

Welcome

The employers' offer is £19 a week guaranteed minimum for skilled workers by 1971, £15 for unskilled men and £13 for women.

The offer to the women is the only one still causing trouble. The union negotiators want a £14 minimum for the women.

Mrs Castle welcomed the employers' offer to set up, as part of the agreement, a joint working party to consider the properly evaluated grading of the work women do.

Daily Mail 1968

Happy as Minister of Labour

THE text of the letters exchanged between Mr. Gunter and Mr. Wilson were released yesterday afternoon. Mr. Gunter, in a letter dated Saturday, wrote:

DEAR HAROLD:

I have to inform you that I no longer desire to be a member of your Government and am therefore tendering my resignation.

I have the feeling that the best service I can render to the folk from whence I came is that I should obtain the freedom of the back benches and of the platforms in the country.

I would like to say how grateful I shall always be to you that you allowed me to be at the Ministry of Labour (now of blessed memory ! !) for three and a half years.

Yours sincerely,

Ray Gunter.

In his reply yesterday, the Prime Minister wrote:

MY DEAR RAY,

I was so sorry to hear of your wish to resign, but of course I respect your decision.

I know that all of our colleagues in the Cabinet will share my sense of loss at your departure. The work you have done through these exciting and formative years has been of great value to the country and the movement to which we all belong.

May I send you my personal thanks for all you have done and my best wishes for the future.

Yours very sincerely,

Harold Wilson.

Daily Telegraph 1968

Stones' fans wait

More than 500 people had gathered in Hyde Park, London, by midnight waiting for this afternoon's free Rolling Stones pop concert.

Daily Mail 1969

Daily Mail 1968

2,000,000 more working days lost by strikes

By ALAN YOUNG

STRIKES have cost 3,874,000 working days in the first nine months of this year—more than two million above the total for the whole of last year.

The figures were given in the Commons yesterday by Mr Roy Hattersley, Parliamentary Secretary to the Employment Ministry.

They horrified Sir Gerald Nabarro, Tory MP for Worcestershire South.

The problem had now reached a crescendo, he protested.

'This is particularly so in the motor industry where £60 million of exports have been lost this year. What is the Minister going to do about it?'

Mr Hattersley had said that In 1967, working days lost totalled 1,751,000. In 1966, it was 2,043,000 and in 1965 2,511,000.

Scourge

He assured Sir Gerald that he did not minimise the importance of the figures.

But the real crescendo was in the days of Tory rule in 1959 and 1962 when appreciably more days were lost.

Shadow Labour Minister, Mr Robert Carr, demanded action—and not more words. The Donovan Report had showed that wildcat strikes had been steadily increasing over the past decade.

'This is a scourge which must be tackled,' he insisted.

Mr Hattersley replied that there had been a great deal of action over the past three weeks.

'Attacking the causes rather than the symptoms may be less dramatic politically, but it will produce the best results' he said.

Sales girl Twiggy on her way to plug a trade gap

TWIGGY left Heathrow Airport, London, yesterday, with an exuberant Justin de Villeneuve, her manager and fiance, to sell Twiggy fashions at the British Trade Week in Copenhagen.

But she will not be modelling. She will be guest of honour at a fashion gala and hopes to bring back orders worth £75,000 for her 60 designs. Justin, 29, said: 'We do big business with the Scandinavian countries.'

Twiggy, 18, was wearing a plum velvet mini-dress, with white stockings and rings on every finger.

Daily Mail 1968

Daily Mail 1968

Mad Mitch's farewell

IN trilby hat and tweeds, Lieut.-Colonel Colin (Mad Mitch' Mitchell marched into civvy street yesterday. In a farewell speech as Commanding Officer of the Argyll and Sutherland Highlanders, he told his men at Seaton Barracks, Plymouth: 'I say goodbye, but I will carry on fighting to save the Argylls.' The regiment, which he led to fame in Aden, is due to be disbanded in 1972. Colonel Mitchell, 42, has said that he would now like to become a Tory MP.

CABINET DROP STRIKE PENALTIES

By VICTOR KNIGHT
and ALAN LAW

I'm happy, says Barbara

PREMIER Harold Wilson agreed last night to drop plans for penalties against wildcat strikers.

In return, the TUC leaders gave a "solemn and binding undertaking" to go to the utmost limit of their existing powers to settle disputes.

Agreement was finally reached after a dramatic series of confrontations at 10 Downing-street lasting seven hours. Jubilant union leaders were also given a firm pledge that the Government have not only abandoned penal clauses for the moment, but for the rest of their term of office.

After the talks, Mr. Wilson said he was certain that the TUC now had "the will, the power and the determination" to deal with the problem of unofficial strikes.

He added: "We take the view that the General Council mean business. We will give them their head."

Mr. Wilson was satisfied that the declaration was "as binding and acceptable as a rule change."

Opposed

At the start of the talks yesterday, Mr. Wilson and Employment Minister Barbara Castle knew that the overwhelming majority of Labour MPs were strongly opposed to fines or other legal sanctions against strikers

So they made a last desperate bid to persuade the TUC leaders to toughen up their own rules.

But acting General Secretary Victor Feather and his colleagues stood firm.

Daily Mirror
1969

THE BEST AGENTS' SCHEME YOU'VE EVER MADE MONEY ON

SELL B.K. WOOLS TO YOUR FRIENDS AND MAKE POUNDS IN YOUR SPARE TIME

HOW B.K. MAKE IT EASY FOR YOU

★ B.K.'s BIG VALUE SELLS ITSELF: To the enthusiastic knitter, B.K.'s value speaks for itself — up to 12/4 per lb. savings over some retail prices.

★ HUGE RANGE FOR YOUR FRIENDS TO CHOOSE FROM: 320 colours. In 19 qualities. In a range of 90 patterns.

★ SUPER LIGHTWEIGHT AGENT'S CASE: Contains one ball of each of the 19 qualities, shade card, pattern book and stationery. The entire kit is so light that it can easily be carried with your other equipment if you're an agent already.

★ B.K. SPECIALITY: An illustrated book containing 57 actual patterns and instructions for machine knitters.

★ BIG COMMISSIONS: You can earn up to 20% commission on your sales. Imagine the luxuries you'll suddenly be able to afford.

★ MAIL ORDER OR COSMETIC AGENT? Remember that you already have established lady customers.

★ Same complete B.K. service for ladies overseas.

Whether you're an agent already, or if you're new to spare-time money making, you can't afford not to find out more about B.K.'s agent scheme. Just fill in the coupon and we'll tell you more, including details of the famous B.K. Guarantee.

NAME ....
ADDRESS ....

B.K. (WOOLS) LTD., Dept. W.O.1, High Street Mills, Heckmondwike.

Woman's Own
1969

● Lillian Board (20) British silver medallist in the Mexico Olympic Games, recently started a new career —as a trainee designer with Russell Hall Sportswear of Redruth, Cornwall.

During her two weeks' 'indoctrination' into the art of making sportswear Lillian tried her hand at making her own track suit and expressed herself 'quite pleased' with the result. 'I thoroughly enjoyed it', she said. 'I have always been keen on dressmaking and found it good fun.'

Lillian will now take a two-year college course, after which she will work as a designer nearer her London home. D. B. Hallett, the firm's managing director, tells SPORTS TRADER:

Sports Trader
1969

Islington
Gazette
1970

London says: 'Goodbye dollies'

London has said goodbye to the last of its "hello dollies"—and been introduced to a completely automatic telephone service.

On Thursday, December 3, the capital's last manual exchange was closed and replaced by a modern Crossbar automatic exchange costing £375,000, the first of its kind in London.

This means that for the first time anyone living in any part of the London telephone region can dial a call without asking the operator for it. In this region, which includes parts of the home counties, there are 392 exchanges serving four million phones.

Guest Lecturers

THE VERY REV. ANTONY CYPRIAN BRIDGE, Dean of Guildford Cathedral. Special interest in art, including Greek and Byzantine; author of *Images of God*, a study in the relationship between symbolism in the arts and religious thought.

ANTHONY A. M. BRYER, Esq., D.Phil., Lecturer in Medieval History, University of Birmingham; Research Fellow, Athens University, Greece, 1962. Byzantinist, working on the Greeks of Trebizond in the Pontus (Asia Minor) where he has undertaken field research. Participant in the recent BBC "Study Session" series on Byzantine history and art; author of several specialised articles.

GERALD CADOGAN, Esq., M.A., Research Lecturer of Christ Church, Oxford, and formerly Macmillan Student of the British School of Archaeology at Athens. Is working in Minoan and Mycenaean archaeology. Author of *The Minoan Palaces of Crete*.

H. W. CATLING, Esq., M.A., D.Phil., F.S.A., Fellow of Linacre College, Oxford: is Senior Assistant Keeper in the Ashmolean Museum, Oxford, in charge of Greek Antiquities; former Student at the British School at Athens; and Archaeological Survey Officer in Cyprus, 1955–59. Has travelled widely in Greece. He has written a book on *Cypriot Bronzework* and contributed to learned journals.

THE VERY REV. DR. HENRY CHADWICK, D.D., Mus.B., F.B.A., Dean of Christ Church, lately Regius Professor of Divinity in the University of Oxford. 1962–64 Gifford Lecturer in the University of St. Andrews. Much of his work has been on early Christianity in the Greek East. Publications include: *Origen contra Celsum*; *Alexandrian Christianity*; a Pelican *History of the Early Church*; *Early Christian Thought and the Classical Tradition*; *The Sentences of Sextus*; and a book on Lessing.

PROFESSOR G. E. F. CHILVER, M.A., D.Phil., Professor of Classical Studies and Dean of Humanities at the University of Kent at Canterbury; lately Senior Tutor of The Queen's College, Oxford, and University Lecturer in Ancient History. Author of *Cisalpine Gaul*, and other publications on the history of Rome.

J. N. COLDSTREAM, Esq., M.A., F.S.A., Reader in Greek at Bedford College, University of London. Formerly Scholar of King's College, Cambridge, Assistant Keeper in the Greek and Roman Department of the British Museum, and Macmillan Student at the British School, Athens. Has taken part in excavations at Knossos, Kythera, and Motya in Sicily. Author of *Greek Geometric Pottery*.

SIR MORTIMER WHEELER, C.H., C.I.E., M.C., F.R.S., F.B.A., Director of the University of London Institute of Archaeology, 1934–44. Director-General of Archaeology in India, 1944–48. Led Government Missions to Iran and Afghanistan, 1945–46. Adviser in Archaeological matters to the Government of Pakistan, 1948–50. Professor of the Archaeology of the Roman Provinces, University of London, 1948–55. Secretary of the British Academy, 1949–68, and Past President of the Society of Antiquaries. Publications include: *The Indus Civilization*; *Early India and Pakistan*; *Hill-forts of Northern France*; *Archaeology from the Earth*; *Rome beyond the Imperial Frontiers*; *Roman Art and Architecture*; *Flames Over Persepolis*; and books and papers on European and Indian archaeological subjects.

MISS L. H. JEFFERY, M.A., D.Phil., F.B.A., F.S.A., Fellow and Tutor in Ancient History at Lady Margaret Hall, Oxford, and a member of the British School of Archaeology at Athens. Publications mainly on Greek inscriptions (*The Local Scripts of Archaic Greece*, and contributions to various periodicals etc.); general field the Archaic and Early Classical age of Greece, with a particular interest in its art.

Swan Hellenic Cruises 1970

☐ At Cannon Row police station Mr Owen was given special treatment. Senior officers ordered canteen staff to prepare ham and chips, bread and butter and a cup of tea for his evening meal, which was delivered to his cell by a constable. Normally prisoners do no better than sausages and beans. Mr Owen's slices of bread were also cut diagonally – to add a special touch. – *Daily Telegraph* (H. A. Ramsay)

New Statesman 1970

Woman's Own 1969

❝We put everyone in the picture❞
by Mrs. Yvonne Eaton

"I can't say if there's anything wrong with the picture, because it's gone dark—but my husband says it's the picture valve . . ."

A pretty vague query, but I'm used to them. Having extracted essential information like the name and address from the distraught caller, I pack off our service engineer on his errand of mercy and sit back.

In the 10 years that my husband John and I have owned our electrical shop in Swanwick, Derbyshire, customers may come and go but the descriptions of their ailing TVs stay the same: "black lines"; "white lines"; "the picture valve" and finally, in a hushed and fearful whisper, "there's smoke coming out of the back!"

Of course, we have two engineers who do outside repair jobs during the week, but I can't remember when we last had a Christmas when John didn't have to turn out in response to a sorry plea for help!

I'm kept pretty busy, too, but now that my two daughters Judith and Maureen are grown-up and married I'm only too pleased to have a job which I can do with my husband.

Life in a shop is always varied—in one day I can be a window-dresser, tea-masher, saleslady, typist and nursemaid. The last is specially important, since it's up to me to keep little minds occupied and sticky fingers out of harm's way while Mum and Dad put their heads together over a purchase.

Having one's own small business is like living with a child—demanding but fascinating. I'm used to the kitchen table being strewn with bits from a radio or tape-recorder that John is working on, and to the small crowd of people who assemble outside when we have a colour set on in the shop-window.

This year Prince Charles' Investiture proved to be our biggest box-office success, with Wimbledon a close second—though to our surprise *that* audience was mostly children!

Of course the nicest thing about running any shop must be the constant contact with people. Swanwick is in a mining area on the fringe of the Peak District and most of our trade is with mining families or girls who work in one or other of the nearby hosiery factories.

These girls are always bang up to date and usually they only need a nice neat transistor to complete the swinging image!

But my favourite customers are the old-age pensioners. Paying the latest instalment on a TV or radio becomes a regular outing with a cosy chat at the end of it.

The popular subject for discussion is favourite programmes—and you'd be surprised at the number of frail old ladies who love nothing better than to watch a fearsome bout of wrestling or a bloodthirsty thriller.

One old dear told me recently of an odd smell which pervaded her living-room in waves. She was unable to decide whether it came from the dog or the TV. So she sprayed both with a well-known deodorant.

I presume it must have worked, because the dog is well and my husband hasn't received an SOS yet!

John and I both feel that the independent shopkeeper has an important part to play in a small community like ours—whether it's providing people with goods, good service, or just a friendly ear!

Wool Record 1970

Another way for the worsted manufacturer

Woman's Own 1969

by Charles M. Bottomley

WHEN the Atkins Report was first published there were several shocks for some sectors of the wool-textile industry. Some dismay was created among worsted weavers at the prospect of seeing the number of weaving establishments halved. The report recommends (page 262) that the number of weaving mills should be reduced from 120 to only 60 by the mid 1970's. This recommended reduction to 50% of the present number (percentagewise the most severe fall of any section) was, putting it mildly, a dramatic one. It follows that it will be difficult to achieve, if done in the way suggested—namely by total closure.

The problem

As the state of trade has definitely worsened since publication of the report, the issue has weighed much more heavily on the firms which are most hard-pressed. If closure is really necessary, need this be the end of the line for the particular manufacturer?

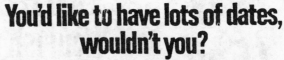

THINGS START TO MOVE!

From that time it started to happen frequently. 'I believe that when Spirit wants you for a purpose they really get things going. It was a good thing for me, being the sceptic that I was, when I received such clear visions."

There are many fascinating incidents in this medium's career, but the most intriguing involved her friend Phyllis Barrable.

"I was cleaning the house and I heard a child's voice say, 'Go and see Aunty Phyl' but I completely ignored this. Four times I heard the voice say it and finally I found myself running across to my friend's home. I felt mad but when I opened the door I found Phyl sitting with a flannel to her nose which was pouring with blood."

She had been sending thoughts to me for several minutes.

It was in Mrs. Barrable's home that Freda Fell was to hear direct voice communications.

Doctors say 'End sick notes'

By WILLIAM BRECKON
Medical Correspondent

BRITAIN'S doctors are to press for action to cut their work in signing sickness certificates.

The British Medical Association Council is to look into other ways of dealing with sickness benefit.

One solution could be 'do-it-yourself' certificates for illnesses lasting less than a week.

Five hundred delegates at the association's annual meeting in Aberdeen yesterday instructed the council to deal urgently with the problem.

Doctors complained that signing certificates used up valuable time and harmed their relationship with patients.

Dr James Cameron, chairman of the association's committee which looks after family doctors' interests, said : 'Self-certification is taking place now. The doctor merely signs the certificate.'

Trusted

If 'do-it-yourself' certificates were introduced workers would be trusted to certify for themselves the sickness which kept them off work.

Pilot trials have shown that there is no increase in absenteeism

Doctors argue that it is often impossible to tell whether a man has had a minor illness— for example diarrhoea or a bad headache—and they have to take his word for it.

The Government has refused in the past to abolish certificates. There are unlikely to be any quick changes.

MPs have alleged that scroungers are taking money in sickness and unemployment benefit.

Industrial health expert Dr Peter Taylor, who tried the sickness-without-certificates plan at Shell Haven, Essex, said last night : 'In two and a half years only two men out of 1,500 abused the system.'

The National Coal Board said 'We find the opinion of a medical man indispensable. The men are subject to stresses and strains which need skilled opinions.'

EMPLOYERS
Nourish your assets

People form your most valuable asset—and the most subject to depreciation. Staff morale and efficiency can plunge after a few rushed or empty 'lunches' in a row. If only one man's not on form, everybody suffers. But Luncheon Vouchers will *nourish* your flourishing assets in over 14,000 restaurants throughout the British Isles. By allowing a proper lunch every day, LV's ensure a more contented, efficient and productive work force every afternoon of the week. Nourish *your* staff asset with Luncheon Vouchers. They'll appreciate it.

PROFIT FROM READING OUR BROCHURE
All Luncheon Voucher benefits – including a Tax Concession – are detailed, for your eyes only, in our latest brochure. Ask your secretary to put it in front of you – or, if you wish to be really discreet, coupon us yourself.

Suddenly, you seem to need twice as much money as you did before. Yet an account (or two) at Westminster makes it all so much simpler, somehow. How ? See below.

WIFE TO SUPPORT

How to get happily married and stay solvent ever after

This is a tough time for people in love and about to get married. You've got to make your money go further. But Westminster Bank says you can do it–read here how they can give you real help.

IN the early hours of Friday morning Mr. Harold Wilson must have been wondering what had gone wrong with an election campaign that had — until the results began to flow — been virtually unanimously praised for the audacious rightness of its timing and the professional brilliance of its execution.

It should be noted for the record, incredible as it now seems, that only ten days ago there was much more interest in what would happen to Mr. Heath after his defeat than in the size of a Labour majority that was taken for granted.

Explanations and excuses have poured out since Friday. Fortunately for those who write about politics, no-one knows why the electorate confounded the pollsters and the prophets. A Swiss pundit has suggested that it was due in part to the shock of England's defeat in the World Cup!

It is possible with hindsight to see that Labour incorrectly judged the pacing of the campaign. Mr. Wilson once observed that a week is a long time in politics. Three weeks, with saturation television coverage, is very much longer. Calm confidence is all very well, but it allowed Mr. Heath to make the running. For a fortnight he gained sympathy as a gallant runner in a lost race, but in fact he was picking the issues that were discussed.